A TALE OF A TUB

JONATHAN SWIFT

Jonathan Swift
from the picture by Charles Jervas in the Bodleian Library, Oxford

JONATHAN SWIFT

A Tale of a Tub

With Other Early Works

1696 — 1707

Edited by Herbert Davis

Oxford: Basil Blackwell : 1965

Printed in Great Britain
at the Shakespeare Head Press
Saint Aldates, Oxford.

First printed in this edition, 1939
Reprinted (photolitho), 1957
Reprinted, 1965

PRINTED IN GREAT BRITAIN
BY THE COMPTON PRINTING WORKS (LONDON) LTD., LONDON, N.1
FOR BASIL BLACKWELL & MOTT LTD.
AND BOUND BY
THE KEMP HALL BINDERY, OXFORD

The PREFACE

THE writings in prose of Jonathan Swift have been re-printed a good many times since 1735, when George Faulkner with the consent and assistance of Swift himself printed at Dublin the first four volumes of a collected edition. But the last of these editions was completed by Temple Scott in 1908, and after serving us well for thirty years is now in part out of print, and in part out of date. Since then, critical editions of some of the prose works have been published by the Clarendon Press, and a volume of Selections by the Nonesuch Press.

In undertaking another complete edition now, I wish to attempt three things which still remain to be done. The first is to provide a text of the works giving, not the earliest form either of the written manuscript or first printed edition, but the final corrected and revised versions which appeared during Swift's lifetime. For we now have evidence from the letters to Charles Ford, printed for the first time in 1935, which shows how careful Swift was that the Dublin edition of his collected works 'should be printed correctly rather than otherwise.' And further evidence is available in Swift's own copy of the four volumes of *Miscellanies*, published in London, 1727–1732, which contain autograph corrections of spelling and punctuation, proving that his interest in correctness extended to the smallest details. On the other hand it is true, as Hawkesworth pointed out, that Faulkner's text contains many errors; for neither Swift himself nor his friends nor his printers took sufficient care in reading the proofs. It has seemed advisable therefore in printing from these later editions to correct such errors as show themselves when the text is collated with the earliest editions or compared with the original manuscript. The bibliographical notes and the list of variants provided at the end of each volume show what text has been used and what corrections have been made.

Secondly, I have attempted for the first time to arrange the prose works as far as possible in the order in which they were written. But, even if they could all be dated accurately enough, they could obviously not be placed in strict chronological sequence like the *Letters* and the *Poems*. It seemed more convenient, for instance, to group together the papers contributed to a periodical, or the papers concerned with Partridge; and to print the sermons, which it is impossible to date, together with other works dating from the earlier years of Swift's residence at the Deanery. Other undated pieces, with fragments and marginalia, will be printed in the last volume.

Thirdly, I wish to exclude from the canon of Swift's writings some papers, hitherto accepted as his work, which we now have evidence enough to reject; and also to separate from his authentic writings all such pieces as we may consider at all doubtful. They will be found at the end of the volumes in the appendices.

The arrangement of text and comment in these volumes has been adopted out of consideration for those who may prefer to read what Swift wrote, undisturbed by comment, reference, or textual trivialities. Those who wish to have at hand information about the occasion of these publications, and the further course of some of these controversies may be willing to turn back to the Introduction; and those who are concerned with the slighter matters of variants, additions or changes in the text, often not un-illuminating, may refer to the notes at the end of the volume.

In the Introduction I have given full references to other studies, and have tried to acknowledge my great indebtedness to former editors; in particular to Professor Nichol Smith, who with his unfailing kindness was always willing to discuss these early works of Swift, which he had already examined so thoroughly, and to help me with my fresh problems in planning this undertaking. I should like also to thank Professor F. P. Wilson and Mr John Hayward for valuable suggestions.

I am especially indebted to Mr Harold Williams, with whom I should have preferred to collaborate in this task, for his promise to contribute introductory essays to some of the later volumes, and for his most generous offer to give me the benefit of his advice on all general matters connected with this edition, and to allow me to make use of any books and pamphlets in his collection. Dr Francis Bourke has kindly promised his aid in choosing and obtaining reproductions of portraits of Swift and his friends to be used as frontispieces.

I am most grateful to Lord Rothschild for so hospitably giving me the use of his library, and for permission to print from unpublished manuscripts in his collection, and from copies of printed books containing Swift's autograph corrections.

Cornell University, November, 1938   H. D.

The CONTENTS

THE PREFACE   *page* v

INTRODUCTION   ix

Resolutions when I Come to be Old   xxxvii

TEXT OF THE EARLY WORKS

    A Tale of a Tub   1
    The Battle of the Books   137
    The Mechanical Operation of the Spirit   167
    The Contests & Dissensions in Athens & Rome   193
    Meditation on a Broomstick   237
    Thoughts on Various Subjects   241
    A Tritical Essay upon the Faculties of the Mind   246
    Prefaces to Temple's Works   253

APPENDIX
    Additions to *A Tale of a Tub* published in 1720   273

TEXTUAL NOTES   296

INDEX

ILLUSTRATIONS

Jonathan Swift, from the picture by Charles Jervas in the
    Bodleian Library, Oxford   *frontispiece*

When I come to be old. *Facsimile of* M.S.   *to face page* xxxvii

A Tale of a Tub: Frontispiece   xxxix

The *Pulpit*, the *Ladder*, and the *Stage-Itinerant*   34

I . . . *have provided each of you . . . a new Coat . . . in my Will full*
    Instructions   44

Very fairly kicks them both out of Doors   76

Both unanimously entred upon this great Work   85

In Bedlam   111

Jack . . . got upon a great Horse, and eat Custard   131

The Battel of the Books: Frontispiece   137

FACSIMILES *of* TITLE-PAGES

A Tale of a Tub, 1710   *page* xxxix

The Battel of the Books, 1710   137

The Mechanical Operation of the Spirit, 1710   167

The Contests and Dissensions in Athens and Rome, 1701   193

A Meditation upon a Broom-Stick, 1710   237

Letters Written by Sir W. Temple, Bar[t], 1700   255

Miscellanea. By the late Sir William Temple, Bar, 1701   261

Letters to the King. By Sir W. Temple, Bar[t], 1703   265

Memoirs. Part III. By Sir William Temple Baronet, 1709   267

Miscellaneous Works, Comical & Diverting:
    By T.R.D.J.S.D.O.P.I.I., 1720   275

The INTRODUCTION

W E do not know when Swift began to write, or whether he showed in youth any signs of latent power; but it is generally supposed that his mind matured slowly. The only claim he himself made to any precociousness was that when 'he was three years old he could read any chapter in the Bible'; but this may have been intended to prove the piety of his English nurse rather than his own early talent. He regarded his life at Trinity College, Dublin, as entirely unsatisfactory: 'He was so discouraged and sunk in his spirits, that he too much neglected his academic studies; for some parts of which he had no great relish by nature, and turned himself to reading history and poetry.'* Nevertheless the tradition persists that during his later years at Trinity, after taking his degree in 1686, he made some sort of start in his career as a satirist. First, there is the story,† which comes from Deane Swift, and is corroborated by the Rev. John Lyon, a prebendary of St Patrick's, who looked after Swift in the final stages of his illness, that *A Tale of a Tub* was begun in the College, and that the manuscript in his handwriting was seen by several persons in 1686, when Swift was but nineteen years old. Secondly, there is the conjecture, made by Dr Barrett,‖ Provost of Trinity College, in 1808, that Swift was, at least in part, responsible for a scandalous oration, the *Tripos*

---

*Quoted from text given by John Forster in *The Life of Jonathan Swift*, London, 1875, p. 12.

†See Hawkesworth's *Life of Swift*, with MS. notes by the Rev. John Lyon (Forster Collection), pp. 15, 24. See also Introduction to *A Tale of a Tub*, edited by A. C. Guthkelch and D. Nichol Smith, Clarendon Press, 1920, pp. xxix–xxxiv. I am indebted throughout to this admirable edition, in which the many difficult problems concerning the composition of the *Tale* are fully discussed, a number of important documents illustrating it are reprinted, and the text elucidated by explanatory notes to which the reader is referred for a more detailed commentary than is possible here.

‖*An Essay on the earlier part of the life of Swift*, London, 1808, pp. 18 ff. See also Mr Harold Williams's remarks, *Poems*, Clarendon Press, 1937, pp. 1055–6.

read by his friend John Jones, at Trinity College, on July 11 1688. There are some Hudibrastic verses in it which it is not impossible that Swift may have thrown off; but as the affair caused a mild scandal and Jones was heavily censured, it is remarkable that no one before Barrett should have suggested that Swift was also guilty, if he had been concerned in it. There is no real evidence that Swift had written anything before he left the College, just before completing his seven years' residence. At any rate, it has never been maintained that he had written anything of importance enough to prove either to himself or his friends that he was a man of letters or a poet.

In his Autobiography Swift puts the events of the next three years (1688–91) into a short paragraph:

> The troubles then breaking out, he went to his mother, who lived in Leicester; and after continuing there some months, he was received by Sir William Temple, whose father had been a great friend to the family, and who was now retired to his house called Moor Park, near Farnham in Surrey; where he continued for about two years. For he happened before twenty years old, by a surfeit of fruit to contract a giddiness and coldness of stomach, that almost brought him to his grave; and this disorder pursued him with intermissions of two or three years to the end of his life. Upon this occasion he returned to Ireland, in 1690, by advice of physicians, who weakly imagined that his native air might be of some use to recover his health; but growing worse, he soon went back to Sir William Temple; with whom growing into some confidence, he was often trusted with matters of great importance.*

Here he remembers in connection with his first visit to Moor Park nothing but his illness; he makes no comment on the year spent in Ireland; but when he comes to the second visit to Moor Park, which lasted from Christmas 1691 until May 1694, he speaks of it as the beginning of a new kind of life: 'he went back to Sir William Temple ; with whom growing into some con-

*Forster, *op. cit.* p. 13.

fidence, he was often trusted with matters of great importance.'
We know that this visit was also the beginning of intense literary
activity. It is true that he had written some poetry while he was
still in Ireland. Two Odes at least belong probably to 1691: one
called the *Ramble*, written to a young lady in Ireland, a poem
which has been lost, but referred to by Swift in a letter as an
example to show that he could not write anything easy to be
understood; the other, an *Ode to the King On his Irish Expedition* . . . , which has recently been restored to the Swift canon.*
He had also met someone, who seems to have recognized his
genius, and encouraged him to turn it to account, for he repeats
in a letter a remark which evidently made a profound impression
upon him at this time:

> And this is it which a person of great honour in Ireland
> (and who was pleased to stoop so low as to look into my
> mind), used to tell me, that my mind was like a conjured
> spirit, that would do mischief if I would not give it employ-
> ment.†

So, having failed to obtain employment as Sir Robert Southwell's secretary,‖ and having no chance of a fellowship at Trinity
College, Swift set out to make a career for himself out of poetry.
Through his connection with Sir William Temple, he might
well hope for the patronage of the King; and, as he had been in
Ireland at the time of William's successful campaign, this was a
natural subject to choose for his purpose. But no sooner had he
settled again in the quiet retirement of Moor Park, than he was
seized by a furor poeticus, which drove him to attempt all kinds
of subjects. In a state of unusual excitement and enthusiasm he
wrote on February 11, 1692:

> there is something in me which must be employed, and when
> I am alone turns all, for want of practice, into speculation and
> thought; insomuch that in these seven weeks I have been here,

---

*See *Poems*, pp. 4–10; and *Correspondence of Swift*, edited by F.
Elrington Ball, London, 1910–14, i, 366.
†*Corr*. i, 4.   ‖*Corr*. i, 1–2 & *notes*.

I have writ, and burnt and writ again, upon almost all manner of subjects, more perhaps than any man in England.*

And still three months later, if we may judge from the letter he wrote on May 3, 1692, to his cousin Thomas Swift, he was enjoying the same full happy activity, and rejoicing with youthful and almost bashful enthusiasm in the first fruits of his poetry. He was proud that his *Ode to the Athenian Society* had been printed, and 'quoted very honourably.' He confessed that he was over-fond of all his writings—'I find when I write what pleases me I am Cowley to myself and can read it a hundred times over.'†

There is no doubt that Swift delighted in these Odes, so contemptuously dismissed by most of his admirers, and further that he was praised for them by his friends, and particularly by Sir William Temple, who suggested subjects, and encouraged him in this kind of poetry. He wrote the *Ode to the Athenian Society* because 'Sir William speaking to me so much in their praise, made me zealous for their cause'; he sent it to the Society to be printed, because 'a person of very great learning and honour' and 'some others, the best of my acquaintance . . . have all been pleased to tell me, that they are sure it will not be unwelcome.' ||

He was set to work by Sir William and by Lady Giffard on a verse translation of Virgil, and did about two hundred lines to their complete satisfaction, more indeed than to his own, for he confessed that he found some passages made 'confounded, silly nonsense in English' and proposed to leave them out, but was not allowed to do so.*

During these months at the beginning of 1692, just before he went up to Oxford to receive an M.A. degree in June, Swift seems to have been perfectly happy and to have been able to write in an atmosphere of friendly encouragement, which kept him on good terms with all the world. He is as fond of the work of his friends as of his own; and as for Sir William Temple, 'I never read his writings'—he says—'but I prefer him to all others at present in England, which I suppose is all but a piece of self-

---

Corr. i, 4.   †*Corr*. i, 363, 4. ||*Corr*. i, 7.
                                Corr. I, 365.

love, and the likeness of humours makes one fond of them as if they were one's own.'* In the *Ode to the Honble Sir William Temple* which was written at this time, there is a certain playfulness and ease, which shows that Swift was enjoying himself— 'two fond lovers..., the Muse and I '†—and not very seriously trying 'to quench this foolish Fire...in Wisdom and Philosophy.' This pleasant life at Moor Park had given him his first experience of the poetic passion,

> ... kindled first with Indolence and Ease,
> And since too oft debauch'd by Praise.‖

But Swift was perhaps never wholly unaware of certain dangers in the situation, owing to the difficulty of adapting himself to Temple's standards both in life and in letters; of fitting his tongue to these exalted strains of poetic eulogy and curbing his spirit for the duties of a courtly prebend. He could not get the ease and clarity he desired even though writing 'but in praise of an old shoe'; and his poetry was always likely to change under his hands into satire. For five months he struggled with the first nine stanzas of his *Ode to Dr. William Sancroft*, and soon after abandoned it unfinished. Here was a subject he felt worthy of his efforts; the Archbishop was one for whom he had the greatest admiration, and he had often conversed with the Bishop of Ely about him two or three years before.* He seemed to find it difficult to understand why he could not write the poem more easily, not being able at the moment perhaps to realize the conflict between his own natural bent and an assumed manner which he was trying to make his own. It is curious to watch Swift struggling with the folds of his borrowed singing-robes, as he tries to wrap them round him; sometimes impatiently shaking himself free, as he turns from compliment to satire or invective and then attains a more forceful and direct utterance. In the twelfth stanza there is a passage of invective against the Dissenters, which could easily have been developed further into a sketch for the character of Jack in *A Tale of a Tub*:

*Ibid.
‖Poems*, p. 33.

†*To Mr. Congreve; Poems*, p. 49.
Corr. i, 363–4.

> Some angel say, what were the nation's crimes,
> That sent these wild reformers to our times;
>   Say what their senseless malice meant,
>   To tear Religion's lovely face;
> Strip her of ev'ry ornament and grace,
>   In striving to wash off th' imaginary paint:

But he restrains himself and leaves the stanza unfinished. The stern figure of Cato bars his way—Temple, we know, did not approve of satire. The spring of poetry must not be sullied by the impurities of party bitterness or the language of controversy.

> Check in thy satire, angry muse,
> Or a more worthy subject chuse:
> Let not the outcasts of this outcast age,
> Provoke the honour of my Muse's rage,
>   Nor be thy mighty spirit rais'd,
>   Since Heaven and Cato both are pleas'd—*

It is interesting to put the question whether, at this time or earlier, Swift had any other outlet for his bent towards satire, even though we cannot answer it. There is no word in any of the few available letters to suggest that he had by him even the rudiments of a satire in prose; and it is difficult to believe that if *A Tale of a Tub* had been begun or even thought of so early as this, and before Swift had taken orders, he would not have mentioned it in the *Apology*, when he was defending it as a youthful work. At any rate even if Swift had written an early satire in prose, prompted by Archbishop Sharp's sermon in 1686,† it had certainly been put aside. Neither in prose satire nor in Hudibrastic verse could Swift hope for the approval of Sir William Temple, nor would they be likely to help him to obtain the preferment promised by the King.

For two years he waited, with growing impatience, and for most of that time he continued to retain the confidence of Temple, to be used by him in important affairs, and to share with

---

*Poems, p. 42.

†See Guthkelch & Nichol Smith, pp. xxix-xxxiv; and Émile Pons, *Swift: les années de jeunesse et le Conte du tonneau*, Strasbourg, 1925, pp. 248–252.

him his literary tastes and activities. But in the winter of 1693
he wrote his final Odes—and these no longer Pindaric, but in
rhyming couplets—the first

> vainly spent
> In satire, to my Congreve's praises meant,*

the second, *Occasioned by Sir William Temple's Late Illness and
Recovery*, written December 1693, turning at the end into a dia-
tribe against the Muse who had cheated him so long, and from
whose enchantments he now tears himself free:

> . . . from this hour
> I here renounce thy visionary pow'r;
> And since thy essence on my breath depends,
> Thus with a puff the whole delusion ends.†

For five years Swift wrote no more poetry; and then he began in
another manner occasionally to scribble verses.

After freeing himself from this delusion, Swift next determined to break away entirely from his dependence on Temple.
Leaving him in anger in the summer of 1694, he returned again
to Ireland to make his own way in the Church. After some delay
he was admitted to deacon's and priest's orders, and on January
28, 1695, was appointed to the prebend of Kilroot, on the shores
of Belfast Lough, where he remained until May 1696. This was
hardly an equivalent for a prebend at Westminster or Windsor,
and there was only one thing for an ambitious man to do there,
and that was to write. There he could give his conjured spirit
employment, in its own way, unchecked by the disapproval of
Temple, and no longer misled by the delusion that he wanted to
write poetry like Cowley's. Now he was free to indulge his wit,
to write in clear direct prose, and to give full play to the spirit
of irony and ridicule. He began—to quote his own words—'a
satire, that would be useful and diverting: he resolved to proceed
in a manner, that should be altogether new, the world having
been already too long nauseated with endless repetitions upon
every subject.' And in '1696, eight years before it was published,'
he had 'finished the greatest part' of *A Tale of a Tub*. ‖That is

---

*Poems, p. 48.   †*Poems*, p. 55.   ‖See below, p. 1.

Swift's own account in the *Apology*, which he wrote, anony-
mously, of course, for the fifth edition in 1710. There is no
reason why he should have invented that story and chosen that
particular date, if the *Tale* had really been written earlier.
Though it contains a number of images* which belong to the
earliest stages of Swift's thought, and some striking verbal
parallels† with lines in the *Odes*, and though it may have roots
which go as far back as his last years at Trinity College, we may
be fairly certain that it was at Kilroot that Swift first conceived
the plan of a satire on the numerous gross corruptions in religion, which should at the same time justify the position of the
Church of England, and show it to be free from the extravagances of Papists and fanatics alike. It has been pointed out that
at Kilroot Swift's 'ancestral prejudices against the Noncon-
formists were likely to be confirmed';‖ and if the *Tale* is read
with an eye to the actual conditions in Ireland, Swift's point of
view will often be better understood.

The Digressions, which were concerned with the abuses in
learning, could hardly have been begun while Swift was still at
Kilroot; in their present form they probably date from 1697,
and contain later insertions. Nevertheless, it should not be forgotten that Temple's *Essay on Ancient and Modern Learning*, which
had appeared in 1690, had been attacked by Wotton in his
Reflections in 1694, and this may have first drawn Swift's attention to the pedants, and to the possibility of enlarging his satire
to include the world of learning. And it was in 1695, in the
Preface to his edition of *The Epistles of Phalaris*, that Boyle
carried the dispute further by his attack upon Bentley.

In May 1696, Swift left Ireland to rejoin Temple, 'with better
prospect of interest.'* He was soon provided with more material for his satire. A second edition of Wotton's *Reflections*
appeared in June 1697; and to this Bentley had added an

---

*Pons, pp. 246–7; 325–6.

†To those already noted by Monsieur Pons may be added another
echo from a phrase in the *Ode to Congreve*, l. 212, which is apparent
as soon as the correct reading of the first edition is restored; see
below, p. 109, l. 1–2, & textual note.

‖See Guthkelch & Nichol Smith, p. xli.   *Corr*. i, 18.

Appendix, his *Dissertation on the Epistles of Phalaris*, in which he replied vigorously to Boyle's attack, and proved with a series of masterly arguments that the Epistles, which Temple had praised so highly, were not only spurious, but without any value. Temple himself refused to be drawn into the dispute, but the Christ Church wits prepared an amusing reply, half of which was written by Dean Atterbury;* it appeared in March 1698, under the title of *Dr. Bentley's Dissertation . . . examin'd by the Honourable Charles Boyle Esq.*, and in spite of Bentley's impregnable position, it was regarded at the time as a great triumph, and went into three editions within a year.†

Swift also came to the assistance of Temple by writing a skit on the whole quarrel, a mock-heroic in prose, perhaps the only safe way of replying to Bentley. It was called *A Full and True Account of the Battel Fought last Friday Between the Antient and the Modern Books in St. James's Library*. It was begun in 1697,

---

*See Guthkelch & Nichol Smith, p. 257, *n.* 2. See also A. T. Bartholomew, *Bibliography of Bentley*, Cambridge, 1908, pp. 26–41.

†Professor F. P. Wilson kindly lent me a copy of the second edition with pencilled notes by Lord Macaulay, recording that he read it twice, in 1835 and 1836. Though he remarks in a note to p. 289, 'the Christ Church men were drunk with the vanity which has always characterized their college' his final comment was most laudatory; 'This is, I think, a masterpiece in its way—indeed quite as great an one as Bentley's Answer. As the Miser says in Molière, it is easy to make a fine entertainment with plenty of money; but the proof of a great artist is to make one without money. I do not suppose that there is in the whole history of letters a single instance of so good a fight made with such small means—so fair a face put on so bad a cause. The whole learning of the Oxford Confederacy was a scanty store yet they have contrived to make it look immense. Here and there to be sure there is an unlucky error into which no really good scholar could probably have fallen. But these gross instances are rare. The little literature which the party had is beat out to the leaf, and spread over so vast a surface, that the mass shines as brightly as Bentley's solid gold.

On the whole this work raises Atterbury prodigiously in my opinion. The part which relates to Aesop is evidently by a different and an inferior hand.'

b

but probably not completed until after the appearance of Boyle's *Examination*, as this is clearly referred to in the account of Boyle's exploit, which brings the book to a close. And the same quarrel with Bentley and Wotton is responsible for several sections or at least passages in the *Tale*, which must therefore be later than 1697. It is possible that the *Battle* or even the *Tale* may be referred to in a letter written by Temple on March 30, 1698, in which he praises Boyle's *Examination* and continues

> You needed no Excuse for anything in your former Letter, nor Mr — for giving you the Occasion for it. What he saw, was written to a Friend—who had undertaken—without my Knowledge: Which I afterwards diverted, having no mind to enter the list with such a Mean, Dull, Unmannerly Pedant.*

That may well mean that Temple had persuaded Swift not to print the *Battle*; and it is quite possible that Temple may also have seen the *Tale*, and have prevented Swift from risking even anonymous publication, until he had obtained for him the promised preferment in England. For Swift had resigned his Irish prebend in January, 1698, and at almost the same moment Lord Sunderland's resignation had destroyed his best hopes:'my Lord Sunderland fell, and I with him,' as he put it in a letter† to his successor at Kilroot. And within the year following his hopes were again frustrated by Temple's own death.

At some time during the year 1699, that is to say, either just before or just after the death of Temple, Swift jotted down on a small scrap of paper a few warnings for his old age, under the heading, *Resolutions when I come to be old*.‖ They have been regarded as a sort of confession in which, having reached the age of thirty-two, Swift notes certain dangerous tendencies in his own character to be guarded against in his old age. But they may well be rather the fruit of his recent observation and experience of others. He had lived for some years in close intimacy with an old man, whose behaviour would sometimes serve as a warning as well as an example. We may gather from other sources, for instance, that Temple had a good opinion of himself, and was

---

*Quoted by Guthkelch & Nichol Smith, pp. xlv–vi.
†*Corr*. i, 24.
‖ See facsimile of original in the Forster Collection, reproduced by kind permission of the Victoria and Albert Museum, p. xxxvii

inclined 'to scorn present Ways, and Wits, and Fashions, and Men and War.' And there are some others among these *Resolutions* which would bear a similar interpretation.

It might be expected that as soon as he had left Moor Park Swift would have felt free to publish his book—*A Tale of a Tub,* and make a bid for the reputation of a wit. But his first impulse was to try and use directly what influence he still possessed at Court; and at the same time to proceed with the publication of Temple's *Letters.* The first two volumes appeared in 1700. He had probably written the Preface and left the text with the printer before leaving for Ireland as chaplain to the Earl of Berkeley in the autumn of 1699, if we may judge from a small scrap of manuscript in his handwriting, containing a few sentences which he evidently decided to omit.

... Man; yet not knowing how soon I may cross the Seas into Ireland, where some Concerns are like suddenly to call me; and remembering how near I have been perishing more than once in that Passage, I am more unwilling to venture those Papers than my self; because if the Publication should fayl with me, I am convinced it would be a very generall Loss. For I am sure that in them may be learnt the true Interest of our Nation both at home and abroad; as well as those of the Neighbors we are most concerned in; together with the Principles, Dispositions, and Abilityes most requisite or necessary to fitt and enable any Gentleman for the service of His Country.

I have therefore ventured to publish them upon those Reasons; But will not stick to confess that I have been a little tempted to it by the Advantage I propose to my self from the Impression of a Book which I have Reason to think will be received with as much and as generall Kindness and Esteem as any Writings that have appeared since those of this Noble Author; and be entertained with equal Applause both at home and abroad.*

When he returned to England with Lord Berkeley in April, 1701, he found the Whigs in difficulties, Somers, Lord Chancel-

---

*In the possession of Lord Rothschild, who generously allowed me to print it here.

lor until the previous year, with three other Whig ministers who
were held responsible for the Partition Treaties, had been impeached by the House of Commons. Swift immediately took
advantage of the situation, and came to their aid with his first
political tract—*A Discourse of the Contests and Dissensions between
the Nobles and the Commons in Athens and Rome, with the Consequences they had upon both those States*. It was written with such
dignity and judgment that it was generally supposed to have
come from the pen of one of the Whig leaders. It was an effective
defence, though it only appeared after the impeachments had
been dropped. It was concerned with the general problem of the
balance of power within a commonwealth between the few and
the many; and it was a particular warning against the dangers of
the undue influence of popular assemblies, and the folly they
had so often shown by impeaching their greatest leaders. Aristides—'the most renowned for his exact justice and knowledge
in the law'—is drawn in such a way as to bear an unmistakable
likeness to Lord Somers; Themistocles—'a most fortunate admiral'—is clearly intended for Admiral Russell, Lord Orford;
Pericles—'an excellent orator and a man of letters'—for Lord
Halifax; and Phocion—'renowned for his negotiations abroad'
—for the Earl of Portland.* It has often been said that this tract
is colourless, and shows little of Swift's intensity or satirical
power; and that it is not at all like *A Tale of a Tub*. That may be
true; but the *Discourse* is exactly what might be expected from
the editor of Sir William Temple's *Letters*, who had said that
'this author has advanced our English tongue to as great a
perfection as it can well bear;' †and who was at this very time
occupied with the publication of Temple's *Miscellanea*, which
was entered in the Stationers' Register on July 28, 1701. For
his first entry into political controversy Swift was not unwilling to borrow something of the manner, as well as some of
the political wisdom of Temple.

It contributed greatly to his reputation, in the way he had
intended it should. It brought him into touch with men like
Somers and Burnet and Peterborough; and it brought him an
audience with the king,‖ in which he gave his views on the

political situation in Ireland: and though he returned to Ireland before the end of the year, he had every reason to hope that he would not remain long as the vicar of Laracor. Unfortunately we have very little knowledge of the details of his life at this period. We have no letters between July 16, 1700, and December 16, 1703. We know only that after the death of William III on March 8, 1702, Swift came to England again, and spent the summer there, partly occupied in preparing for publication the Third Volume of Temple's *Letters*.* The next year he remained in Ireland until November 11, and then set out on his journey to London, with the manuscript of *A Tale of a Tub* almost completed. We must look at the political changes after the Queen's accession for an indication of the reasons why Swift now decided that the time was opportune for publication.

Encouraged by the Queen's loyalty to the Church of England, the Tories were making a determined attempt to limit the power of the Whig party by bringing in a Bill against Occasional Conformity. It had already been thrown out once by the House of Lords. A second attempt was being made to get it passed just at the moment when Swift arrived in London, and the most violent party feelings were aroused; he notes

> the highest and warmest reign of party and faction, that I ever knew or read of . . . I observed the dogs in the street much more contumelious and quarrelsome than usual; . . . the very ladies are split asunder into High Church and Low . . . For the rest, the whole body of the clergy, with a great majority of the House of Commons, were violent for this bill. As great a majority of the Lords, amongst whom all the Bishops, but four, were against it. The Court and the rabble, as extremes often agree, were trimmers.†

He confesses that he was himself much at a loss; finally he was persuaded by his Whig friends that the Bill would really harm the Church, and he went so far as to write against it, though his pamphlet was not finished in time to be published.

Moreover, he still calls himself a Whig and boasts that the number of Whigs daily increases. But he was evidently much

---

*See below, p. 265.   †*Corr.* i, 38–9.

perturbed by the conflict, and anxious to find support for his own position in the assurances of his friends that 'several, who were against this bill, do love the Church, and do hate or despise Presbytery.' Finally not knowing what to think, he determined to think no more—and instead, to satisfy perhaps his ancestral prejudices, he throws out, for the wits of all parties to play with, *A Tale of a Tub*. It was provided with a Dedication* addressed to Lord Somers, the Whig leader, and it was a satire against extremes in religion and learning. It was clearly intended to express the attitude of a moderate Churchman. Swift was contemptuous of the pamphlet war that was being carried on so violently by Leslie against Presbyterians and Low Churchmen. Such pamphlets are 'the vilest things in nature'; 'Pox on the Dissenters and Independents! I would as soon trouble my head to write against a louse or a flea.'†

And so, as soon as he had finished the arrangements for the publication of his volume, he resolved to 'retire like a discontented courtier,' finding 'nothing but the good words and wishes of a decayed Ministry, whose lives and mine will probably wear out before they can serve either my little hopes, or their own ambition.'‖

In this volume, which he had taken such pains to write, Swift was indeed concerned with many things besides Dissenters and Independents. He ranges widely over the field of human folly and absurdity, as far as it had come, whether through reading or experience, under his observation as a young man. It is his one important book written before the age of forty—his one youthful work. It is indeed in style and manner so different from his other works that its authenticity has been challenged. 'I doubt,' said Dr Johnson, 'if the *Tale of a Tub* was his: it has so much

---

* This was probably written in 1704, like the *Bookseller to the Reader*. It is just possible that the phrase DETUR DIGNISSIMO may have been another hit at Bentley, who was fond of boasting that in exerting his influence as Master of Trinity College, he followed 'that excellent Rule, DETUR DIGNIORI'; but in a notorious 'election for Fellowships about 1703 or 1704 he had ventured for *once* only, as he said, to recede from it.' See Whiston's *Memoirs*, 1749, i, 121.

†*Corr.* i, 43–4.   ‖*Corr.* i, 47.

more thinking, more knowledge, more power, more colour, than any of his works which are indisputably his. If it was his, I shall only say, he was *impar sibi*.' And again, 'It exhibits a vehemence and rapidity of mind, a copiousness of images, and vivacity of diction, such as he afterwards never possessed, or never exerted.'*

We have now sufficient evidence that Swift was the sole author of the volume; nevertheless Johnson's impression was a true one. The *Tale* is unlike anything else that Swift wrote; it is the work of a young man 'with his reading fresh in his head.' In the copiousness of its imagery and in the vivacity of its diction, it bears the marks of the time when it was written. Not that Swift was directly influenced by the fashions of the century in which he grew up; he is concerned rather to make fun of them, to play with them, and thus to free himself entirely from their power. Johnson gave too little heed to Swift's warning in the *Apology*, that he has sometimes indulged in parodies, and personated the style and manner of other writers, whom he has a mind to expose. For this reason the book is more concerned with literature than anything else he ever wrote; and every reader who is acquainted with the writings of the seventeenth century will find recurring evidence of the range of Swift's reading, and enjoy his turns and somersaults of its phrase and thought. And in the form and shape of the work as a whole, with its elaborate paraphernalia of introductions and prefaces and digressions, and all its carefully planned irregularities, we are given a superb and exuberant caricature of the heroics and extravagances of seventeenth-century art and thought. The solemnities of its learning and the passionate enthusiasms of its fanatic zeal are turned into a huge joke.

The *Tale* itself in its straightforward simplicity has the quality of a fable, and requires little explanation or comment. The Digressions are loaded with the spoils of Swift's wide reading, † and are a light-hearted challenge to the critics and commentators to follow him if they can over a course set with obstacles for

---

*Quoted by Guthkelch & Nichol Smith, pp. xvi–vii.

†For an account of Swift's reading at this time, see Guthkelch & Nichol Smith, pp. l–lvii.

every kind of pedantry—irony and parody and contemptuous ridicule and triumphant wit, and an unusual amount of common sense. He is not content with general satire on the weaknesses of the time, but points his moral here and there at the expense of particular persons, whose reputations seem to him undeserved, or whose exploits provoke his censure. Thus Dryden is introduced as the inventor of all the advertizing and money-making devices that Swift despised, and in the later *Apology* and *Notes* more specific references* to Dryden and L'Estrange are added lest his meaning should have been overlooked. Here Swift shows the real grounds of his dislike of Dryden, and some others not named, 'who having spent their Lives in Faction, and Apostacies, and all manner of Vice, pretended to be Sufferers for Loyalty and Religion.' And it must not be forgotten that one function of *A Tale of a Tub* was to reply to Dryden's *Hind and the Panther*. A few contemporaries—Tate, the Laureate; Durfey, the popular poet; and Rymer and Dennis, a pair of modern critics—are casually introduced to form a suitable entourage for Dryden. But above all Swift is concerned with pedantry and the conceit of learning; and here ready at hand and suitable to his purpose are Dr Bentley and his young disciple William Wotton, B.D., whose exploits are told at length in the *Battle of the Books*, but who are here made to serve again as victims for parody and ridicule. Sections III, V and VII all bear marks of the dispute with Bentley, and some of the methods of scholarship here made fun of—the use of indexes, abstracts and lexicons—had already been ridiculed in Boyle's *Examination*. To the contemporary reader they would have a familiar ring, and Swift's witty elaboration of the same theme would be peculiarly effective. This is, I think, what Swift meant when he claimed that his wit was all his own. Boyle scoffs again and again at the learning that is derived 'from turning an Index or a Lexicon,' 'next anagrams and acrosticks the lowest diversion a man can betake himself to,' † but Swift enlarges and plays with the idea through a whole paragraph, in a way which serves at the same time to burlesque the fantastic

*See below, pp. 3, 42.
†*Examination*, 3rd ed., 1699, p. 68, 145.

game of hunting after similes and metaphors in remote corners, so common in pulpit rhetoric and metaphysical wit. Similarly Boyle comments on Bentley's fondness for flinging the term *Ass* at his opponents, and throws him back 'an *Asinine Proverb*' out of Aristophanes. * But Swift takes up the same game in his digression concerning Criticks and seizing upon the term 'ass' as a hieroglyph for a 'true critic' runs it down in the very manner of a Bentley, gathering quotations very much to the purpose, and tossing off a paragraph which surges along just like a passage from the *Dissertation*:

> For first; *Pausanias* is of opinion . . .and, that he can possibly mean no other . . . is, I think, manifest enough . . . But *Herodotus* holding the very same *Hieroglyph*, speaks much plainer, and almost *in terminis* . . . Upon which Relation *Ctesias* yet refines, mentioning the very same Animal about *India*, adding, *That whereas all other* ASSES *wanted a* Gall, *these horned ones were so redundant in that Part, that their Flesh was not to be eaten because of its extream* Bitterness.†

An even better example of original wit is the famous passage in Section II devoted to an account of the philosophy of clothes, which is a natural elaboration of the metaphor of the coats left to the three brothers. It is a mixture of parody and punning, tricked out with remote allusions and phrases caught from the controversies of seventeenth-century philosophers and theologians. And then finally, in the midst of this clowning, the whip-strokes of the satirist cutting into shreds the poor garments man has taken for a covering.

> Is not Religion a *Cloak*, Honesty a *Pair of Shoes*, worn out in the Dirt, Self-love a *Surtout*, Vanity a *Shirt*, and Conscience a *Pair of Breeches*, which, tho' a Cover for Lewdness as well as Nastiness, is easily slipt down for the Service of both.

And again:

> 'Tis true indeed, that these Animals, which are vulgarly called *Suits of Cloaths*, or *Dresses*, do according to certain Compositions receive different Appellations. If one of them

---

Ibid., p. 220.   †See below, p. 60.

be trimm'd up with a Gold Chain, and a red Gown, and a white Rod, and a great Horse, it is called a *Lord-Mayor*; If certain Ermins and Furs be placed in a certain Position, we stile them a *Judge*, and so, an apt Conjunction of Lawn and black Sattin, we intitle a *Bishop*. *

Had the volume contained no more than this, it would have been amusing enough to have run into several editions, and provocative enough to call forth some answers; and it might have served to give Swift a reputation less brilliant but more safe, and have interfered less with his advancement in the Church. But once mounted, Swift took little care to stay his course until his energy was exhausted; as it is, the volume he printed may be only part of what he wrote. He seems to have believed that there was nothing in it that could possibly give offence to intelligent and right-minded readers. He had not like some proceeded to dangerous heights; he had only endeavoured to strip himself of as many real prejudices as he could. † He was not content to leave us any illusions about mankind. There remained still one chapter to be added to all the anatomies and utopias of the seventeenth century, another useful project to be set forth. This would provide him with the theme for another digression, 'concerning the Original, the Use and Improvement of *Madness* in a Commonwealth.' ||

It is an extraordinary composition in three parts: the first, an examination of the origin of that state of frenzy in single men, which has been the source of the greatest actions that have been performed in the world; the second, a consideration of delusion as the foundation of human happiness; the third, a

---

*See below, p. 47 and notes by Guthkelch & Nichol Smith pp. 77–9, and Pons, pp. 321–7.

†*Apology*, p. 1.

|| *Sect. IX*, pp. 102 ff. Cf. Defoe, *Review*, August 1, 1706, III, 365–8. It is strange that there is no specific reference to *A Tale of a Tub* either here, or earlier in the *Review* for November, 1–10, 1705 (II, Nos. 104–6) where Defoe is attacking the virulence of the High-Church party, and proposes regulating the Press 'by obliging the author of every book to set his name to the book, in a manner particular etc.'

proposal to investigate the students of Bedlam, that such excellent material might be made use of to provide the commonwealth with persons most fitted to succeed in the army, the
law-courts, and in business and politics. The madness which
takes the form of religious fanaticism is dealt with separately in
the account of the sect of the Aeolists, * and in the Fragment at
the end of the volume, called *A Discourse concerning the Mechanical
Operation of the Spirit.* This might very well have been a part of
one of the 'Treatises speedily to be published,' announced at
the beginning of the book—*An Analytical Discourse upon Zeal,
Histori-theo-physi-logically considered.* But though he assumes this
historical and analytical manner, his aim is polemical; he will
ruthlessly expose the quackery and knavery of these pedlars of
religion:

> Who, that sees a little paultry Mortal, droning, and dream-
> ing, and drivelling to a Multitude, can think it agreeable to
> common good Sense, that either Heaven or Hell should be
> put to the Trouble of Influence or Inspection upon what he is
> about? Therefore, I am resolved immediately, to weed this
> Error out of Mankind, by making it clear, that this Mystery,
> of venting spiritual Gifts is nothing but a *Trade*, acquired by
> as much Instruction, and mastered by equal Practice and
> Application as others are. †

Swift is not more violent in his attack than many churchmen
and their opponents in the quarrels between the sects after the
Reformation; but his method is different and seemed to his
friends as well as his enemies often dangerously near to blasphemy. This is due to his lack of restraint in verbal play and
punning. For him no words are sacred; they have good and bad
associations, and once they have been perverted for the use of
canting hypocrites, he treats them as so much foulness and corruption. It makes no difference to him that the same words may
once have been used to better purpose by the prophets and the
saints. All the romantic terminology of faith and love, human
and divine, seems to him no better than a game of leap-frog
between heaven and earth; and every kind of enthusiasm it em-

---

Sect. VIII, pp. 95 ff.   †See below, pp. 180-1.

bodies, however high it may soar, is left by him lying ignomini-
ously in a ditch.*

It is hardly surprising that, when the book first appeared, none
of those suspected of having written it were willing to accept the
compliment; one indeed, later a friend of Swift, Dr King of
Christ Church, published his *Remarks on the tale of a Tub* within
a month, just to prove his innocence by witnessing against it. †

Wotton's *Observations upon The Tale of a Tub* did not appear
until 1705, when the *Tale* had reached its fourth edition. A few
others 'flirted at it' but nothing was published in its defence,
though the author could well assume by the way it had been
received 'that those who approve it are a great majority among
the men of taste.' ‖ Atterbury remarked in a private letter* that
it was very well written and would do good service, though he
feared it would do the author's reputation and interest in the
world more harm than the wit could do him good.

Swift concerned himself in his *Apology* to answer only two of
the criticisms made against it. The first of these was the grave
accusation that—to quote Wotton's words—'it is one of the
Prophanest Banters upon the Religion of Jesus Christ, as such,
that ever yet appeared.'† Swift met this with an utter denial.
Though the book might possibly contain a few youthful sallies,
deserving rebuke, he would forfeit his life if any opinion could
be fairly deduced from that book, contrary to religion or morality. The other criticism—that his wit was not his own—he indig-
nantly repudiated, and had little difficulty in answering the particular charges of borrowing which Wotton had brought forward. ‖

But more recently other sources both of the *Tale* and the
Battle have been suggested, which make it necessary to examine

---

*See below, p. 190.

†See Quintana, R. *The Mind and Art of Jonathan Swift*, New
York, 1936, p. 75 & notes. This chapter gives a good short analysis
of the *Tale* and is of particular value in calling attention to the
admirable form of the whole work.

‖*Apology*, p. 1.   *Quoted by Quintana, p. 75.

†Reprinted by Guthkelch & Nichol Smith, p. 321.

‖ *Apology*, pp. 7–8.

once again Swift's claim that through the whole book he has
not borrowed one single hint from any writer in the world. In
writing *The Battle of the Books* Swift was dealing with a topic
which had been the centre of controversy* in France and in
England for more than a generation, and he was bound to use as
his material some ideas which had been dealt with before. Swift
never bothered to invent material when he could find it ready to
hand; and particularly in controversy he never ignored the main
struggle in order to engage in some corner of the field in trivial
strife on matters of small importance so as to give an impression
of originality. Indeed he was not only content to take over the
idea of a battle between the forces of the Ancients and the
Moderns, but he seems to have picked out his chief combatants
on both sides from among those mentioned by Sir William
Temple;† and certain details and even phrases have close paral-
lels in the *Histoire Poëtique de la Guerre nouvellement declarée entre les
Anciens et les Modernes* by François de Callières, which was published in 1688, though the tone and style of the book as a whole
are quite different, and Swift declared that he had never heard of
it.‖ In the *Tale* likewise, the allegory of the father's will and the
legacy of the coats to the three sons may have been suggested by
Archbishop Sharp's sermon in 1686, or by the story of the Three
Rings, which represented the Jewish, Christian and Moham-
medan churches, as it appeared in Boccaccio and elsewhere.*

But none of these general similarities seriously affect Swift's
claim that his wit was all his own. And he would doubtless have
been content to use some of his later critics as he did William
Wotton, and collect from their work passages to serve as foot-
notes to his treatise: 'The Part of Minellius or Farnaby would
have fallen in with their Genius and might be serviceable to

---

*For a very full and admirable account of the whole controversy
of the Ancients and the Moderns, see R. F. Jones, *Ancients and
Moderns, the Background of the Battle of the Books*. (Washington Univ.
Studies, new series 6), St. Louis, 1936.

†See Guthkelch & Nichol Smith, p. xlvi and 244 *n.*

‖ Discussed fully by Pons, pp. 271–4.

* See Guthkelch & Nichol Smith, pp. xxxiv–vi.

many Readers who cannot enter into the abstruser Parts of that Discourse.'*

For the fifth edition, published in 1710, Swift suggested to his printer Benjamin Tooke that a Key should be added made up of quotations from Wotton's *Observations*, and Tooke improved upon this by arranging Wotton's comments as footnotes to the passages referred to, and inserting them among the other foot-notes, almost certainly provided by Swift himself for this edi-tion. The marginal notes and references, which had appeared in all the earlier editions were left in their place. Just before this edition was ready, early in 1710, Curll published *A Complete Key to the* Tale of a Tub; *With some Account of the Authors, The Oc(c)asion and Design of Writing it, and Mr. Wotton's* Remarks *examin'd.*† This had the appearance of a reply to Wotton and a defence of the authors of the *Tale*, whom it describes thus:

> It was perform'd by a couple of young Clergymen in the Year 1697, who having been Domestick Chaplains to Sir *William Temple*, thought themselves oblig'd to take up his Quarrel in Relation to the Controversy then in Dispute between him and Mr. *Wotton* concerning *Ancient* and *Modern* Learning. . . . *Thomas Swift* is Grandson to Sir *William D'Avenant*, *Jonathan Swift* is Cousin German to *Thomas Swift* both Retainers to Sir *William Temple.*

Thomas was said to have begun the *Tale of a Tub* and intended to have it very regular.

> But when he had not yet gone half way, his Companion bor-rowing the *Manuscript* to peruse, carried it with him to *Ireland*, and having kept it seven Years at last publish'd it imperfect. ‖

This story Swift contemptuously noticed in his *Postscript* to the *Apology*. He dealt with it more fully in a Letter to Benjamin Tooke from Dublin, June 29, 1710, which must be quoted here because it also provides adequate documentary proof that Swift was the sole author of the book, and responsible for the addi-tions added in 1710.

Sir,

    I was in the country when I received your letter with the Apology enclosed in it; and I had neither health nor humour to finish that business. But the blame rests with you, that if you thought it time, you did not print it when you had it. I have just now your last, with the Complete Key. I believe it is so perfect a Grub-street piece, it will be forgotten in a week. But it is strange that there can be no satisfaction against a bookseller for publishing names in so bold a manner. I wish some lawyer could advise you how I might have satisfaction; for at this rate, there is no book, however vile, which may not be fastened on me.

    I cannot but think that little parson cousin of mine is at the bottom of this: for, having lent him a copy of some part of, etc. and he showing it, after I was gone for Ireland, and the thing abroad, he affected to talk suspiciously, as if he had some share in it. If he should happen to be in town, and you light upon him, I think you ought to tell him gravely, that, if he be the author, he should set his name to the, etc. and rally him a little upon it: and tell him, if he can explain some things, you will, if he pleases, set his name to the next edition. I should be glad to see how far the foolish impudence of a dunce could go.

    Well; I will send you the thing, now I am in town, as soon as possible. But I dare say, you have neither printed the rest, nor finished the cuts; only are glad to lay the fault on me. I shall, at the end, take a little contemptible notice of the thing you sent me; and I dare say it will do you more good than hurt. . . .*

Tooke replied on July 10 that he wished to get the volume out as soon as possible without waiting for the cuts and gives some suggestions about details; as to Thomas Swift he says simply—and this is decisive evidence from the publisher of the book—'I neither know him nor ever heard of him till the Key mentioned him.'† A warning should perhaps be added that

---

* *Corr.* i, 183–4; also reprinted by Guthkelch & Nichol Smith, pp. 343–4.   † *Corr.* i, 186.

there exist a number of copies of *A Tale of a Tub*, with manuscript notes added by early readers, which at first sight seem to provide further evidence of dual authorship; certain sections are marked as being by Thomas Swift, and explanatory notes added in the margin. But all such copies as have been examined turn out to have no other authority than Curll's *Key*.*

Once again, in 1720, another unauthorized edition of *A Tale of a Tub* appeared 'with considerable *Additions*, & explanatory *Notes*, never before printed.' The story of the dual authorship was repeated, but with a note that 'since they don't think fit publickly to own it, wherever I mention their names 'tis not upon any other affirmation than as they are the *reputed Authors*.' † The addition consists of a Table or Index or Key to the *Tale*, into which is inserted an 'Abstract of what follows after Sect IX in the Manuscript' containing the *History of Martin*, with 'A Digression on the nature usefulness and necessity of Wars and Quarrels': and later, just before the *Battle of the Books*, 'A Project for the universal benefit of Mankind.' These abstracts are said to have been made by a gentleman from a manuscript which contains a great deal more than what is printed. Though the authenticity of this additional material was immediately challenged by Justus van Effen in the introduction to his French translation of the *Tale* in 1721, ‖ it was reprinted by Nichols in his *Supplement to Dr. Swift's Works* (1779) and inserted in the text by Sir Walter Scott, and later editors. Here, it is reprinted separately in the Appendix to this volume, as there seems to be no doubt that it was an entirely unauthentic continuation of the *Tale*, against which Swift had expressly warned his readers.*

*   *   *

The remaining works included in this volume were first col-

---

* A copy however was found by Mr J. A. Rice, with notes which were almost certainly in the handwriting of Thomas Swift; but the notes provided no evidence that he was the author of any of it.

† See below, p. 279.   ‖ See Guthkelch & Nichol Smith, p. lx.
* See below, p. 282.

lected by Swift in the *Miscellanies in Prose and Verse* printed by Benjamin Tooke in 1711.

The Meditation on a Broomstick is there dated August 1704; but this cannot be correct if we are to accept the story of its composition given by Thomas Sheridan in his *Life of Swift*: that it was written during one of Swift's visits to the Berkeleys as a parody of the Hon.Robert Boyle's *Meditations*, a devotional work which the Countess was particularly fond of, which she desired Swift to read to her day by day. Not sharing her enthusiasm for the book, Swift on one occasion substituted this meditation of his own. 'Lady Berkeley, a little surprised at the oddity of the title, stopped him, repeating the words, "A Meditation on a Broomstick! Bless me, what a strange subject! But there is no knowing what useful lessons of instruction this wonderful man may draw from things apparently the most trivial. Pray let us hear what he says upon it." Swift then, with an inflexible gravity of countenance, proceeded to read the Meditation, in the same solemn tone which he had used in delivering the former. Lady Berkeley, not at all suspecting a trick, in the fullness of her prepossession, was every now and then, during the reading of it, expressing her admiration of this extraordinary man, who could draw such fine moral reflections from so contemptible a subject; with which, though Swift must have been inwardly not a little tickled, yet he preserved a most perfect composure of features, so that she had not the least room to suspect any deceit. Soon after, some company coming in, Swift pretended business, and withdrew, foreseeing what was to follow. Lady Berkeley, full of the subject, soon entered upon the praises of those heavenly Meditations of Mr. Boyle. "But," said she, "the doctor has just been reading one to me, which has surprised me more than all the rest." One of the company asked which of the Meditations she meant. She answered directly, in the simplicity of her heart, "I mean, that excellent Meditation on a Broom-stick." The company looked at each other with some surprise, and could scarce refrain from laughing. But they all agreed that they had never heard of such a Meditation before. "Upon my word," said my lady, "there it is, look into that book, and convince yourselves." One of them opened the book, and found it there indeed, but in Swift's

c

handwriting; upon which a general burst of laughter ensued; and my lady, when the first surprise was over, enjoyed the joke as much as any of them.'*

It is one of Sheridan's good stories, told convincingly; and there is perhaps no reason to suspect that on some such occasion the parody was written. But if the incident took place at Cranford, it must have been before June 1704, when Swift returned to Ireland. It may have occurred during Swift's visit to Berkeley Castle in the summer of 1702, when, as we know, he wrote the *Ballad on the Game of Traffic*.† There are certain rather close similarities of phrase ‖ in the *Meditation* and in Section II of *A Tale of a Tub*, which was probably written not later than 1702.

The Hon. Robert Boyle's *Occasional Reflections upon Several Subjects with a Discourse touching occasional Meditations* was first published in 1665. As will be seen later Swift indulged also in parody of some of Boyle's scientific works. Perhaps the extravagant eulogy of some of Boyle's friends, as well as the opinion of Lady Berkeley, may have led Swift to make fun of him. Joseph Glanvil had observed in 1665, for instance, 'that had this great person lived in those days when men godded their benefactors he could not have missed one of the first places among their deified mortals.' And Ralph Cudworth in a letter of 1684 to Boyle, flatters him thus: 'You have outdone Sir Francis Bacon in your natural experiments; and you have not insinuated anything, as he is thought to have done, tending to irreligion, but the contrary.'*

We know very little of Swift's activities after his return to Ireland in June 1704. He certainly spent part of his time in Dublin, and during the lord-lieutenancy of the Earl of Pembroke was frequently at the Castle, where great punning contests took place. Of his writings at this time there remain, besides a few verses,† only a group of aphorisms and another parody, which first appeared in the *Miscellanies*, 1711.

---

* T. Sheridan, *Life of Swift*, (1784), pp. 43-4.
† *Poems*, p. 74.   ‖ Noted by Émile Pons, pp. 325-6.
*See Boyle, *Works* (1744), I, 56, 76.
†*Poems*, pp. 78-96.

Various Thoughts, Moral and Diverting is dated October the 1st, 1706, which perhaps indicates the time when Swift first brought together a group of these aphorisms for publication. Further additions were made later both for the *Miscellanies*, 1727, and the *Works*, 1735; but these later collections were the joint work of Swift and Pope and perhaps other friends. They will be printed together in the last volume of this edition.

These *Thoughts* may be accepted as entirely Swift's work, and as dating from this period. His admiration for the *Maximes* of La Rochefoucauld began early, and lasted throughout his life, and may well have prompted and shaped these *Thoughts*. Some may go back as far as 1696, jotted down at odd times as the fruit of Swift's reading and meditation; or they may even be regarded as little scraps left over from his work on *A Tale of a Tub*, further comments on such themes as Time, Posterity, the infancy of the present age and such like. Generally the tone is impersonal, and there seems to be little reference to any particular occasion or circumstances; but sometimes we find a remark which both in form and intention reveals so fully the play of Swift's mind that we are tempted to ask what it was that first prompted it—for example: 'What they *do* in heaven we are ignorant of; what they do *not* we are told expressly; that they neither marry, nor are given in Marriage.' *

A Tritical Essay upon the Faculties of the Mind is dated August the 6th, 1707. It is possible that here too Swift was parodying some particular essay; but it has not yet been found. It may have been prompted by a general dislike of the commonplaces of moralists, as indicated in the Preface: 'I have been of late offended with many writers of essays and moral discourses, for running into stale topics and threadbare quotations, and not handling their subject fully and closely.'†

It is too thorough a parody to be witty; and it is perhaps not often read. But it is a part of Swift's campaign against dullness, an early disciplinary measure against the banalities of composition, and the product of the same didactic energy which was much later to be directed against the banalities of Polite Conversation.

---

*See below, p. 244.   †See below, p. 246.

Swift did not complete his editorial task of bringing out Sir William Temple's *Works* until 1709, when he published the *Memoirs Part III*. But it is convenient to add that Preface to the other pieces which will be found in this volume. Out of deference to the opinion of some persons nearly concerned, he had withheld this last portion of the *Memoirs* until those whose proceedings had been condemned by Temple were all dead. The volume contains no dedication, but provides him with an opportunity of paying compliments to persons in power, such as Sunderland, the Secretary of State, and Godolphin, the Lord Treasurer. He also uses the preface to reply to the criticisms that had been made against Temple's other writings, and vindicates him from the charge brought forward by Wotton that his language abounds in French words and turns of expression.*

The book was printed from Swift's own manuscript copy without the knowledge and without the permission of the Temple family. Lady Giffard, Temple's sister, enraged at this, immediately published an advertisement, in which Swift was accused of printing from 'an unfaithful copy,' the original autographs being still in the hands of the family. In a letter, dated November 9, 1709, Swift replied to these accusations with dignity and restraint, and gave an account of the way in which all Temple's *Works* had been published by him—not from the autographs, but from copies 'made from the originals under his direction, and corrected all along by his orders.'

This final attack on Swift by members of Temple's family not unnaturally roused for a moment his earlier feelings of resentment; and he allowed himself in one bitter phrase to remind Lady Giffard of the limited advantages which the privilege of Temple's friendship had brought him: 'I pretend not to have had the least share in Sir William Temple's confidence above his relatives or his commonest friends—I have but too good reason to think otherwise.' † This lends some support to what has been said above about the circumstances which shaped the early course of Swift's literary career, before the publication of *A Tale of a Tub*.

*See below, p. 268.   †*Corr.* i, 172.

When I come to be old   1699

Not to marry a young Woman.

Not to keep young Company unless they realy desire it.

Not to be peevish or morose, or suspicious

Not to scorn present Ways, or Witt, or Fashions, or Men, or Warr, &c

Not to be fond of Children, ~~or lett them come near me hardly~~

– not to tell the same Story over & over to the same People.

Not to be covetous.

Not to neglect Decency, or cleanlyness, for fear of falling into Nastyness.

Not to be severe with your People, but give Allowances to their youthfull

    follyes, and Weaknesses.

– not to be influenced by, or give ear to knavish tatling Servants, or others

Not to be too free of advise nor trouble any but those that desire it.

To desire some good Friend to inform me wch of these Resolutions I

break, or neglect, & wherein; and reform accordingly.

Not to talk much, nor of my self.

Not to boast of my former beauty, or strength, or favour with Ladyes, &c.

– not to hearken to Flatteryes, nor conceive I can be beloved by a young

    woman, et eos qui hereditatem captant odisse ac vitare.

– not to be positive or opiniatre.

Not to sett up for observing all these Rules; for fear I should observe none.

Not to marry a young Woman.

Not to keep young Company unless they realy desire it.

Not to be peevish or morose, or suspicious.

Not to scorn present Ways, or Wits, or Fashions, or Men, or War, &c.

Not to be fond of Children, or let them come near me hardly.

Not to tell the same Story over & over to the same People.

Not to be covetous.

Not to neglect decency, or cleenlyness, for fear of falling into Nastyness.

Not to be over severe with young People, but give Allowances for their youthfull follyes, and Weaknesses.

Not to be influenced by, or give ear to knavish tatling Servants, or others.

Not to be too free of advise nor trouble any but those that desire it.

To desire some good Friends to inform me wch of these Resolutions I break, or neglect, & wherein; and reform accordingly.

Not to talk much, nor of my self.

Not to boast of my former beauty, or strength, or favor with Ladyes, &c.

Not to hearken to Flatteryes, nor conceive I can be beloved by a young woman. et eos qui hereditatem captant odisse ac vitare.

Not to be positive or opiniatre.

Not to sett up for observing all these Rules, for fear I should observe none.

To front the Title.

B.L. was delin. J. Sturt sculp.

A TALE OF A TUB.

Written for the Univerſal Improvement of Mankind.

Diu multumque deſideratum.

To which is added,

An ACCOUNT of a BATTEL

BETWEEN THE

Antient and Modern BOOKS in St. *James's* Library.

Baſima eacabaſa eanaa irrauriſta. diarba da caeotaba fobor camelanthi. *Iren. Lib.* 1. C. 18.

————*Juvatque novos decerpere flores,*
Inſignemque meo capiti petere inde coronam,
Unde prius nulli velarunt tempora Muſæ. Lucret.

The Fifth EDITION: With the Author's Apology and Explanatory Notes. By *W. W--tt--n*, B. D. and others.

LONDON: Printed for *John Nutt*, near *Stationers-Hall.* MDCCX.

Treatises wrote by the same Author, most of them mentioned in the following Discourses; which will be speedily published.

A *Character of the present Set of* Wits *in this Island.*
A Panegyrical Essay upon the Number THREE.
A Dissertation upon the principal Productions of Grub-street.

Lectures upon a Dissection of Human Nature.

A Panegyrick upon the World.

An Analytical Discourse upon Zeal, Histori-theo-physi-logically *considered.*

A general History of Ears.

A modest Defence of the Proceedings of the Rabble *in all Ages.*

A Description of the Kingdom of Absurdities.

A Voyage into England, *by a Person of Quality in* Terra Australis incognita, *translated from the Original.*

A Critical Essay upon the Art of Canting, *Philosophically, Physically, and Musically considered.*

AN

APOLOGY

For the, &c.

IF *good and ill Nature equally operated upon Mankind, I might have saved my self the Trouble of this Apology; for it is manifest by the Reception the following Discourse hath met with, that those who approve it, are a great Majority among the Men of Tast; yet there have been two or three Treatises written expresly against it, besides many others that have flirted at it occasionally, without one Syllable having been ever published in its Defence, or even Quotation to its Advantage, that I can remember, except by the Polite Author of a late Discourse between a Deist and a Socinian.*

Therefore, since the Book seems calculated to live at least as long as our Language, and our Tast admit no great Alterations, I am content to convey some Apology along with it.

The greatest Part of that Book was finished above thirteen Years since, 1696, *which is eight Years before it was published. The Author was then young, his Invention at the Height, and his Reading fresh in his Head. By the Assistance of some Thinking, and much Conversation, he had endeavour'd to Strip himself of as many real Prejudices as he could; I say real ones, because under the Notion of Prejudices, he knew to what dangerous Heights some Men have proceeded. Thus prepared, he thought the numerous and gross Corruptions in Religion and Learning might furnish Matter for a Satyr, that would be useful and diverting: He resolved to proceed in a manner, that should be altogether new, the World having been already too long nauseated with endless Repetitions upon every Subject. The Abuses in Religion he proposed to set forth in the Allegory of the Coats, and the three Brothers, which was to make up the Body of the Discourse. Those in Learning he chose to introduce by way of Digressions. He was then a young Gentleman much in the World, and wrote to the Tast of those who were like himself; therefore in order to allure them, he gave a Liberty to his Pen, which might not suit with ma-*

b

turer Years, *or graver* Characters, *and which he could have easily corrected with a very few* Blots, *had he been Master of his Papers for a Year or two before their Publication.*

Not that he would have governed his Judgment by the ill-placed Cavils of the Sour, the Envious, the Stupid, and the Tastless, which he mentions with disdain. He acknowledges there are several youthful Sallies, which from the Grave and the Wise may deserve a Rebuke. But he desires to be answerable no farther than he is guilty, and that his Faults may not be multiply'd by the ignorant, the unnatural, and uncharitable Applications of those who have neither Candor to suppose good Meanings, nor Palate to distinguish true Ones. After which, he will forfeit his Life, if any one Opinion can be fairly deduced from that Book, which is contrary to Religion or Morality.

Why should any Clergyman of our Church be angry to see the Follies of Fanaticism and Superstition exposed, tho' in the most ridiculous Manner? since that is perhaps the most probable way to cure them, or at least to hinder them from farther spreading. Besides, tho' it was not intended for their Perusal; it raillies nothing but what they preach against. It contains nothing to provoke them by the least Scurrillity upon their Persons or their Functions. It Celebrates the Church of England as the most perfect of all others in Discipline and Doctrine, it advances no Opinion they reject, nor condemns any they receive. If the Clergy's Resentments lay upon their Hands, in my humble Opinion, they might have found more proper Objects to employ them on: Nondum tibi defuit Hostis; I mean those heavy, illiterate Scriblers, prostitute in their Reputations, vicious in their Lives, and ruin'd in their Fortunes, who to the shame of good Sense as well as Piety, are greedily read, meerly upon the Strength of bold, false, impious Assertions, mixt with unmannerly Reflections upon the Priesthood, and openly intended against all Religion; in short, full of such Principles as are kindly received, because they are levell'd to remove those Terrors that Religion tells Men will be the Consequence of immoral Lives. Nothing like which is to be met with in this Discourse, tho' some of them are pleased so freely to censure it. And I wish, there were no other Instance of what I have too frequently observed, that many of that Reverend Body are not always very nice in distinguishing between their Enemies and their Friends.

Had the Author's Intentions met with a more candid Interpretation from some whom out of Respect he forbears to name, he might have been *encouraged to an Examination of Books written by some of those Au-thors above-described, whose Errors, Ignorance, Dullness and Villany, he thinks he could have detected and exposed in such a Manner, that the Persons who are most conceived to be infected by them, would soon lay them aside and be ashamed: But he has now given over those Thoughts, since the* weightiest *Men in the* weightiest *Stations are pleased to think it a more dangerous Point to laugh at those Corruptions in Re-ligion, which they themselves must disapprove, than to endeavour pulling up those very Foundations, wherein all Christians have agreed.*

He thinks it no fair Proceeding, that any Person should offer deter-minately to fix a name upon the Author of this Discourse, who hath all along concealed himself from most of his nearest Friends: Yet several have gone a farther Step, and pronounced another Book to Letter of *have been the Work of the same Hand with this; which* Enthusiasm. *the Author directly affirms to be a thorough mistake; he having yet never so much as read that Discourse, a plain Instance how little Truth, there often is in general Surmises, or in Conjectures drawn from a Similitude of Style, or way of thinking.*

Had the Author writ a Book to expose the Abuses in Law, or in Physick, he believes the Learned Professors in either Faculty, would have been so far from resenting it, as to have given him Thanks for his Pains, especially if he had made an honourable Reservation for the true Practice of either Science: But Religion they tell us ought not to be ridiculed, and they tell us Truth, yet surely the Corruptions in it may; for we are taught by the tritest Maxim in the World, that Religion being the best of Things, its Corruptions are likely to be the worst.

There is one Thing which the judicious Reader cannot but have ob-served, that some of those Passages in this Discourse, which appear most liable to Objection are what they call Parodies, where the Author per-sonates the Style and Manner of other Writers, whom he has a mind to expose. I shall produce one Instance, it is in the [42nd] Page. Dryden, L'Estrange, *and some others I shall not name, are here levelled at, who having spent their Lives in Faction, and Apostacies, and all manner of Vice, pretended to be Sufferers for Loyalty and Religion. So* Dryden *tells us in one of his Prefaces of his Merits and Suffering, thanks God that he* possesses his Soul in Patience: *In other Places he talks at the same Rate, and* L'Estrange *often uses the like Style, and I believe the Reader may find more Persons to give that Passage an Application: But*

this is enough to direct those who may have over-look'd the Authors In-
tention.

   There are three or four other Passages which prejudiced or ignorant
Readers have drawn by great Force to hint at ill Meanings; as if they
glanced at some Tenets in Religion, in answer to all which, the Author
solemnly protests he is entirely Innocent, and never had it once in his
Thoughts that any thing he said would in the least be capable of such In-
terpretations, which he will engage to deduce full as fairly from the most
innocent Book in the World. And it will be obvious to every Reader, that
this was not any part of his Scheme or Design, the Abuses he notes being
such as all Church of England *Men agree in, nor was it proper for his*
Subject to meddle with other Points, than such as have been perpetually
controverted since the Reformation.

   To instance only in that Passage about the three wooden Machines
mentioned in the Introduction: In the Original Manuscript there was a
description of a Fourth, which those who had the Papers in their Power,
blotted out, as having something in it of Satyr, that I suppose they thought
was too particular, and therefore they were forced to change it to the
Number Three, *from whence some have endeavour'd to squeeze out a*
dangerous Meaning that was never thought on. And indeed the Conceit
was half spoiled by changing the Numbers; that of Four *being much more*
Cabalistick, and therefore better exposing the pretended Virtue of
Numbers, a Superstitition there intended to be ridicul'd.

   Another Thing to be observed is, that there generally runs an Irony
through the Thread of the whole Book, which the Men of Tast will observe
and distinguish, and which will render some Objections that have been
made, very weak and insignificant.

   This Apology being chiefly intended for the Satisfaction of future Rea-
ders, it may be thought unnecessary to take any notice of such Treatises as
have been writ against this ensuing Discourse, which are already sunk
into waste Paper and Oblivion; after the usual Fate of common Ans-
werers to Books, which are allowed to have any Merit: They are indeed
like Annuals that grow about a young Tree, and seem to vye with it for
a Summer, but fall and die with the Leaves in Autumn, and are never
heard of any more. When Dr. Eachard *writ his Book about the Con-*
tempt of the Clergy, numbers of those Answerers immediately started up,
whose Memory if he had not kept alive by his Replies, it would now be
utterly unknown that he were ever answered at all. There is indeed an

Exception, when any great Genius thinks it worth his while to expose a foolish Piece; so we still read Marvel's *Answer to* Parker *with Pleasure, tho' the Book it answers be sunk long ago; so the Earl of* Orrery's *Remarks will be read with Delight, when the Dissertation he exposes will neither be sought nor found; but these are no Enterprises for common Hands, nor to be hoped for above once or twice in an Age. Men would be more cautious of losing their Time in such an Undertaking, if they did but consider, that to answer a Book effectually, requires more Pains and Skill, more Wit, Learning, and Judgment than were employ'd in the Writing it. And the Author assures those Gentlemen who have given themselves that Trouble with him, that his Discourse is the Product of the Study, the Observation, and the Invention of several Years, that he often blotted out much more than he left, and if his Papers had not been a long time out of his Possession, they must have still undergone more severe Corrections; and do they think such a Building is to be battered with Dirt-Pellets however envenom'd the Mouths may be that discharge them. He hath seen the Productions but of two Answerers, One of which first appear'd as from an unknown hand, but since avowed by a Person, who upon some Occasions hath discover'd no ill Vein of Humor. 'Tis a Pity any Occasions should put him under a necessity of being so hasty in his Productions, which otherwise might often be entertaining. But there were other Reasons obvious enough for his Miscarriage in this; he writ against the Conviction of his Talent, and enter'd upon one of the wrongest Attempts in Nature, to turn into ridicule by a Weeks Labour, a Work which had cost so much time, and met with so much Success in ridiculing others, the manner how he has handled his Subject, I have now forgot, having just look'd it over when it first came out, as others did, meerly for the sake of the Title.*

The other Answer is from a Person of a graver Character, and is made up of half Invective, and half Annotation. In the latter of which he hath generally succeeded well enough. And the Project at that time was not amiss, to draw in Readers to his Pamphlet, several having appear'd desirous that there might be some Explication of the more difficult Passages. Neither can he be altogether blamed for offering at the Invective Part, because it is agreed on all hands that the Author had given him sufficient Provocation. The great Objection is against his manner of treating it, very unsuitable to one of his Function. It was determined by a fair Majority, that this Answerer had in a way not to be pardon'd, drawn his Pen against a certain great Man then alive, and universally reverenced for every good Quality that could possibly enter into the Composition of the most accomplish'd Person; it was observed, how he was pleased and affected to have that noble Writer call'd his Adversary, and it was a Point of Satyr well directed, for I have been told, Sir W. T. was sufficiently mortify'd at the Term. All the Men of Wit and Politeness were immediately up in Arms, through Indignation, which prevailed over their Contempt, by the Consequences they apprehended from such an Example, and it grew to be Porsenna's Case; Idem trecenti juravimus. In short, things were ripe for a general Insurrection, till my Lord Orrery had a little laid the Spirit, and settled the Ferment. But his Lordship being principally engaged with another Antagonist, it was thought necessary in order to quiet the Minds of Men, that this Opposer should receive a Reprimand, which partly occasioned that Discourse of the Battle of the Books, and the Author was farther at the Pains to insert one or two Remarks on him in the Body of the Book.

This Answerer has been pleased to find Fault with about a dozen Passages, which the Author will not be at the Trouble of defending, farther than by assuring the Reader, that for the greater Part the Reflecter is entirely mistaken, and forces Interpretations which never once entered into the Writer's Head, nor will he is sure into that of any Reader of Tast and Candor; he allows two or three at most there produced to have been deliver'd unwarily, for which he desires to plead the Excuse offered already, of his Youth, and Franckness of Speech, and his Papers being out of his Power at the Time they were published.

But this Answerer insists, and says, what he chiefly dislikes, is the Design; what that was I have already told, and I believe there is not a Person in England who can understand that Book, that ever imagined it to have been any thing else, but to expose the Abuses and Corruptions in Learning and Religion.

But it would be good to know what Design this Reflecter was serving, when he concludes his Pamphlet with a Caution to Readers, to beware of thinking the Authors Wit was entirely his own, surely this must have had some Allay of Personal Animosity, at least mixt with the Design of serving the Publick by so useful a Discovery; and it indeed touches the Author in a very tender Point, who insists upon it, that through the whole Book he has not borrowed one single Hint from any Writer in the World; and he thought, of all Criticisms, that would never have been one,

He conceived it was never disputed to be an Original, whatever Faults it might have. However this Answerer produces three Instances to prove this Author's Wit is not his own in many Places. *The first is, that the Names of* Peter, Martin *and* Jack *are borrowed from a Letter of the late Duke of* Buckingham. *Whatever Wit is contained in those three Names, the Author is content to give it up, and desires his Readers will substract as much as they placed upon that Account; at the same time protesting solemnly that he never once heard of that Letter, except in this Passage of the Answerer: So that the Names were not borrowed as he affirms, tho' they should happen to be the same; which however is odd enough, and what he hardly believes; that of* Jack, *being not quite so obvious as the other two. The second Instance to shew* the Author's Wit is not his own, *is* Peter*'s* Banter *(as he calls it in his* Alsatia *Phrase) upon Transubstantiation, which is taken from the same Duke's Conference with an* Irish *Priest, where a* Cork *is turned into a* Horse. *This the Author confesses to have seen, about ten Years after his Book was writ, and a Year or two after it was published. Nay, the Answerer overthrows this himself; for he allows the Tale was writ in* 1697; *and I think that Pamphlet was not printed in many Years after. It was necessary, that Corruption should have some Allegory as well as the rest; and the Author invented the properest he could, without enquiring what other People had writ, and the commonest Reader will find, there is not the least Resemblance between the two Stories. The third Instance is in these Words:* I have been assured, that the Battle in St. *James*'s Library, is *mutatis mutandis*, taken out of a *French* Book, entituled, *Combat des livres*, if I misremember not. *In which Passage there are two Clauses observable:* I have been assured; *and,* if I misremember not. *I desire first to know, whether if that Conjecture proves an utter falshood, those two Clauses will be a sufficient Excuse for this worthy Critick. The Matter is a Trifle; but, would he venture to pronounce at this Rate upon one of greater Moment? I know nothing more contemptible in a Writer than the Character of a Plagiary; which he here fixes at a venture, and this, not for a Passage, but a whole Discourse, taken out from another Book only* mutatis mutandis. *The Author is as much in the dark about this as the Answerer; and will imitate him by an Affirmation at Random; that if there be a word of Truth in this Reflection, he is a paultry, imitating Pedant, and the Answerer is a Person of Wit, Manners and Truth. He takes his Boldness, from never having* seen any such Treatise in his Life nor heard of it before; and he is sure it is impossible for two Writers of different Times and Countries to agree in their Thoughts after such a Manner, that two continued Discourses shall be the same only mutatis mutandis. Neither will he insist upon the mistake of the Title, but let the Answerer and his Friend produce any Book they please, he defies them to shew one single Particular, where the judicious Reader will affirm he has been obliged for the smallest Hint; giving only Allowance for the accidental encountring of a single Thought, which he knows may sometimes happen; tho' he has never yet found it in that Discourse, nor has heard it objected by any body else.

So that if ever any design was unfortunately executed, it must be that of this Answerer, who when he would have it observed that the Author's Wit is not his own, is able to produce but three Instances, two of them meer Trifles, and all three manifestly false. If this be the way these Gentlemen deal with the World in those Criticisms, where we have not Leisure to defeat them, their Readers had need be cautious how they rely upon their Credit; and whether this Proceeding can be reconciled to Humanity or Truth, let those who think it worth their while, determine.

It is agreed, this Answerer would have succeeded much better, if he had stuck wholly to his Business as a Commentator upon the Tale of a Tub, wherein it cannot be deny'd that he hath been of some Service to the Publick, and has given very fair Conjectures towards clearing up some difficult Passages; but, it is the frequent Error of those Men (otherwise very commendable for their Labors) to make Excursions beyond their Talent and their Office, by pretending to point out the Beauties and the Faults; which is no part of their Trade, which they always fail in, which the World never expected from them, nor gave them any thanks for endeavouring at. The Part of Min-ellius, or Farnaby would have fallen in with his Genius, and might have been serviceable to many Readers who cannot enter into the abstruser Parts of that Discourse; but Optat ephippia bos piger. The dull, unwieldy, ill-shaped Ox would needs put on the Furniture of a Horse, not considering he was born to Labour, to plow the Ground for the Sake of superior Beings, and that he has neither the Shape, Mettle nor Speed of that nobler Animal he would affect to personate.

It is another Pattern of this Answerer's fair dealing, to give us Hints that the Author is dead, and yet to lay the Suspicion upon somebody, I know not who, in the Country; to which can be only returned, that *he is absolutely mistaken in all his Conjectures; and surely Conjectures are at best too light a Pretence to allow a Man to assign a Name in Publick. He condemns a Book, and consequently the Author, of whom he is utterly ignorant, yet at the same time fixes in Print, what he thinks a disadvantageous Character upon those who never deserved it. A Man who receives a Buffet in the Dark may be allowed to be vexed; but it is an odd kind of Revenge to go to Cuffs in broad day with the first he meets with, and lay the last Nights Injury at his Door. And thus much for this* discreet, candid, pious, *and* ingenious *Answerer.*

How the Author came to be without his Papers, is a Story not proper to be told, and of very little use, being a private Fact of which the Reader would believe as little or as much as he thought good. He had however a blotted Copy by him, which he intended to have writ over, with many Alterations, and this the Publishers were well aware of, having put it into the Booksellers Preface, that they apprehended a surreptitious Copy, which was to be altered, *&c. This though not regarded by Readers, was a real Truth, only the surreptitious Copy was rather that which was printed, and they made all hast they could, which indeed was needless; the Author not being at all prepared; but he has been told, the Bookseller was in much Pain, having given a good Sum of Money for the Copy.*

In the Authors Original Copy there were not so many Chasms as appear in the Book; and why some of them were left he knows not; had the Publication been trusted to him, he should have made several Corrections of Passages against which nothing hath been ever objected. He should likewise have altered a few of those that seem with any Reason to be excepted against, but to deal freely, the greatest Number he should have left untouch'd, as never suspecting it possible any wrong Interpretations could be made of them.

The Author observes, at the End of the Book there is a Discourse called A Fragment; *which he more wondered to see in Print than all the rest. Having been a most imperfect Sketch with the Addition of a few loose Hints, which he once lent a Gentleman who had designed a Discourse of somewhat the same Subject; he never thought of it afterwards, and it was a sufficient Surprize to see it pieced up together, wholly out of the Method and Scheme he had intended, for it was the Ground-work of a much larger Discourse, and he was sorry to observe the Materials so foolishly employ'd.*

There is one farther Objection made by those who have answered this Book, as well as by some others, that Peter *is frequently made to repeat Oaths and Curses. Every Reader observes it was necessary to know that* Peter *did Swear and Curse. The Oaths are not printed out, but only supposed, and the Idea of an Oath is not immoral, like the Idea of a Prophane or Immodest Speech. A Man may laugh at the Popish Folly of cursing People to Hell, and imagine them swearing, without any crime; but lewd Words, or dangerous Opinions though printed by halves, fill the Readers Mind with ill Idea's; and of these the Author cannot be accused. For the judicious Reader will find that the severest Stroaks of Satyr in his Book are levelled against the modern Custom of Employing Wit upon those Topicks, of which there is a remarkable Instance in the* [92nd] *Page, as well as in several others, tho' perhaps once or twice exprest in too free a manner, excusable only for the Reasons already alledged. Some Overtures have been made by a third Hand to the Bookseller for the Author's altering those Passages which he thought might require it. But it seems the Bookseller will not hear of any such Thing, being apprehensive it might spoil the Sale of the Book.*

The Author cannot conclude this Apology, without making this one Reflection; that, as Wit is the noblest and most useful Gift of humane Nature, so Humor is the most agreeable, and where these two enter far into the Composition of any Work, they will render it always acceptable to the World. Now, the great Part of those who have no Share or Tast of either, but by their Pride, Pedantry and Ill Manners, lay themselves bare to the Lashes of Both, think the Blow is weak, because they are insensible, and where Wit hath any mixture of Raillery; 'Tis but calling it Banter, *and the work is done. This Polite Word of theirs was first borrowed from the Bullies in* White-Fryars, *then fell among the Footmen, and at last retired to the Pedants, by whom it is applied as properly to the Productions of Wit, as if I should apply it to Sir* Isaac Newton's *Mathematicks, but, if this* Bantring *as they call it, be so despisable a Thing, whence comes it to pass they have such a perpetual Itch towards it themselves? To instance only in the Answerer already mentioned; it is grievous to see him in some of his Writings at every turn going out of his way to be waggish, to tell us of a* Cow *that prickt up her Tail, and in his answer to this Discourse, he says it is all a Farce and a Ladle; With other Passages equally shining. One may say of these* Impedimenta Literarum, *that Wit ows them a Shame; and they cannot take wiser*

Counsel than to keep out of harms way, or at least not to come till they are sure they are called.

To conclude; with those Allowances above-required, this Book should be read, after which the Author conceives, few things will remain which may not be excused in a young Writer. He wrote only to the Men of Wit and Tast, and he thinks he is not mistaken in his Accounts, when he says they have been all of his side, enough to give him the vanity of telling his Name, wherein the World with all its wise Conjectures, is yet very much in the dark, which Circumstance is no disagreeable Amusement either to the Publick or himself.

The Author is informed, that the Bookseller has prevailed on several Gentlemen, to write some explanatory Notes, for the goodness of which he is not to answer, having never seen any of them, nor intends it, till they appear in Print, when it is not unlikely he may have the Pleasure to find twenty Meanings, which never enter'd into his Imagination.

June 3. 1709.

POSTSCRIPT.

SInce the writing of this which was about a Year ago; a Prostitute Bookseller hath publish'd a foolish Paper, under the Name of Notes on the Tale of a Tub, with some Account of the Author, and with an Insolence which I suppose is punishable by Law, hath presumed to assign certain Names. It will be enough for the Author to assure the World, that the Writer of that Paper is utterly wrong in all his Conjectures upon that Affair. The Author farther asserts that the whole Work is entirely of one Hand, which every Reader of Judgment will easily discover. The Gentleman who gave the Copy to the Bookseller, being a Friend of the Author, and using no other Liberties besides that of expunging certain Passages where now the Chasms appear under the Name of Desiderata. But if any Person will prove his Claim to three Lines in the whole Book, let him step forth and tell his Name and Titles, upon which the Bookseller shall have Orders to prefix them to the next Edition, and the Claimant shall from henceforward be acknowledged the undisputed Author.

TO
The Right Honourable,
JOHN
Lord SOMMERS.

My LORD,

THO' the Author has written a large Dedication, yet That being address'd to a Prince, whom I am never likely to have the Honor of being known to; A Person, besides, as far as I can observe, not at all regarded, or thought on by any of our present Writers; And, being wholly free from that Slavery, which Booksellers usually lie under, to the Caprices of Authors; I think it a wise Piece of Presumption, to inscribe these Papers to your Lordship, and to implore your Lordship's Protection of them. God and your Lordship know their Faults, and their Merits; for as to my own Particular, I am altogether a Stranger to the Matter; And, tho' every Body else should be equally ignorant, I do not fear the Sale of the Book, at all the worse, upon that Score. Your Lordship's Name on the Front, in Capital Letters, will at any time get off one Edition: Neither would I desire any other Help, to grow an Alderman, than a Patent for the sole Priviledge of Dedicating to your Lordship.

I should now, in right of a Dedicator, give your Lordship a List of your own Virtues, and at the same time, be very unwilling to offend your Modesty; But, chiefly, I should celebrate your Liberality towards Men of great Parts and small Fortunes, and give you broad Hints, that I mean my self. And, I was just going on in the usual Method, to peruse a hundred or two of Dedications, and transcribe an Abstract, to be applied to your Lordship; But, I was diverted by a certain Accident. For, upon the

Covers of these Papers, I casually observed written in large
Letters, the two following Words, *DETUR DIGNISSIMO;*
which, for ought I knew, might contain some important Meaning. But, it unluckily fell out, that none of the Authors I employ,
understood *Latin* (tho' I have them often in pay, to translate out
of that Language) I was therefore compelled to have recourse to
the Curate of our Parish, who Englished it thus, *Let it be given to
the Worthiest;* And his Comment was, that the Author meant, his
Work should be dedicated to the sublimest Genius of the Age,
for Wit, Learning, Judgment, Eloquence and Wisdom. I call'd
at a Poet's Chamber (who works for my Shop) in an Alley hard
by, shewed him the Translation, and desired his Opinion, who
it was that the Author could mean; He told me, after some Consideration, that Vanity was a Thing he abhorr'd; but by the Description, he thought Himself to be the Person aimed at; And, at
the same time, he very kindly offer'd his own Assistance *gratis*,
towards penning a Dedication to Himself. I desired him, however, to give a second Guess; Why then, said he, It must be I, or
my Lord *Sommers*. From thence I went to several other Wits of
my Acquaintance, with no small Hazard and Weariness to my
Person, from a prodigious Number of dark, winding Stairs; But
found them all in the same Story, both of your Lordship and
themselves. Now, your Lordship is to understand, that this Proceeding was not of my own Invention; For, I have somewhere
heard, it is a Maxim, that those, to whom every Body allows the
second Place, have an undoubted Title to the First.

THIS infallibly convinced me, that your Lordship was the
Person intended by the Author. But, being very unacquainted in
the Style and Form of Dedications, I employ'd those Wits aforesaid, to furnish me with Hints and Materials, towards a Panegyrick upon your Lordship's Virtues.

IN two Days, they brought me ten Sheets of Paper, fill'd up on
every Side. They swore to me, that they had ransack'd whatever
could be found in the Characters of *Socrates, Aristides, Epami-
nondas, Cato, Tully, Atticus*, and other hard Names, which I cannot
now recollect. However, I have Reason to believe, they imposed
upon my Ignorance, because, when I came to read over their
Collections, there was not a Syllable there, but what I and every

body else knew as well as themselves: Therefore, I grievously suspect a Cheat; and, that these Authors of mine, stole and transcribed every Word, from the universal Report of Mankind. So that I look upon my self, as fifty Shillings out of Pocket, to no manner of Purpose.

IF, by altering the Title, I could make the same Materials serve for another Dedication (as my Betters have done) it would help to make up my Loss: But, I have made several Persons, dip here and there in those Papers, and before they read three Lines, they have all assured me, plainly, that they cannot possibly be applied to any Person besides your Lordship.

I expected, indeed, to have heard of your Lordship's Bravery, at the Head of an Army; Of your undaunted Courage, in mounting a Breach, or scaling a Wall; Or, to have had your Pedigree trac'd in a Lineal Descent from the House of *Austria*; Or, of your wonderful Talent at Dress and Dancing; Or, your Profound Knowledge in *Algebra*, *Metaphysicks*, and the Oriental Tongues. But to ply the World with an old beaten Story of your Wit, and Eloquence, and Learning, and Wisdom, and Justice, and Politeness, and Candor, and Evenness of Temper in all Scenes of Life; Of that great Discernment in Discovering, and Readiness in Favouring deserving Men; with forty other common Topicks: I confess, I have neither Conscience, nor Countenance to do it. Because, there is no Virtue, either of a Publick or Private Life, which some Circumstances of your own, have not often produced upon the Stage of the World; And those few, which for want of Occasions to exert them, might otherwise have pass'd unseen or unobserved by your *Friends*, your *Enemies* have at length brought to Light.

'TIS true, I should be very loth, the Bright Example of your Lordship's Virtues should be lost to After-Ages, both for their sake and your own; but chiefly, because they will be so very necessary to adorn the History of a *late Reign*; And That is another Reason, why I would forbear to make a Recital of them here; Because, I have been told by Wise Men, that as Dedications have run for some Years past, a good Historian will not be apt to have Recourse thither, in search of Characters.

THERE is one Point, wherein I think we Dedicators would do

well to change our Measures; I mean, instead of running on so far, upon the Praise of our Patrons *Liberality*, to spend a Word or two, in admiring their *Patience*. I can put no greater Compliment on your Lordship's, than by giving you so ample an Occasion to exercise it at present. Tho', perhaps, I shall not be apt to reckon much Merit to your Lordship upon that Score, who having been formerly used to tedious Harangues, and sometimes to as little Purpose, will be the readier to pardon this, especially, when it is offered by one, who is with all Respect and Veneration,

    My LORD,

        Your Lordship's most Obedient,

          and most Faithful Servant,

            The Bookseller.

THE
BOOKSELLER
TO THE
READER.

IT is now *Six Years* since these *Papers* came first to my *Hands,* which seems to have been about a *Twelvemonth* after they were writ: For, the *Author* tells us in his *Preface* to the first *Treatise,* that he hath calculated it for the *Year* 1697, and in several *Passages* of that *Discourse,* as well as the second, it appears, they were written about that *Time.*

As to the *Author,* I can give no manner of *Satisfaction;* However, I am credibly informed that this *Publication* is without his *Knowledge;* for he concludes the *Copy* is lost, having lent it to a *Person,* since dead, and being never in *Possession* of it after: So that, whether the *Work* received his last *Hand,* or, whether he intended to fill up the defective *Places,* is like to remain a *Secret.*

If I should go about to tell the *Reader,* by what *Accident,* I became *Master* of these *Papers,* it would, in this unbelieving *Age,* pass for little more than the *Cant,* or *Jargon* of the *Trade.* I, therefore, gladly spare both him and my self so unnecessary a *Trouble.* There yet remains a difficult *Question,* why I publish'd them no sooner. I forbore upon two *Accounts:* First, because I thought I had better *Work* upon my *Hands;* and Secondly, because, I was not without some *Hope* of hearing from the *Author,* and receiving his *Directions.* But, I have been lately alarm'd with *Intelligence* of a surreptitious *Copy,* which a certain great *Wit* had new polish'd and refin'd, or as our present *Writers* express themselves, fitted to the Humor of the *Age;* as they have already done, with great *Felicity,* to Don Quixot, Boccalini, la Bruyere and other *Authors.* However, I thought it fairer *Dealing,* to offer the whole *Work* in its *Naturals.* If any *Gentleman* will please to furnish me with a *Key,* in order to explain the more difficult *Parts,* I shall very gratefully acknowledge the *Favour,* and print it by it self.

c

THE

Epistle Dedicatory,

TO

His Royal Highness

PRINCE POSTERITY.

SIR,

I HERE present *Your Highness* with the Fruits of a very few leisure Hours, stollen from the short Intervals of a World of Business, and of an Employment quite alien from such Amusements as this: The poor Production of that Refuse of Time which has lain heavy upon my Hands, during a long Prorogation of Parliament, a great Dearth of Forein News, and a tedious Fit of rainy Weather: For which, and other Reasons, it cannot chuse extreamly to deserve such a Patronage as that of *Your Highness*, whose numberless Virtues in so few Years, make the World look upon You as the future Example to all Princes: For altho' *Your Highness* is hardly got clear of Infancy, yet has the universal learned World already resolv'd upon appealing to Your future Dictates with the lowest and most resigned Sub-

---

The Citation out of Irenæus *in the* Title-Page, *which seems to be all* Gibberish, *is a Form of Initiation used antiently by the* Marcosian Hereticks. W. Wotton.

It is the usual Style of decry'd Writers to appeal to Posterity, *who is here represented as a Prince in his Nonage, and* Time *as his Governour, and the Author begins in a way very frequent with him, by personating other Writers, who sometimes offer such Reasons and Excuses for publishing their Works as they ought chiefly to conceal and be asham'd of.*

mission: Fate having decreed You sole Arbiter of the Productions of human Wit, in this polite and most accomplish'd Age. Methinks, the Number of Appellants were enough to shock and startle any Judge of a Genius less unlimited than Yours: But in order to prevent such glorious Tryals, the *Person* (it seems) to whose Care the Education of *Your Highness* is committed, has resolved (as I am told) to keep you in almost an universal Ignorance of our Studies, which it is Your inherent Birth-right to inspect.

It is amazing to me, that this *Person* should have Assurance in the face of the Sun, to go about persuading *Your Highness*, that our Age is almost wholly illiterate, and has hardly produc'd one Writer upon any Subject. I know very well, that when *Your Highness* shall come to riper Years, and have gone through the Learning of Antiquity, you will be too curious to neglect inquiring into the Authors of the very age before You: And to think that this *Insolent*, in the Account he is preparing for Your View, designs to reduce them to a Number so insignificant as I am asham'd to mention; it moves my Zeal and my Spleen for the Honor and Interest of our vast flourishing Body, as well as of my self, for whom I know by long Experience, he has profess'd, and still continues a peculiar Malice.

'Tis not unlikely, that when *Your Highness* will one day peruse what I am now writing, You may be ready to expostulate with Your *Governour* upon the Credit of what I here affirm, and command Him to shew You some of our Productions. To which he will answer, (for I am well informed of his Designs) by asking *Your Highness*, where they are? and what is become of them? and pretend it a Demonstration that there never were any, because they are not then to be found: Not to be found! Who has mislaid them? Are they sunk in the Abyss of Things? 'Tis certain, that in their own Nature they were *light* enough to swim upon the Surface for all Eternity. Therefore the Fault is in Him, who tied Weights so heavy to their Heels, as to depress them to the Center. Is their very Essence destroyed? Who has annihilated them? Were they drowned by *Purges* or martyred by *Pipes*? Who administred them to the Posteriors of ——? But that it may no longer be a Doubt with *Your Highness*, who is to be the Author of this universal Ruin; I beseech You to observe that large and terrible *Scythe* which your *Governour* affects to bear continually about him. Be pleased to remark the Length and Strength, the Sharpness and Hardness of his *Nails* and *Teeth*: Consider his baneful abominable *Breath*, Enemy to Life and Matter, infectious and corrupting: And then reflect whether it be possible for any mortal Ink and Paper of this Generation to make a suitable Resistance. Oh, that *Your Highness* would one day resolve to disarm this Usurping * *Maitre du Palais*, of his furious Engins, and bring Your Empire † *hors de Page*.

It were endless to recount the several Methods of Tyranny and Destruction, which Your *Governour* is pleased to practise upon this Occasion. His inveterate Malice is such to the Writings of our Age, that of several Thousands produced yearly from this renowned City, before the next Revolution of the Sun, there is not one to be heard of: Unhappy Infants, many of them barbarously destroyed, before they have so much as learnt their *Mother-Tongue* to beg for Pity. Some he stifles in their Cradles, others he frights into Convulsions, whereof they suddenly die; Some he flays alive, others he tears Limb from Limb: Great Numbers are offered to *Moloch*, and the rest tainted by his Breath, die of a languishing Consumption.

But the Concern I have most at Heart, is for our Corporation of *Poets*, from whom I am preparing a Petition to *Your Highness*, to be subscribed with the Names of one hundred thirty six of the first Rate, but whose immortal Productions are never likely to reach your Eyes, tho' each of them is now an humble and an earnest Appellant for the Laurel, and has large comely Volumes ready to shew for a Support to his Pretensions. The *never-dying* Works of these illustrious Persons, Your *Governour*, Sir, has devoted to unavoidable Death, and *Your Highness* is to be made believe, that our Age has never arrived at the Honor to produce one single Poet.

We confess *Immortality* to be a great and powerful Goddess, but in vain we offer up to her our Devotions and our Sacrifices, if *Your Highness*'s *Governour*, who has usurped the *Priesthood*,

---

* *Comptroller*.   † *Out of Guardianship*.

must by an unparallel'd Ambition and Avarice, wholly intercept and devour them.

To affirm that our Age is altogether Unlearned, and devoid of Writers in any kind, seems to be an Assertion so bold and so false, that I have been sometime thinking, the contrary may almost be proved by uncontroulable Demonstration. 'Tis true indeed, that altho' their Numbers be vast, and their Productions numerous in proportion, yet are they hurryed so hastily off the Scene, that they escape our Memory, and delude our Sight. When I first thought of this Address, I had prepared a copious List of *Titles* to present *Your Highness* as an undisputed Argument for what I affirm. The Originals were posted fresh upon all Gates and Corners of Streets; but returning in a very few Hours to take a Review, they were all torn down, and fresh ones in their Places: I enquired after them among Readers and Booksellers, but I enquired in vain, the *Memorial of them was lost among Men, their Place was no more to be found*: and I was laughed to scorn, for a *Clown* and a *Pedant*, without all Taste and Refinement, little versed in the Course of *present* Affairs, and that knew nothing of what had pass'd in the best Companies of Court and Town. So that I can only avow in general to *Your Highness*, that we do abound in Learning and Wit; but to fix upon Particulars, is a Task too slippery for my slender Abilities. If I should venture in a windy Day, to affirm to *Your Highness*, that there is a huge Cloud near the *Horizon* in the Form of a *Bear*, another in the *Zenith* with the Head of an *Ass*, a third to the Westward with Claws like a *Dragon*; and *Your Highness* should in a few Minutes think fit to examine the Truth; 'tis certain, they would all be changed in Figure and Position, new ones would arise, and all we could agree upon would be, that Clouds there were, but that I was grosly mistaken in the *Zoography* and *Topography* of them.

BUT Your *Governour*, perhaps, may still insist, and put the Question: What is then become of those immense Bales of Paper, which must needs have been employ'd in such Numbers of Books? Can these also be wholly annihilate, and so of a sudden as I pretend? What shall I say in return of so invidious an Objection? It ill befits the Distance between *Your Highness* and Me, to send You for ocular Conviction to a *Jakes*, or an *Oven*; to the

Windows of a *Bawdy-house*, or to a sordid *Lanthorn*. Books, like Men their Authors, have no more than one Way of coming into the World, but there are ten Thousand to go out of it, and return no more.

I profess to *Your Highness*, in the Integrity of my Heart, that what I am going to say is literally true this Minute I am writing: What Revolutions may happen before it shall be ready for your Perusal, I can by no means warrant: However I beg You to accept it as a Specimen of our Learning, our Politeness and our Wit. I do therefore affirm upon the Word of a sincere Man, that there is now actually in being, a certain Poet called *John Dryden*, whose Translation of *Virgil* was lately printed in a large Folio, well bound, and if diligent search were made, for ought I know, is yet to be seen. There is another call'd *Nahum Tate*, who is ready to make Oath that he has caused many Rheams of Verse to be published, whereof both himself and his Bookseller (if lawfully required) can still produce authentick Copies, and therefore wonders why the World is pleased to make such a Secret of it. There is a Third, known by the Name of *Tom Durfey*, a Poet of a vast Comprehension, an universal Genius, and most profound Learning. There are also one Mr. *Rymer*, and one Mr. *Dennis*, most profound Criticks. There is a Person styl'd Dr. *Bentley*, who has written near a thousand Pages of immense Erudition, *giving a full and true Account* of a certain *Squable* of wonderful Importance between himself and a Bookseller: He is a Writer of infinite Wit and Humour; no Man raillyes with a better Grace, and in more sprightly Turns. Farther, I avow to *Your Highness*, that with these Eyes I have beheld the Person of *William Wotton*, B.D. who has written a good sizeable Volume against a *Friend of Your Governor* (from whom, alas! he must therefore look for little Favour) in a most gentlemanly Style, adorned with utmost Politeness and Civility; replete with Discoveries equally valuable for their Novelty and Use: and embellish'd with *Traits* of Wit so poignant and so apposite, that he is a worthy Yokemate to his foremention'd *Friend*.

Why should I go upon farther Particulars, which might fill a Volume with the just Elogies of my cotemporary Brethren? I shall bequeath this Piece of Justice to a larger Work: wherein I intend to write a Character of the present Set of *Wits* in our Nation: Their Persons I shall describe particularly, and at Length, their Genius and Understandings in *Mignature*.

IN the mean time, I do here make bold to present *Your Highness* with a faithful Abstract drawn from the Universal Body of all Arts and Sciences, intended wholly for your Service and Instruction: Nor do I doubt in the least, but *Your Highness* will peruse it as carefully, and make as considerable Improvements, as *other* young *Princes* have already done by the many Volumes of late Years written for a Help to their Studies.

THAT *Your Highness* may advance in Wisdom and Virtue, as well as Years, and at last out-shine all Your Royal Ancestors, shall be the daily Prayer of,

S I R ,

Decemb.
  1697.

Your Highness's

Most devoted, &c.

THE
PREFACE.

THE Wits of the present Age being so very numerous and penetrating, it seems, the Grandees of *Church* and *State* begin to fall under horrible Apprehensions, lest these Gentlemen, during the intervals of a long Peace, should find leisure to pick Holes in the weak sides of Religion and Government. To prevent which, there has been much Thought employ'd of late upon certain Projects for taking off the Force, and Edge of those formidable Enquirers, from canvasing and reasoning upon such delicate Points. They have at length fixed upon one, which will require some Time as well as Cost, to perfect. Mean while the Danger hourly increasing, by new Levies of Wits all appointed (as there is Reason to fear) with Pen, Ink, and Paper which may at an hours Warning be drawn out into Pamphlets, and other Offensive Weapons, ready for immediate Execution: It was judged of absolute necessity, that some present Expedient be thought on, till the main Design can be brought to Maturity. To this End, at a Grand Committee, some Days ago, this important Discovery was made by a certain curious and refined Observer; That Sea-men have a Custom when they meet a *Whale*, to fling him out an empty *Tub*, by way of Amusement, to divert him from laying violent Hands upon the Ship. This Parable was immediately mythologiz'd: The *Whale* was interpreted to be *Hobbes's Leviathan*, which tosses and plays with all other Schemes of Religion and Government, whereof a great many are hollow, and dry, and empty, and noisy, and wooden, and given to Rotation. This is the *Leviathan* from whence the terrible Wits of our Age are said to borrow their Weapons. The *Ship* in danger, is easily understood to be its old Antitype the *Commonwealth*. But, how to analyze the *Tub*, was a Matter of difficulty; when after long Enquiry and Debate, the literal Meaning was preserved: And it was decreed, that in order to prevent these *Leviathans* from tossing and sporting with the *Commonwealth*, (which of it self is too apt to *fluctuate*) they should be diverted from that Game by a *Tale of a Tub*. And my Genius being conceived to lye not unhappily that way, I had the Honor done me to be engaged in the Performance.

THIS is the sole Design in publishing the following Treatise, which I hope will serve for an *Interim* of some Months to employ those unquiet Spirits, till the perfecting of that great Work: into the Secret of which, it is reasonable the courteous Reader should have some little Light.

IT is intended that a large Academy be erected, capable of containing nine thousand seven hundred forty and three Persons; which by modest Computation is reckoned to be pretty near the current Number of *Wits* in this Island. These are to be disposed into the several Schools of this Academy, and there pursue those Studies to which their Genius most inclines them. The Undertaker himself will publish his Proposals with all convenient speed, to which I shall refer the curious Reader for a more particular Account, mentioning at present only a few of the Principal Schools. There is first, a large *Pederastick* School, with *French* and *Italian* Masters. There is also, the *Spelling* School, *a very spacious Building*: the School of *Looking Glasses*: The School of *Swearing*: the School of *Criticks*: the School of *Salivation*: The School of *Hobby-Horses*: The School of *Poetry*: * The School of *Tops*: the School of *Spleen*: The School of *Gaming*: with many others too tedious to recount. No Person to be admitted Member into any of these Schools, without an Attestation under two sufficient Persons Hands, certifying him to be a *Wit*.

BUT, to return. I am sufficiently instructed in the Principal Duty of a Preface, if my Genius were capable of arriving at it. Thrice have I forced my Imagination to make the *Tour* of my Invention, and thrice it has returned empty; the latter having been wholly drained by the following Treatise. Not so, my more successful Brethren the *Moderns*, who will by no means let slip a

---

* *This I think the Author should have omitted, it being of the very same Nature with the* School of Hobby-Horses, *if one may venture to censure one who is so severe a Censurer of others, perhaps with too little Distinction.*

Preface or Dedication, without some notable distinguishing
Stroke, to surprize the Reader at the Entry, and kindle a Wonderful Expectation of what is to ensue. Such was that of a most
ingenious Poet, who solliciting his Brain for something new,
compared himself to the *Hangman*, and his Patron to the *Patient*:
This was * *Insigne, recens, indictum ore alio*. When I
went thro' That necessary and noble † Course of   * *Hor.*
Study, I had the happiness to observe many such †*Reading Prefa-*
egregious Touches, which I shall not injure the   *ces,* &c.
Authors by transplanting: Because I have re-
marked, that nothing is so very tender as a *Modern* Piece of Wit,
and which is apt to suffer so much in the Carriage. Some things
are extreamly witty *to day*, or *fasting*, or *in this place*, or *at eight a
clock*, or *over a Bottle*, or *spoke by Mr*. What d'y'call'm, or *in a
Summer's Morning*: Any of which, by the smallest Transposal or
Misapplication, is utterly annihilate. Thus, *Wit* has its Walks and
Purlieus, out of which it may not stray the breadth of an Hair,
upon peril of being lost. The *Moderns* have artfully fixed this
Mercury, and reduced it to the Circumstances of Time, Place and
Person. Such a Jest there is, that will not pass out of *Covent-Gar-
den*; and such a one, that is no where intelligible but at *Hide-Park*
Corner. Now, tho' it sometimes tenderly affects me to consider,
that all the towardly Passages I shall deliver in the following
Treatise, will grow quite out of date and relish with the first
shifting of the present Scene: yet I must need subscribe to the
Justice of this Proceeding: because, I cannot imagine why we
should be at Expence to furnish Wit for succeeding Ages, when
the former have made no sort of Provision for ours; wherein I
speak the Sentiment of the very newest, and consequently the
most Orthodox Refiners, as well as my own. However, being
extreamly sollicitous, that every accomplished Person who has
got into the Taste of Wit, calculated for this present Month of
August, 1697, should descend to the very *bottom* of all the *Sublime*
throughout this Treatise; I hold fit to lay down this general
Maxim. Whatever Reader desires to have a thorow Comprehension of an Author's Thoughts, cannot take a better Method, than

* *Something extraordinary, new and never hit upon before.*

by putting himself into the Circumstances and Postures of Life,
that the Writer was in, upon every important Passage as it
flow'd from his Pen; For this will introduce a Parity and strict
Correspondence of Idea's between the Reader and the Author.
Now, to assist the diligent Reader in so delicate an Affair, as
far as brevity will permit, I have recollected, that the shrewdest
Pieces of this Treatise, were conceived in Bed, in a Garret: At
other times (for a Reason best known to my self) I thought fit to
sharpen my Invention with Hunger; and in general, the whole
Work was begun, continued, and ended, under a long Course of
Physick, and a great want of Money. Now, I do affirm, it will be
absolutely impossible for the candid Peruser to go along with
me in a great many bright Passages, unless upon the several
Difficulties emergent, he will please to capacitate and prepare
himself by these Directions. And this I lay down as my principal
Postulatum.

BECAUSE I have profess'd to be a most devoted Servant of all
Modern Forms: I apprehend some curious *Wit* may object
against me, for proceeding thus far in a Preface, without de-
claiming, according to the Custom, against the Multitude of
Writers whereof the whole Multitude of Writers most reasonably complains. I am just come from perusing some hundreds of
Prefaces, wherein the Authors do at the very beginning address
the gentle Reader concerning this enormous Grievance. Of
these I have preserved a few Examples, and shall set them down
as near as my Memory has been able to retain them.

One begins thus;

For a Man to set up for a Writer, when the Press swarms with, &c.

Another;

*The Tax upon Paper does not lessen the Number of Scriblers, who
daily pester*, &c.

Another;

*When every little Would-be-wit takes Pen in hand, 'tis in vain to enter
the Lists*, &c.

Another;

To observe what Trash the Press swarms with, &c.

Another;

SIR, *It is meerly in Obedience to your Commands that I venture*

*into the Publick; for who upon a less Consideration would be of a Party
with such a Rabble of Scriblers,* &c.

Now, I have two Words in my own Defence, against this Objection. First: I am far from granting the Number of Writers,
a Nuisance to our Nation, having strenuously maintained the
contrary in several Parts of the following Discourse. Secondly:
I do not well understand the Justice of this Proceeding, because
I observe many of these polite Prefaces, to be not only from the
same Hand, but from those who are most voluminous in their
several Productions. Upon which I shall tell the Reader a short
Tale.

A Mountebank in Leicester-Fields, *had drawn a huge Assembly
about him. Among the rest, a fat unweildy Fellow, half stifled in the
Press, would be every fit crying out, Lord! what a filthy Crowd is here?
Pray, good People, give way a little, Bless me! what a Devil has rak'd
this Rabble together: Z——ds, what squeezing is this! Honest Friend,
remove your Elbow. At last, a* Weaver *that stood next him could hold
no longer: A Plague confound you* (said he) *for an over-grown Sloven;
and who* (in the Devil's Name) *I wonder, helps to make up the Crowd
half so much as your self? Don't you consider* (with a Pox) *that you take
up more room with that Carkass than any five here? Is not the Place as
free for us as for you? Bring your own Guts to a reasonable Compass* (and
be d——n'd) *and then I'll engage we shall have room enough for us all.*

There are certain common Privileges of a Writer, the Benefit
whereof, I hope, there will be no Reason to doubt; Particularly,
that where I am not understood, it shall be concluded, that something very useful and profound is couch't underneath: And
again, that whatever word or Sentence is Printed in a different
Character, shall be judged to contain something extraordinary
either of *Wit* or *Sublime.*

As for the Liberty I have thought fit to take of praising my
self, upon some Occasions or none; I am sure it will need no Excuse, if a Multitude of great Examples be allowed sufficient
Authority: For it is here to be noted, that *Praise* was originally a
Pension paid by the World: but the *Moderns* finding the Trouble
and Charge too great in collecting it, have lately bought out the
Fee-Simple; since which time, the Right of Presentation is wholly
in our selves. For this Reason it is, that when an Author makes

his own Elogy, he uses a certain form to declare and insist upon
his Title, which is commonly in these or the like words, *I speak
without Vanity*; which I think plainly shews it to be a Matter of
Right and Justice. Now, I do here once for all declare, that in
every Encounter of this Nature, thro' the following Treatise, the
Form aforesaid is imply'd; which I mention, to save the Trouble
of repeating it on so many Occasions.

'TIs a great Ease to my Conscience that I have writ so elaborate and useful a Discourse without one grain of Satyr intermixt;
which is the sole point wherein I have taken leave to dissent
from the famous Originals of our Age and Country. I have observ'd some Satyrists to use the Publick much at the Rate that
Pedants do a naughty Boy ready Hors'd for Discipline: First expostulate the Case, then plead the Necessity of the Rod, from
great Provocations, and conclude every Period with a Lash. Now,
if I know any thing of Mankind, these Gentlemen might very
well spare their Reproof and Correction: For there is not,
through all Nature, another so callous and insensible a Member
as the *World's Posteriors*, whether you apply to it the *Toe* or the
Birch. Besides, most of our late Satyrists seem to lye under a sort
of Mistake, that because *Nettles* have the Prerogative to Sting,
therefore all *other Weeds* must do so too. I make not this Comparison out of the least Design to detract from these worthy
Writers: For it is well known among *Mythologists*, that *Weeds*
have the Preeminence over all other Vegetables; and therefore
the first *Monarch* of this Island, whose Taste and Judgment were
so acute and refined, did very wisely root out the *Roses* from the
Collar of the *Order*, and plant the *Thistles* in their stead as the
nobler Flower of the two. For which Reason it is conjectured by
profounder Antiquaries, that the Satyrical Itch, so prevalent in
this part of our Island, was first brought among us from beyond
the *Tweed*. Here may it long flourish and abound; May it survive
and neglect the Scorn of the World, with as much Ease and Contempt as the World is insensible to the Lashes of it. May their
own Dullness, or that of their Party, be no Discouragement for
the Authors to proceed; but let them remember, it is with *Wits*
as with *Razors*, which are never so apt to *cut* those they are employ'd on, as when they have *lost their Edge*. Besides, those whose

Teeth are too rotten to bite, are best of all others, qualified to revenge that Defect with their Breath.

I am not like other Men, to envy or undervalue the Talents I cannot reach; for which Reason I must needs bear a true Honour to this large eminent Sect of our *British* Writers. And I hope, this little Panegyrick will not be offensive to their Ears, since it has the Advantage of being only designed for themselves. Indeed, Nature her self has taken order, that Fame and Honour should be purchased at a better Pennyworth by Satyr, than by any other Productions of the Brain; the World being soonest provoked to *Praise* by *Lashes*, as Men are to *Love*. There is a Problem in an ancient Author, why Dedications, and other Bundles of Flattery run all upon stale musty Topicks, without the smallest Tincture of any thing New; not only to the torment and nauseating of the *Christian* Reader, but (if not suddenly prevented) to the universal spreading of that pestilent Disease, the Lethargy, in this Island: whereas, there is very little Satyr which has not something in it untouch'd before. The Defects of the former are usually imputed to the want of Invention among those who are Dealers in that kind: But, I think, with a great deal of Injustice; the Solution being easy and natural. For, the Materials of Panegyrick being very few in Number, have been long since exhausted: For, as Health is but one Thing, and has been always the same, whereas Diseases are by thousands, besides new and daily Additions; So, all the Virtues that have been ever in Mankind, are to be counted upon a few Fingers, but his Follies and Vices are innumerable, and Time adds hourly to the Heap. Now, the utmost a poor Poet can do, is to get by heart a List of the Cardinal Virtues, and deal them with his utmost Liberality to his Hero or his Patron: He may ring the Changes as far as it will go, and vary his Phrase till he has talk'd round; but the Reader quickly finds, * *Plutarch.* it is all * *Pork*, with a little variety of Sawce: For there is no inventing Terms of Art beyond our Idea's; and when Idea's are exhausted, Terms of Art must be so too.

BUT, tho' the Matter for Panegyrick were as fruitful as the Topicks of Satyr, yet would it not be hard to find out a sufficient Reason, why the latter will be always better received than the first. For, this being bestowed only upon one or a few Persons at a time, is sure to raise Envy, and consequently ill words from the rest, who have no share in the Blessing: But Satyr being levelled at all, is never resented for an offence by any, since every indivi- dual Person makes bold to understand it of others, and very wisely removes his particular Part of the Burthen upon the shoulders of the World, which are broad enough, and able to bear it. To this purpose, I have sometimes reflected upon the Difference between *Athens* and *England*, with respect to the Point before us. In the *Attick* * Commonwealth, * *Vid. Xenoph.* it was the Privilege and Birth-right of every Citi- zen and Poet, to rail aloud and in publick, or to expose upon the Stage by Name, any Person they pleased, tho' of the greatest Figure, whether a *Creon*, an *Hyperbolus*, an *Alcibiades*, or a *Demo- sthenes*: But on the other side, the least reflecting word let fall against the *People* in general, was immediately caught up, and revenged upon the Authors, however considerable for their Quality or their Merits. Whereas, in *England* it is just the Reverse of all this. Here, you may securely display your utmost *Rhetorick* against Mankind, in the Face of the World; tell them, "*That all are* "*gone astray; That there is none that doth good, no not one; That we live* "*in the very Dregs of Time; That Knavery and Atheism are Epidemick* "*as the Pox; That Honesty is fled with Astræa*; with any other Com- mon places *equally* new and eloquent, which are furnished by the * *Splendida bilis.* And when you have done, the * *Hor.* whole Audience, far from being offended, shall return you thanks as a Deliverer of precious and useful Truths. Nay farther; It is but to venture your Lungs, and you may preach in *Covent-Garden* against Foppery and Fornication, and *something else*: Against Pride, and Dissimulation, and Bribery, at *White Hall*: You may expose Rapine and Injustice in the *Inns* of *Court* Chappel: And in a *City* Pulpit be as fierce as you please, against Avarice, Hypocrisie and Extortion. 'Tis but a *Ball* bandied to and fro, and every Man carries a *Racket* about Him to strike it from himself among the rest of the Company. But on the other side, whoever should mistake the Nature of things so far, as to drop but a single Hint in publick, How *such a one*, starved half

---

* *Spleen.*

the Fleet, and half-poison'd the rest: How *such a one*, from a true Principle of *Love* and *Honour*, pays no Debts but for *Wenches* and *Play*: How *such a one* has got a Clap and runs out of his Estate: * How *Paris* bribed by *Juno* and *Venus*, loath to offend either Party, slept out the whole Cause on the Bench: Or, how *such an Orator* makes long Speeches in the Senate with much Thought, little Sense, and to no Purpose; whoever, I say, should venture to be thus particular, must expect to be imprisoned for *Scandalum Magnatum*: to have *Challenges* sent him; to be sued for *Defamation*; and to be *brought before the Bar of the House*.

BUT I forget that I am expatiating on a Subject, wherein I have no concern, having neither a Talent nor an Inclination for Satyr; On the other side, I am so entirely satisfied with the whole present Procedure of human Things, that I have been for some Years preparing Materials towards *A Panegyrick upon the World*; to which I intended to add a Second Part, entituled, *A Modest Defence of the Proceedings of the Rabble in all Ages*. Both these I had Thoughts to publish by way of Appendix to the following Treatise; but finding my Common-Place-Book fill much slower than I had reason to expect, I have chosen to defer them to another Occasion. Besides, I have been unhappily prevented in that Design, by a certain Domestick Misfortune, in the Particulars whereof, tho' it would be very seasonable, and much in the *Modern* way, to inform the *gentle Reader*, and would also be of great Assistance towards extending this Preface into the Size now in Vogue, which by Rule ought to be *large* in proportion as the subsequent Volume is *small*; Yet I shall now dismiss our impatient Reader from any farther Attendance at the *Porch*; and having duly prepared his Mind by a preliminary Discourse, shall gladly introduce him to the sublime Mysteries that ensue.

---

* Juno *and* Venus *are Money and a Mistress, very powerful Bribes to a Judge, if Scandal says true. I remember such Reflexions were cast about that time, but I cannot fix the Person intended here.*

A TALE

OF A

TUB, &c.

SECT. I.

The INTRODUCTION.

WHOEVER hath an Ambition to be heard in a Crowd, must press, and squeeze, and thrust, and climb with indefatigable Pains, till he has exalted himself to a certain Degree of Altitude above them. Now, in all Assemblies, tho' you wedge them ever so close, we may observe this peculiar Property; that, over their Heads there is Room enough; but how to reach it, is the difficult Point; It being as hard to get quit of *Number* as of *Hell*;

> **——— Evadere ad auras,*
> *Hoc opus, hic labor est.*

To this End, the Philosopher's Way in all Ages has been by erecting certain *Edifices in the Air*; But, whatever Practice and Reputation these kind of Structures have formerly possessed, or may still continue in, not excepting even that of *Socrates*, when he was suspended in a Basket to help Contemplation; I think, with due Submission, they seem to labour under two In-

---

* *But to return, and view the cheerful Skies;*
  In this the Task and mighty Labour lies.

d

conveniences. *First*, That the Foundations being laid too high, they have been often out of *Sight*, and ever out of *Hearing*. *Secondly*, That the Materials, being very transitory, have suffer'd much from Inclemencies of Air, especially in these North-West Regions.

THEREFORE, towards the just Performance of this great Work, there remain but three Methods that I can think on; Whereof the Wisdom of our Ancestors being highly sensible, has, to encourage all aspiring Adventurers, thought fit to erect three wooden Machines, for the Use of those Orators who desire to talk much without Interruption. These are, the *Pulpit*, the *Ladder*, and the *Stage-Itinerant*. For, as to the *Bar*, tho' it be compounded of the same Matter, and designed for the same Use, it cannot however be well allowed the Honor of a fourth, by reason of its level or inferior Situation, exposing it to perpetual Interruption from Collaterals. Neither can the *Bench* it self, tho raised to a proper Eminency, put in a better Claim, whatever its Advocates insist on. For if they please to look into the original Design of its Erection, and the Circumstances or Adjuncts subservient to that Design, they will soon acknowledge the present Practice exactly correspondent to the Primitive Institution, and both to answer the Etymology of the Name, which in the *Phœnician* Tongue is a Word of great Signification, importing, if literally interpreted, *The Place of Sleep*; but in common Acceptation, *A Seat well bolster'd and cushion'd, for the Repose of old and gouty Limbs: Senes ut in otia tuta recedant*. Fortune being indebted to them this Part of Retaliation, that, as formerly, they have long *Talkt*, whilst others *Slept*, so now they may *Sleep* as long whilst others *Talk*.

BUT if no other Argument could occur to exclude the *Bench* and the *Bar* from the List of Oratorial Machines, it were sufficient, that the Admission of them would overthrow a Number which I was resolved to establish, whatever Argument it might cost me; in imitation of that prudent Method observed by many other Philosophers and great Clerks, whose chief Art in Division has been, to grow fond of some proper mystical Number, which their Imaginations have rendred Sacred, to a Degree, that they force common Reason to find room for it in every part of Nature;

reducing, including, and adjusting every *Genus* and *Species* within that Compass, by coupling some against their Wills, and banishing others at any Rate. Now among all the rest, the profound Number *THREE* is that which hath most employ'd my sublimest Speculations, nor ever without wonderful Delight. There is now in the Press, (and will be publish'd next Term) a Panegyrical Essay of mine upon this Number, wherein I have by most convincing Proofs, not only reduced the *Senses* and the *Elements* under its Banner, but brought over several Deserters from its two great Rivals *SEVEN* and *NINE*.

Now, the first of these Oratorial Machines in Place as well as Dignity, is the *Pulpit*. Of *Pulpits* there are in this Island several sorts; but I esteem only That made of Timber from the *Sylva Caledonia*, which agrees very well with our Climate. If it be upon its Decay, 'tis the better, both for Conveyance of Sound, and for other Reasons to be mentioned by and by. The Degree of Perfection in Shape and Size, I take to consist, in being extreamly narrow, with little Ornament, and best of all without a Cover; (for by antient Rule, it ought to be the only uncover'd *Vessel* in every Assembly where it is rightfully used) by which means, from its near Resemblance to a Pillory, it will ever have a mighty Influence on human Ears.

Of *Ladders* I need say nothing: 'Tis observed by Foreigners themselves, to the Honor of our Country, that we excel all Nations in our Practice and Understanding of this Machine. The ascending Orators do not only oblige their Audience in the agreeable Delivery, but the whole World in their *early* Publication of these Speeches; which I look upon as the choicest Treasury of our *British* Eloquence, and whereof I am informed, that worthy Citizen and Bookseller, Mr. *John Dunton*, hath made a faithful and a painful Collection, which he shortly designs to publish in Twelve Volumes in Folio, illustrated with Copper-Plates. A Work highly useful and curious, and altogether worthy of such a Hand.

The last Engine of Orators, is the * *Stage Itinerant*, erected

---

* *Is the* Mountebank's Stage, *whose Orators the Author determines either to the* Gallows *or a* Conventicle.

with much Sagacity, † *sub Jove pluvio, in triviis & quadriviis.* It is the great Seminary of the two former, and its Orators are sometimes preferred to the One, and sometimes to the Other, in proportion to their Deservings, there being a strict and perpetual Intercourse between all three.

FROM this accurate Deduction it is manifest, that for obtaining Attention in Publick, there is of necessity required a *superiour Position of Place.* But, altho' this Point be generally granted, yet the Cause is little agreed in; and it seems to me, that very few Philosophers have fallen into a true, natural Solution of this *Phænomenon.* The deepest Account, and the most fairly digested of any I have yet met with, is this, That Air being a heavy Body, and therefore (according to the System of * *Epicurus*) continually descending, must needs be more so, when loaden and press'd down by Words; which are also Bodies of much Weight and Gravity, as it is manifest from those deep *Impressions* they make and leave upon us; and therefore must be delivered from a due Altitude, or else they will neither carry a good Aim, nor fall down with a sufficient Force.

Lucret.
Lib. 2.

> * *Corpoream quoque enim vocem constare fatendum est,*
> *Et sonitum, quoniam possunt impellere Sensus.* Lucr. *Lib.* 4.

AND I am the readier to favour this Conjecture, from a common Observation; that in the several Assemblies of these Orators, Nature it self hath instructed the Hearers, to stand with their Mouths open, and erected parallel to the Horizon, so as they may be intersected by a perpendicular Line from the Zenith to the Center of the Earth. In which Position, if the Audience be well compact, every one carries home a Share, and little or nothing is lost.

I confess, there is something yet more refined in the Contrivance and Structure of our Modern Theatres. For, First; the Pit is sunk below the Stage with due regard to the Institution above-deduced; that whatever *weighty* Matter shall be delivered thence (whether it be *Lead* or *Gold*) may fall plum into the Jaws of cer-

---

† *In the Open Air, and in Streets where the greatest Resort is.*
* *'Tis certain then, that* Voice *that thus can wound*
Is all Material; Body *every* Sound.

tain *Criticks* (as I think they are called) which stand ready open to devour them. Then, the Boxes are built round, and raised to a Level with the Scene, in deference to the Ladies, because, That large Portion of Wit laid out in raising Pruriences and Protuberances, is observ'd to run much upon a Line, and ever in a Circle. The whining Passions and little starved Conceits, are gently wafted up by their own extreme Levity, to the middle Region, and there fix and are frozen by the frigid Understandings of the Inhabitants. Bombast and Buffoonry, by Nature lofty and light, soar highest of all, and would be lost in the Roof, if the prudent Architect had not with much Foresight contrived for them a fourth Place, called *the Twelve-Peny Gallery*, and there planted a suitable Colony, who greedily intercept them in their Passage.

Now this Physico-logical Scheme of Oratorial Receptacles or Machines, contains a great Mystery, being a Type, a Sign, an Emblem, a Shadow, a Symbol, bearing Analogy to the spacious Commonwealth of Writers, and to those Methods by which they must exalt themselves to a certain Eminency above the inferiour World. By the *Pulpit* are adumbrated the Writings of our *Modern Saints* in *Great Britain*, as they have spiritualized and refined them from the Dross and Grossness of *Sense* and *Human Reason*. The Matter, as we have said, is of rotten Wood, and that upon two Considerations; Because it is the Quality of rotten Wood to give *Light* in the Dark: And secondly, Because its Cavities are full of Worms: which is a * Type with a Pair of Handles, having a Respect to the two principal Qualifications of the Orator, and the two different Fates attending upon his Works.

THE *Ladder* is an adequate Symbol of *Faction* and of *Poetry*, to both of which so noble a Number of Authors are indebted for their Fame. † Of *Faction*, because   *   *   *   *   *

---

* *The Two Principal Qualifications of a Phanatick Preacher are, his Inward Light, and his Head full of Maggots, and the Two different Fates of his Writings are, to be burnt or Worm eaten.*

† *Here is pretended a Defect in the Manuscript, and this is very frequent with our Author, either when he thinks he cannot say any thing worth Reading, or when he has no mind to enter on the Subject, or when it is a Matter of little Moment, or perhaps to amuse his Reader (whereof he is frequently very fond) or lastly, with some Satyrical Intention.*

*	*	*	*	*	*	*	*	*

Hiatus in MS.

*	*	*	*	*	*	*	*	*
*	*	*	*	*	*	*	*	*

*   *   *   * Of *Poetry*, because its Orators do *perorare* with a Song; and because climbing up by slow Degrees, Fate is sure to turn them off before they can reach within many Steps of the Top: And because it is a Preferment attained by transferring of Propriety, and a confounding of *Meum* and *Tuum*.

UNDER the *Stage-Itinerant* are couched those Productions designed for the Pleasure and Delight of Mortal Man; such as, *Six-peny-worth of Wit*, Westminster *Drolleries, Delightful Tales, Compleat Jesters*, and the like; by which the Writers of and for *GRUB-STREET*, have in these latter Ages so nobly triumph'd over *Time*; have clipt his Wings, pared his Nails, filed his Teeth, turn'd back his Hour-Glass, blunted his Scythe, and drawn the Hob-Nails out of his Shoes. It is under this Classis, I have presumed to list my present Treatise, being just come from having the Honor conferred upon me, to be adopted a Member of that Illustrious Fraternity.

Now, I am not unaware, how the Productions of the *Grub-street* Brotherhood, have of late Years fallen under many Prejudices, nor how it has been the perpetual Employment of two *Junior* start-up Societies, to ridicule them and their Authors, as unworthy their established Post in the Commonwealth of Wit and Learning. Their own Consciences will easily inform them, whom I mean; Nor has the World been so negligent a Looker on, as not to observe the continual Efforts made by the Societies of *Gresham* and of * *Will*'s to edify a Name and Reputation upon the Ruin of OURS. And this is yet a more feeling Grief to Us upon the Regards of Tenderness as well as of Justice, when we reflect on their Proceedings, not only as unjust, but as ungrateful, undutiful, and unnatural. For, how can it be forgot by the

---

* Will'*s* Coffee-House, *was formerly the Place where the Poets usually met, which tho it be yet fresh in memory, yet in some Years may be forgot, and want this Explanation.*

World or themselves, (to say nothing of our own Records, which are full and clear in the Point) that they both are Seminaries, not only of our *Planting*, but our *Watering* too? I am informed, Our two *Rivals* have lately made an Offer to enter into the Lists with united Forces, and Challenge us to a Comparison of Books, both as to *Weight* and *Number*. In Return to which, (with Licence from our *President*) I humbly offer two Answers: First, We say, the proposal is like that which *Archimedes* made upon a * *smaller* Affair, including an   *Viz. *About* moving the Earth.* impossibility in the Practice; For, where can they find Scales of *Capacity* enough for the first, or an Arithmetician of *Capacity* enough for the Second. Secondly, We are ready to accept the Challenge, but with this Condition, that a third indifferent Person be assigned, to whose impartial Judgment it shall be left to decide, which Society each Book, Treatise or Pamphlet do most properly belong to. This Point, God knows, is very far from being fixed at present; For, We are ready to produce a Catalogue of some Thousands, which in all common Justice ought to be entitled to Our Fraternity, but by the revolted and new-fangled Writers, most perfidiously ascribed to the others. Upon all which, we think it very unbecoming our Prudence, that the Determination should be remitted to the Authors themselves; when our Adversaries by Briguing and Caballing, have caused so universal a Defection from us, that the greatest Part of our Society hath already deserted to them, and our nearest Friends begin to stand aloof, as if they were half-ashamed to own Us.

THIS is the utmost I am authorized to say upon so ungrateful and melancholy a Subject; because We are extreme unwilling to inflame a Controversy, whose Continuance may be so fatal to the Interests of Us All, desiring much rather that Things be amicably composed; and We shall so far advance on our Side, as to be ready to receive the two *Prodigals* with open Arms, whenever they shall think fit to return from their *Husks* and their *Harlots*; which I think from the * present Course of their   *Virtuoso Experiments, and Modern Comedies.* Studies they most properly may be said to be engaged in; and like an indulgent Parent, continue to them our Affection and our Blessing.

BUT the greatest Maim given to that general Reception, which the Writings of our Society have formerly received, (next to the transitory State of all sublunary Things,) hath been a superficial Vein among many Readers of the present Age, who will by no means be persuaded to inspect beyond the Surface and the Rind of Things; whereas, *Wisdom* is a *Fox*, who after long hunting, will at last cost you the Pains to dig out: 'Tis a *Cheese*, which by how much the richer, has the thicker, the homelier, and the courser Coat; and whereof to a judicious Palate, the *Maggots* are the best. 'Tis a *Sack-Posset*, wherein the deeper you go, you will find it the sweeter. *Wisdom* is a *Hen*, whose *Cackling* we must value and consider, because it is attended with an *Egg*; But then, lastly, 'tis a *Nut*, which unless you chuse with Judgment, may cost you a Tooth, and pay you with nothing but a *Worm*. In consequence of these momentous Truths, the *Grubæan* Sages have always chosen to convey their Precepts and their Arts, shut up within the Vehicles of Types and Fables, which having been perhaps more careful and curious in adorning, than was altogether necessary, it has fared with these Vehicles after the usual Fate of Coaches over-finely painted and gilt; that the transitory Gazers have so dazzled their Eyes, and fill'd their Imaginations with the outward Lustre, as neither to regard or consider, the Person or the Parts of the Owner within. A Misfortune we undergo with somewhat less Reluctancy, because it has been common to us with *Pythagoras*, *Æsop*, *Socrates*, and other of our Predecessors.

HOWEVER, that neither the World nor our selves may any longer suffer by such misunderstandings, I have been prevailed on, after much importunity from my Friends, to travel in a compleat and laborious Dissertation upon the prime Productions of our Society, which besides their beautiful Externals for the Gratification of superficial Readers, have darkly and deeply couched under them, the most finished and refined Systems of all Sciences and Arts; as I do not doubt to lay open by Untwisting or Unwinding, and either to draw up by Exantlation, or display by Incision.

THIS great Work was entred upon some Years ago, by one of our most eminent Members: He began with the History of

† *Reynard* the *Fox*, but neither lived to publish his Essay, nor to proceed farther in so useful an Attempt which is very much to be lamented, because the Discovery he made, and communicated with his Friends, is now universally received; nor, do I think, any of the Learned will dispute, that famous Treatise to be a compleat Body of Civil Knowledge, and the *Revelation*, or rather the *Apocalyps* of all State-*Arcana*. But the Progress I have made is much greater, having already finished my Annotations upon several Dozens; From some of which, I shall impart a few Hints to the candid Reader, as far as will be necessary to the Conclusion at which I aim.

THE first Piece I have handled is that of *Tom Thumb*, whose Author was a *Pythagorean* Philosopher. This dark Treatise contains the whole Scheme of the *Metempsychosis*, deducing the Progress of the Soul thro' all her Stages.

THE next is Dr. *Faustus*, penn'd by *Artephius*, an Author *bonæ notæ*, and an *Adeptus*; He published it in the *nine hundred eighty fourth Year of his Age; this   *He lived a thousand.* Writer proceeds wholly by *Reincrudation*, or in the *via humida*: And the Marriage between *Faustus* and *Helen*, does most conspicuously dilucidate the fermenting of the *Male* and *Female Dragon*.

WHITTINGTON *and his Cat*, is the Work of that Mysterious *Rabbi, Jehuda Hannasi*, containing a Defence of the *Gemara* of the *Jerusalem Misna*, and its just preference to that of *Babylon*, contrary to the vulgar Opinion.

THE *Hind and Panther*. This is the Master-piece of a famous ||Viz *in the*   Writer || now living, intended for a compleat *Year* 1698.   Abstract of sixteen thousand Schoolmen from *Scotus* to *Bellarmin*.

TOMMY POTTS. Another Piece supposed by the same Hand, by way of Supplement to the former.

THE *Wise Men of* Goatham, *cum Appendice*. This is a Treatise of immense Erudition, being the great Original and Fountain of

---

† *The Author seems here to be mistaken, for I have seen a Latin Edition of* Reynard *the* Fox, *above an hundred Years old, which I take to be the Original; for the rest it has been thought by many People to contain some Satyrical Design in it.*

those Arguments, bandied about both in *France* and *England*, for a just Defence of the *Modern* Learning and Wit, against the Presumption, the Pride, and the Ignorance of the *Antients*. This unknown Author hath so exhausted the Subject, that a penetrating Reader will easily discover, whatever hath been written since upon that Dispute, to be little more than Repetition. * An Abstract of this Treatise hath been lately published by a *worthy Member* of our Society.

THESE Notices may serve to give the Learned Reader an Idea as well as a Taste of what the whole Work is likely to produce: wherein I have now altogether circumscribed my Thoughts and my Studies; and if I can bring it to a Perfection before I die, shall reckon I have well employ'd the † poor Remains of an unfortunate Life. This indeed is more than I can justly expect from a Quill worn to the Pith in the Service of the State, in *Pro's* and *Con's* upon *Popish Plots*, and ‖ *Meal-Tubs*, and *Exclusion Bills*, and *Passive Obedience*, and *Addresses of Lives and Fortunes*; and *Prerogative*, and *Property*, and *Liberty of Conscience*, and *Letters to a Friend*: From an Understanding and a Conscience, threadbare and ragged with perpetual turning; From a Head broken in a hundred places, by the Malignants of the opposite Factions, and from a Body spent with Poxes ill cured, by trusting to Bawds and Surgeons, who, (as it afterwards appeared) were profess'd Enemies to Me and the Government, and revenged their Party's Quarrel upon my Nose and Shins. Four-score and eleven Pamphlets have I writ under three Reigns, and for the Service of six and thirty Factions. But finding the State has no farther Occasion for Me and my Ink, I retire willingly to draw it out into Speculations more becoming a Philosopher, having, to my unspeakable Comfort, passed a long Life, with a Conscience void of Offence.

---

* *This I suppose to be understood of Mr.* Wottons *Discourse of Antient and Modern Learning.*

† *Here the Author seems to personate* L'estrange, Dryden, *and some others, who after having past their Lives in Vices, Faction and Falshood, have the Impudence to talk of Merit and Innocence and Sufferings.*

‖ *In King* Charles *the* II. *Time, there was an Account of a* Presbyterian *Plot, found in a Tub, which then made much Noise.*

BUT to return. I am assured from the Reader's Candor, that the brief Specimen I have given, will easily clear all the rest of our Society's Productions from an Aspersion grown, as it is manifest, out of Envy and Ignorance: That they are of little farther Use or Value to Mankind, beyond the common Entertainments of their Wit and their Style: For these I am sure have never yet been disputed by our keenest Adversaries: In both which, as well as the more profound and mystical Part, I have throughout this Treatise closely followed the most applauded Originals. And to render all compleat, I have with much Thought and Application of Mind, so ordered, that the chief Title prefixed to it, (I mean, That under which I design it shall pass in the common Conversations of Court and Town) is modelled exactly after the Manner peculiar to *Our* Society.

I confess to have been somewhat liberal in the Business of * Titles, having observed the Humor of multiplying them, to bear great Vogue among certain Writers, whom I exceedingly Reverence. And indeed, it seems not unreasonable, that Books, the Children of the Brain, should have the Honor to be Christned with variety of Names, as well as other Infants of Quality. Our famous *Dryden* has ventured to proceed a Point farther, endeavouring to introduce also a Multiplicity of * *God-fathers*; which is an Improvement of much more Advantage, upon a very obvious Account. 'Tis a Pity this admirable Invention has not been better cultivated, so as to grow by this time into general Imitation, when such an Authority serves it for a Precedent. Nor have my Endeavours been wanting to second so useful an Example: But it seems, there is an unhappy Expence usually annexed to the Calling of a God-Father, which was clearly out of my Head, as it is very reasonable to believe. Where the Pinch lay, I cannot certainly affirm; but having employ'd a World of Thoughts and Pains, to split my Treatise into forty Sections, and having entreated forty Lords of my Acquaintance, that they would do me the Honor to stand, they all made it a Matter of Conscience, and sent me their Excuses.

* The Title Page in the Original was so torn, that it was not possible to recover several Titles which the Author here speaks of.

* See Virgil translated, &c.

SECTION II.

ONCE upon a Time, there was a Man who had Three *Sons by one Wife, and all at a Birth, neither could the Mid-Wife tell certainly which was the Eldest. Their Father died while they were young, and upon his Death-Bed, calling the Lads to him, spoke thus,

SONS; *because I have purchased no Estate, nor was born to any, I have long considered of some good Legacies to bequeath You; And at last, with much Care as well as Expence, have provided each of you* (here they are) *a new* † *Coat. Now, you are to understand, that these Coats have two Virtues contained in them: One is, that with good wearing, they will last you fresh and sound as long as you live: The other is, that they will grow in the same proportion with your Bodies, lengthning and widening of themselves, so as to be always fit. Here, let me see them on you before I die. So, very well, Pray Children, wear them clean, and brush them often. You will find in my* ‖ *Will* (here it is) *full Instructions in every particular concerning the Wearing and Management of your Coats; wherein you must be very exact, to avoid the Penalties I have appointed for every Transgression or Neglect, upon which your future Fortunes will entirely depend. I have also commanded in my Will, that you should live together in one House like Brethren and Friends, for then you will be sure to thrive, and not otherwise.*

HERE the Story says, this good Father died, and the three Sons went all together to seek their Fortunes.

I shall not trouble you with recounting what Adventures they met for the first seven Years, any farther than by taking notice, that they carefully observed their Father's Will, and kept their Coats in very good Order; That they travelled thro'

---

* *By these three Sons,* Peter, Martyn *and* Jack; Popery, *the* Church *of* England, *and our* Protestant Dissenters *are designed.* W. Wotton.

† *By his Coats which he gave his Sons, the Garments of the* Israelites. W. Wotton.

An Error (*with Submission*) *of the learned Commentator; for by the Coats are meant the Doctrine and Faith of* Christianity, *by the Wisdom of the Divine Founder fitted to all Times, Places and Circumstances.* Lambin.

‖ *The New Testament.*

several Countries, encountred a reasonable Quantity of **Gyants** and slew certain Dragons.

BEING now arrived at the proper Age for producing themselves, they came up to Town, and fell in love with the Ladies, but especially three, who about that time were in chief Reputation: The * Dutchess *d' Argent, Madame de Grands Titres*, and the Countess *d' Orgueil*. On their first Appearance, our three Adventurers met with a very bad Reception; and soon with great Sagacity guessing out the Reason, they quickly began to improve in the good Qualities of the Town: They Writ, and Raillyed, and Rhymed, and Sung, and Said, and said Nothing; They Drank, and Fought, and Whor'd, and Slept, and Swore, and took Snuff: They went to new Plays on the first Night, haunted the *Chocolate*-Houses, beat the Watch, lay on Bulks, and got Claps: They bilkt Hackney-Coachmen, ran in Debt with Shop-keepers, and lay with their Wives: They kill'd Bayliffs, kick'd Fidlers down Stairs, eat at *Locket*'s, loytered at *Will*'s: They talk'd of the Drawing-Room and never came there, Dined with Lords they never saw; Whisper'd a Dutchess, and spoke never a Word; exposed the Scrawls of their Laundress for Billets-doux of Quality: came ever just from Court and were never seen in it; attended the Levee *sub dio*; Got a list of Peers by heart in one Company, and with great Familiarity retailed them in another. Above all, they constantly attended those Committees of Senators who are silent in the *House*, and loud in the *Coffee-House*, where they nightly adjourn to chew the Cud of Politicks, and are encompass'd with a Ring of Disciples, who lye in wait to catch up their Droppings. The three Brothers had acquired forty other Qualifications of the like Stamp, too tedious to recount, and by consequence, were justly reckoned the most accomplish'd Persons in Town: But all would not suffice, and the Ladies aforesaid continued still inflexible: To clear up which Difficulty, I must with the

---

* *Their Mistresses are the* Dutchess d'Argent, Madamoiselle de Grands Titres, *and the* Countess d'Orgueil, *i. e.* Covetousness, Ambition *and* Pride, *which were the three great Vices that the ancient Fathers inveighed against as the first Corruptions of Christianity.* W. Wotton.

Reader's good Leave and Patience, have recourse to some Points of Weight, which the Authors of that Age have not sufficiently illustrated.

For, * about this Time it happened a Sect arose, whose Tenents obtained and spread very far, especially in the *Grand Monde*, and among every Body of good Fashion. They worshipped a sort of *Idol*, who, as their Doctrine delivered, did daily create Men, by a kind of Manufactory Operation. This † *Idol* they placed in the highest Parts of the House, on an Altar erected about three Foot: He was shewn in the Posture of a *Persian* Emperor, sitting on a *Superficies*, with his Legs interwoven under him. This God had a *Goose* for his Ensign; whence it is, that some Learned Men pretend to deduce his Original from *Jupiter Capitolinus*. At his left Hand, beneath the Altar, *Hell* seemed to open, and catch at the Animals the *Idol* was creating; to prevent which, certain of his Priests hourly flung in Pieces of the uninformed Mass, or Substance, and sometimes whole Limbs already enlivened, which that horrid Gulph insatiably swallowed, terrible to behold. The *Goose* was also held a subaltern Divinity, or *Deus minorum Gentium*, before whose Shrine was sacrificed that Creature, whose hourly Food is humane Gore, and who is in so great Renown abroad, for being the Delight and Favourite of the ‖ *Ægyptian Cercopithecus*. Millions of these Animals were cruelly slaughtered every Day, to appease the Hunger of that consuming Deity. The chief *Idol* was also worshipped as the Inventor of the *Yard* and the *Needle*, whether as the God of Seamen, or on Account of certain other mystical Attributes, hath not been sufficiently cleared.

The Worshippers of this Deity had also a System of their Belief, which seemed to turn upon the following Fundamental. They held the Universe to be a large *Suit of Cloaths*, which *invests* every Thing: That the Earth is *invested* by the Air; The Air is

---

* *This is an Occasional Satyr upon Dress and Fashion, in order to introduce what follows.*

† *By this* Idol *is meant a Taylor.*

‖ *The* Ægyptians *worship'd a Monkey, which Animal is very fond of eating Lice, styled here Creatures that feed on Human Gore.*

invested by the Stars; and the Stars are *invested* by the *Primum Mobile*. Look on this Globe of Earth, you will find it to be a very compleat and fashionable *Dress*. What is that which some call *Land*, but a fine Coat faced with Green? or the Sea, but a Wast-coat of Water-Tabby? Proceed to the particular Works of the Creation, you will find how curious *Journey-man* Nature hath been, to trim up the *vegetable* Beaux: Observe how sparkish a Perewig adorns the Head of a *Beech*, and what a fine Doublet of white Satin is worn by the *Birch*. To conclude from all, what is Man himself but a * *Micro-Coat*, or rather a compleat Suit of Cloaths with all its Trimmings? As to his Body, there can be no dispute; but examine even the Acquirements of his Mind, you will find them all contribute in their Order, towards furnishing out an exact Dress: To instance no more; Is not Religion a *Cloak*, Honesty a *Pair of Shoes*, worn out in the Dirt, Self-love a *Surtout*, Vanity a *Shirt*, and Conscience a *Pair of Breeches*, which, tho' a Cover for Lewdness as well as Nastiness, is easily slipt down for the Service of both.

THESE *Postulata* being admitted, it will follow in due Course of Reasoning, that those Beings which the World calls im-properly *Suits of Cloaths*, are in Reality the most refined Species of Animals, or to proceed higher, that they are Rational Crea-tures, or Men. For, is it not manifest, that They live, and move, and talk, and perform all other Offices of Human Life? Are not Beauty, and Wit, and Mien, and Breeding, their inseparable Proprieties? In short, we see nothing but them, hear nothing but them. Is it not they who walk the Streets, fill up *Parlia-ment*——, *Coffee*—, *Play*—, *Bawdy-Houses*? 'Tis true indeed, that these Animals, which are vulgarly called *Suits of Cloaths*, or *Dresses*, do according to certain Compositions receive different Appellations. If one of them be trimm'd up with a Gold Chain, and a red Gown, and a white Rod, and a great Horse, it is called a *Lord-Mayor*; If certain Ermins and Furs be placed in a certain Position, we stile them a *Judge*, and so, an apt Conjunction of Lawn and black Sattin, we intitle a *Bishop*.

---

* *Alluding to the Word* Microcosm, *or a little World, as Man hath been called by Philosophers.*

OTHERS of these Professors, though agreeing in the main System, were yet more refined upon certain Branches of it; and held that Man was an Animal compounded of two *Dresses*, the *Natural* and the *Celestial Suit*, which were the Body and the Soul: That the Soul was the outward, and the Body the inward Cloathing; that the latter was *ex traduce*; but the former of daily Creation and Circumfusion. This last they proved by *Scripture*, because, *in Them we Live, and Move, and have our Being*: As likewise by Philosophy, because they are *All in All, and All in every Part*. Besides, said they, separate these two, and you will find the Body to be only a sensless unsavory Carcass. By all which it is manifest, that the outward Dress must needs be the Soul.

To this System of Religion were tagged several subaltern Doctrines, which were entertained with great Vogue: as particularly, the Faculties of the Mind were deduced by the Learned among them in this manner: *Embroidery*, was *Sheer wit; Gold Fringe* was *agreeable Conversation, Gold Lace* was *Repartee*, a huge long *Periwig* was *Humor*, and a *Coat full of Powder* was very good *Raillery*: All which required abundance of *Finesse* and *Delicatesse* to manage with Advantage, as well as a strict Observance after Times and Fashions.

I have with much Pains and Reading, collected out of antient Authors, this short Summary of a Body of Philosophy and Divinity, which seems to have been composed by a Vein and Race of Thinking, very different from any other Systems, either *Antient* or *Modern*. And it was not meerly to entertain or satisfy the Reader's Curiosity, but rather to give him Light into several Circumstances of the following Story: that knowing the State of Dispositions and Opinions in an Age so remote, he may better comprehend those great Events which were the issue of them. I advise therefore the courteous Reader, to peruse with a world of Application, again and again, whatever I have written upon this Matter. And so leaving these broken Ends, I carefully gather up the chief Thread of my Story, and proceed.

THESE Opinions therefore were so universal, as well as the Practices of them, among the refined Part of Court and Town, that our three Brother-Adventurers, as their Circumstances then stood, were strangely at a loss. For, on the one side, the three Ladies they address'd themselves to, (whom we have named already) were ever at the very Top of the Fashion, and abhorred all that were below it, but the breadth of a Hair. On the other side, their Father's Will was very precise, and it was the main Precept in it, with the greatest Penalties annexed, not to add to, or diminish from their Coats, one Thread, without a positive Command in the Will. Now, the Coats their Father had left them were, 'tis true, of very good Cloth, and besides, so neatly sown, you would swear they were all of a Piece, but at the same time, very plain, and with little or no Ornament; And it happened, that before they were a Month in Town, great * *Shoulder-knots* came up; Strait, all the World was *Shoulder-knots*; no approaching the Ladies *Ruelles* without the *Quota* of *Shoulder-knots: That Fellow*, cries one, *has no Soul; where is his Shoulder-knot?* Our three Brethren soon discovered their Want by sad Experience, meeting in their Walks with forty Mortifications and Indignities. If they went to the *Play-house*, the Door-keeper shewed them into the Twelve-peny Gallery. If they called a Boat, says a Water-man, *I am first Sculler*: If they stept to the *Rose* to take a Bottle, the Drawer would cry, *Friend, we sell no Ale*. If they went to visit a Lady, a Footman met them at the Door with, *Pray send up your Message*. In this unhappy Case, they

---

The first part of the Tale *is the History of* Peter; *thereby* Popery *is exposed, every Body knows the* Papists *have made great Additions to Christianity, that indeed is the great Exception which the* Church of England *makes against them, accordingly* Peter *begins his Pranks, with adding a* Shoulder-knot *to his Coat.* W. Wotton.

His Description of the Cloth of which the Coat was made, has a farther meaning than the Words may seem to import, "The Coats their Father had left them, were of very good Cloth, and besides so neatly Sown, you would swear it had been all of a Piece, but at the same time very plain with little or no Ornament." *This is the distinguishing Character of the Christian Religion.* Christiana Religio absoluta & simplex, *was* Ammianus Marcellinus's *Description of it, who was himself a Heathen.* W. Wotton.

* *By this is understood the first introducing of Pageantry, and unnecessary Ornaments in the Church, such as were neither for Convenience nor Edification, as a* Shoulder-knot, *in which there is neither Symmetry nor Use.*

e

went immediately to consult their Father's Will, read it over and over, but not a Word of the *Shoulder-knot*. What should they do? What Temper should they find? Obedience was absolutely necessary, and yet *Shoulder-knots* appeared extreamly requisite. After much Thought, one of the Brothers who happened to be more *Book-learned* than the other two, said he had found an Expedient. '*Tis true*, said he, *there is nothing here in this Will*, * totidem verbis, *making mention of* Shoulder-knots, *but I dare conjecture, we may find them* inclusivè, *or* totidem syllabis. This Distinction was immediately approved by all; and so they fell again to examine the Will. But their evil Star had so directed the Matter, that the first Syllable was not to be found in the whole Writing. Upon which Disappointment, he, who found the former Evasion, took heart, and said, *Brothers, there is yet Hopes; for tho' we cannot find them* totidem verbis, *nor* totidem syllabis, *I dare engage we shall make them out* tertio modo, *or* totidem literis. This Discovery was also highly commended, upon which they fell once more to the Scrutiny, and soon picked out *S, H, O, U, L, D, E,* R; when the same Planet, Enemy to their Repose, had wonderfully contrived, that a *K* was not to be found. Here was a weighty Difficulty! But the distinguishing Brother (for whom we shall hereafter find a Name) now his Hand was in, proved by a very good Argument, that *K* was a modern illegitimate Letter, unknown to the Learned Ages, nor any where to be found in antient Manuscripts. 'Tis true, said he, the Word *Calendæ* hath in † *Q.V.C.* been sometimes writ with a *K*, but erroneously, for in the best Copies it is ever spelt with a *C*. And by consequence it was a gross Mistake in our Language to spell *Knot* with a *K*, but that from henceforward, he would take care it should be writ with a *C*. Upon this, all farther Difficulty vanished; *Shoulder-Knots* were

† *Quibusdam Veteribus Codicibus.*

---

* *When the Papists cannot find any thing which they want in Scripture, they go to* Oral *Tradition: Thus* Peter *is introduced satisfy'd with the Tedious way of looking for all the Letters of any Word, which he has occasion for in the* Will, *when neither the constituent Syllables, nor much less the whole Word, were there* in Terminis. W. Wotton.

† *Some antient Manuscripts.*

made clearly out, to be *Jure Paterno*, and our three Gentlemen swaggered with as large and as flanting ones as the best.

BUT, as human Happiness is of a very short Duration, so in those Days were human Fashions, upon which it entirely depends. *Shoulder-Knots* had their Time, and we must now imagine them in their Decline; for a certain Lord came just from *Paris*, with fifty Yards of *Gold Lace* upon his Coat, exactly trimm'd after the Court-Fashion of that *Month*. In two Days, all Mankind appear'd closed up in Bars of * *Gold Lace*: whoever durst peep abroad without his Complement of *Gold Lace*, was as scandalous as a ——, and as ill received among the Women. What should our three Knights do in this momentous Affair? They had sufficiently strained a Point already, in the Affair of *Shoulder-Knots*: Upon Recourse to the Will, nothing appeared there but *altum silentium*. That of the *Shoulder-Knots* was a loose, flying, circumstantial Point; but this of *Gold Lace*, seemed too considerable an Alteration without better Warrant; it did *aliquo modo essentiæ adhærere*, and therefore required a positive Precept. But about this time it fell out, that the Learned Brother aforesaid, had read *Aristotelis Dialectica*, and especially that wonderful Piece *de Interpretatione*, which has the Faculty of teaching its Readers to find out a Meaning in every Thing but it self; like Commentators on the *Revelations*, who proceed Prophets without understanding a Syllable of the Text. *Brothers*, said he, † *You are to be informed, that, of Wills*, duo sunt genera, ‖ *Nuncupatory and scriptory: that in the Scriptory Will here before us, there is no Precept or Mention about Gold Lace*, conceditur: *But*, si idem affirmetur de nuncupatorio, negatur, *For Brothers, if you remember, we heard a Fellow say when we were Boys, that he heard my Father's Man say, that*

---

* *I cannot tell whether the Author means any new Innovation by this Word, or whether it be only to introduce the new Methods of forcing and perverting Scripture.*

† *The next Subject of our Author's Wit, is the Glosses and Interpretations of Scripture, very many absurd ones of which are allow'd in the most Authentick Books of the* Church of Rome. W. Wotton.

‖ *By this is meant* Tradition, *allowed to have equal Authority with the Scripture, or rather greater.*

he heard my Father say, that he would advise his Sons to get Gold Lace *on their Coats, as soon as ever they could procure Money to buy it. By* G---- *that is very true,* cries the other; *I remember it perfectly well,* said the third. And so without more ado they got the largest *Gold Lace* in the Parish, and walk'd about as fine as Lords.

A while after, there came up *all in Fashion,* a pretty sort of * *flame Coloured Sattin* for Linings, and the *Mercer* brought a Pattern of it immediately to our three Gentlemen, *An please your Worships* (said he) † *My Lord C--, and Sir* J. W. *had Linings out of this very Piece last Night; it takes wonderfully, and I shall not have a Remnant left, enough to make my Wife a Pin-cushion by to morrow Morning at ten a Clock.* Upon this, they fell again to romage the Will, because the present Case also required a positive Precept, the Lining being held by Orthodox Writers to be of the Essence of the Coat. After long search, they could fix upon nothing to the Matter in hand, except a short Advice of their Fathers in the Will, ‖ to take care of *Fire,* and put out their *Candles* before they went to Sleep. This tho' a good deal for the Purpose, and helping very far towards Self-Conviction, yet not seeming wholly of Force to establish a Command; and being resolved to avoid farther Scruple, as well as future Occasion for Scandal, says He

---

* *This is Purgatory, whereof he speaks more particularly hereafter, but here only to shew how Scripture was perverted to prove it, which was done by giving equal Authority with the* Canon *to* Apocrypha, *called here a* Codicil annex'd.

It is likely the Author, in every one of these Changes in the Brother's Dresses, referrs to some particular Error in the Church of Rome; *tho' it is not easy I think to apply them all, but by this of* Flame Colour'd Satin *is manifestly intended* Purgatory; *by* Gold Lace *may perhaps be understood, the lofty Ornaments and Plate in the Churches. The* Shoulder-Knots *and* Silver Fringe, *are not so obvious, at least to me; but the* Indian Figures *of Men,* Women *and* Children *plainly relate to the Pictures in the* Romish Churches, *of God like an old Man, of the* Virgin Mary *and our Saviour as a Child.*

† *This shews the Time the Author writ, it being about fourteen Years since those two Persons were reckoned the fine Gentlemen of the Town.*

‖ *That is, to take care of Hell, and, in order to do that, to subdue and extinguish their Lusts.*

that was the Scholar; *I remember to have read in Wills, of a Codicil annexed, which is indeed a Part of the Will, and what it contains hath equal authority with the rest. Now, I have been considering of this same Will here before us, and I cannot reckon it to be compleat for want of such a Codicil. I will therefore fasten one in its proper Place very dexterously; I have had it by me some Time, it was written by a * Dog-keeper of my Grand-father's, and talks a great deal (as good Luck would have it) of this very flame-colour'd Sattin.* The Project was immediately approved by the other two; an old Parchment Scrowl was tagged on according to Art, in the Form of a *Codicil annext*, and the *Sattin* bought and worn.

NEXT Winter, a *Player*, hired for the Purpose by the Corporation of *Fringe-makers*, acted his Part in a new Comedy, all covered with † *Silver Fringe*, and according to the laudable Custom gave Rise to that Fashion. Upon which, the Brothers consulting their Father's Will, to their great Astonishment found these Words; Item, *I charge and command my said three Sons, to wear no sort of* Silver Fringe *upon or about their said Coats*, &c. with a Penalty in case of Disobedience, too long here to insert. However, after some Pause the Brother so often mentioned for his Erudition, who was well Skill'd in Criticisms, had found in a certain Author, which he said should be nameless, that the same Word which in the Will is called *Fringe*, does also signifie a *Broom-stick*; and doubtless ought to have the same Interpretation in this Paragraph. This, another of the Brothers disliked, because of that Epithet, *Silver*, which could not, he humbly conceived, in Propriety of Speech be reasonably applied to a *Broom-stick*: but it was replied upon him, that this Epithet was understood in a *Mythological*, and *Allegorical* Sense. However, he objected again, why their Father should forbid them to wear a *Broom-stick* on their Coats, a Caution that seemed unnatural and impertinent; upon which he was taken up short, as one that spoke irreverently of a *Mystery*, which doubtless was very useful and significant,

---

* *I believe this refers to that part of the* Apocrypha *where mention is made of* Tobit *and his* Dog.

† *This is certainly the farther introducing the Pomps of Habit and Ornament.*

but ought not to be over-curiously pryed into, or nicely reasoned upon. And in short, their Father's Authority being now considerably sunk, this Expedient was allowed to serve as a lawful Dispensation, for wearing their full Proportion of *Silver Fringe*.

A while after, was revived an old Fashion, long antiquated, of *Embroidery* with * *Indian Figures* of Men, Women and Children. Here they had no Occasion to examine the Will. They remembred but too well, how their Father had always abhorred this Fashion; that he made several Paragraphs on purpose, importing his utter Detestation of it, and bestowing his everlasting Curse to his Sons whenever they should wear it. For all this, in a few Days, they appeared higher in the Fashion than any Body else in the Town. But they solved the Matter by saying, that these Figures were not at all the *same* with those that were formerly worn, and were meant in the Will. Besides, they did not wear them in that Sense, as forbidden by their Father, but as they were a commendable Custom, and of great Use to the Publick. That these rigorous Clauses in the Will did therefore require some *Allowance*, and a favourable Interpretation, and ought to be understood *cum grano Salis*.

BUT, Fashions perpetually altering in that Age, the Scholastick Brother grew weary of searching farther Evasions, and solving everlasting Contradictions. Resolved therefore at all Hazards, to comply with the Modes of the World, they concerted Matters together, and agreed unanimously, to † lock up their Father's Will in a *Strong-Box*, brought out of *Greece* or *Italy*, (I have forgot which) and trouble themselves no farther to examine it, but only refer to its Authority whenever they thought fit. In consequence whereof, a while after, it grew a general Mode

---

* *The Images of Saints, the Blessed Virgin, and our Saviour an Infant.*
Ibid. *Images in the* Church of Rome *give him but too fair a Handle.* The Brothers remembred, *&c. The Allegory here is direct.* W. Wotton.

† *The Papists formerly forbad the People the Use of Scripture in a Vulgar Tongue,* Peter *therefore* locks up his Father's Will in a Strong Box, brought out of *Greece* or *Italy. Those Countries are named because the* New Testament *is written in* Greek; *and the* Vulgar Latin, *which is the Authentick Edition of the* Bible *in the Church of* Rome, *is in the Language of old* Italy. W. Wotton.

to wear an infinite Number of *Points*, most of them *tagg'd with Silver*: Upon which the Scholar pronounced * *ex Cathedra*, that *Points* were absolutely *Jure Paterno*, as they might very well remember. 'Tis true indeed, the Fashion prescribed somewhat more than were directly named in the Will; However, that they, as Heirs general of their Father, had power to make and add certain Clauses for publick Emolument, though not deducible, *totidem verbis*, from the Letter of the Will, or else, *Multa absurda sequerentur*. This was understood for *Canonical*, and therefore on the following *Sunday* they came to Church all covered with *Points*.

THE Learned Brother so often mentioned, was reckon'd the best Scholar in all that or the next Street to it; insomuch, as having run something behind-hand with the World, he obtained the Favour from a † *certain Lord*, to receive him into his House, and to teach his Children. A while after, the *Lord* died, and he by long Practice upon his Father's Will, found the way of contriving a *Deed of Conveyance* of that House to Himself and his Heirs: Upon which he took Possession, turned the young Squires out, and received his Brothers in their stead.

---

* *The* Popes *in their Decretals and Bulls, have given their Sanction to very many gainful Doctrines which are now received in the* Church of Rome *that are not mention'd in Scripture, and are unknown to the Primitive Church.* Peter *accordingly pronounces* ex Cathedra, *That* Points *tagged with Silver were absolutely* Jure Paterno, *and so they wore them in great Numbers.* W. Wotton.

† *This was* Constantine the Great, *from whom the* Popes *pretend a Donation of St.* Peter's *Patrimony, which they have been never able to produce.*

Ibid. *The Bishops of* Rome *enjoyed their Priviledges in* Rome *at first by the favour of Emperors, whom at last they shut out of their own Capital City, and then forged a Donation from* Constantine the Great, *the better to justifie what they did. In Imitation of this,* Peter *having run something behind hand in the World, obtained Leave of a certain Lord, &c.* W. Wotton.

S E C T. III.

A Digression concerning Criticks.

THO' I have been hitherto as cautious as I could, upon all Occasions, most nicely to follow the Rules and Methods of Writing, laid down by the Example of our illustrious *Moderns*; yet has the unhappy shortness of my Memory led me into an Error, from which I must immediately extricate my self, before I can decently pursue my Principal Subject. I confess with Shame, it was an unpardonable Omission to proceed so far as I have already done, before I had performed the due Discourses, Expostulatory, Supplicatory, or Deprecatory with my *good Lords* the *Criticks*. Towards some Atonement for this grievous Neglect, I do here make humbly bold to present them with a short Account of themselves and their *Art*, by looking into the Original and Pedigree of the Word, as it is generally understood among us, and very briefly considering the antient and present State thereof.

BY the Word, *Critick*, at this Day so frequent in all Conversations, there have sometimes been distinguished three very different Species of Mortal Men, according as I have read in *Antient Books and Pamphlets*. For first, by this Term were understood such Persons as invented or drew up Rules for themselves and the World, by observing which, a careful Reader might be able to pronounce upon the productions of the *Learned*, form his Taste to a true Relish of the *Sublime* and the *Admirable*, and divide every Beauty of Matter or of Style from the Corruption that Apes it: In their common perusal of Books, singling out the Errors and Defects, the Nauseous, the Fulsome, the Dull, and the Impertinent, with the Caution of a Man that walks thro' *Edenborough* Streets in a Morning, who is indeed as careful as he can, to watch diligently, and spy out the Filth in his Way, not that he is curious to observe the Colour and Complexion of the Ordure, or take its Dimensions, much less to be padling in, or tasting it: but only with a Design to come out as cleanly as he may. These men seem, tho' very erroneously, to have understood the Appellation of, *Critick* in a literal Sence; That one principal part of his Office was to Praise and Acquit; and, that a *Critick*, who sets up to Read, only for an Occasion of Censure and Reproof, is a Creature as barbarous as a *Judge*, who should take up a Resolution to hang all Men that came before him upon a Tryal.

AGAIN; by the Word *Critick*, have been meant, the Restorers of Antient Learning from the Worms, and Graves, and Dust of Manuscripts.

Now, the Races of these two have been for some Ages utterly extinct; and besides, to discourse any farther of them would not be at all to my purpose.

THE Third, and Noblest Sort, is that of the *TRUE CRITICK*, whose Original is the most Antient of all. Every *True Critick* is a Hero born, descending in a direct Line from a Celestial Stem, by *Momus* and *Hybris*, who begat *Zoilus*, who begat *Tigellius*, who begat *Etcætera* the Elder, who begat *Bently*, and *Rymer*, and *Wotton*, and *Perrault*, and *Dennis*, who begat *Etcætera* the Younger.

AND these are the *Criticks* from whom the Commonwealth of Learning has in all Ages received such immense benefits, that the Gratitude of their Admirers placed their Origine in Heaven, among those of *Hercules*, *Theseus*, *Perseus*, and other great Deservers of Mankind. But Heroick Virtue it self hath not been exempt from the Obloquy of Evil Tongues. For it hath been objected, that those Antient Heroes, famous for their Combating so many Giants, and Dragons, and Robbers, were in their own Persons a greater Nuisance to Mankind, than any of those Monsters they subdued; and therefore, to render their Obligations more Compleat, when all *other* Vermin were destroy'd, should in Conscience have concluded with the same Justice upon themselves: as *Hercules* most generously did, and hath upon that Score, procured to himself more Temples and Votaries than the best of his Fellows. For these Reasons, I suppose it is, why some have conceived, it would be very expedient for the Publick Good of Learning, that every *True Critick*, as soon as he had finished his Task assigned, should immediately deliver himself up to Ratsbane, or Hemp, or from some convenient *Altitude*, and that no Man's Pretensions to so illustrious a Character, should by any means be received, before That Operation were performed.

Now, from this Heavenly Descent of *Criticism*, and the close Analogy it bears to *Heroick Virtue*, 'tis easie to Assign the proper Employment of a *True Antient Genuine Critick*; which is, to travel thro' this vast World of Writings: to pursue and hunt those Monstrous Faults bred within them: to drag out the lurking Errors like *Cacus* from his Den; to multiply them like *Hydra*'s Heads; and rake them together like *Augeas*'s Dung. Or else to drive away a sort of *Dangerous Fowl*, who have a perverse Inclination to plunder the best Branches of the *Tree of Knowledge*, like those *Stymphalian* Birds that eat up the Fruit.

THESE Reasonings will furnish us with an adequate Definition of a *True Critick*; that, He is *a Discoverer and Collector of Writers Faults*. Which may be farther put beyond Dispute by the following Demonstration: That whoever will examine the Writings in all kinds, wherewith this antient Sect has honour'd the World, shall immediately find, from the whole Thread and Tenour of them, that the Idea's of the Authors have been altogether conversant, and taken up with the Faults and Blemishes, and Oversights, and Mistakes of other Writers; and let the Subject treated on be whatever it will, their Imaginations are so entirely possess'd and replete with the Defects of other Pens, that the very Quintessence of what is bad, does of necessity distill into their own: by which means the Whole appears to be nothing else but an *Abstract* of the *Criticisms* themselves have made.

HAVING thus briefly consider'd the Original and Office of a *Critick*, as the Word is understood in its most noble and universal Acceptation, I proceed to refute the Objections of those who argue from the Silence and Pretermission of Authors; by which they pretend to prove, that the very Art of *Criticism*, as now exercised, and by me explained, is wholly *Modern*; and consequently, that the *Criticks* of *Great Britain* and *France*, have no Title to an Original so Antient and Illustrious as I have deduced. Now, If I can clearly make out on the contrary, that the most Antient Writers have particularly described, both the Person and the Office of a *True Critick*, agreeable to the Definition laid down by me; their Grand Objection, from the Silence of Authors, will fall to the Ground.

I confess to have for a long time born a part in this general

Error; from which I should never have acquitted my self, but thro' the Assistance of our Noble *Moderns*; whose most edifying Volumes I turn indefatigably over Night and Day, for the Improvement of my Mind, and the good of my Country: These have with unwearied Pains made many useful Searches into the weak sides of the *Antients*, and given us a comprehensive List of them. * Besides, they have proved beyond con-   * *See* Wotton tradiction, that the very finest Things delivered   *of Antient and* of old, have been long since invented, and   *Modern Learning.* brought to Light by much later Pens, and that the noblest Discoveries those *Antients* ever made, of Art or of Nature, have all been produced by the transcending Genius of the present Age. Which clearly shews, how little Merit those *Ancients* can justly pretend to; and takes off that blind Admiration paid them by Men in a Corner, who have the Unhappiness of conversing too little with *present Things.* Reflecting maturely upon all this, and taking in the whole Compass of Human Nature, I easily concluded, that these *Antients*, highly sensible of their many Imperfections, must needs have endeavoured from some Passages in their Works, to obviate, soften, or divert the Censorious Reader, by *Satyr*, or *Panegyrick* upon the *True Criticks*, in Imitation of their *Masters* the *Moderns.* Now, in the *Common-* *Places* of * both these, I was plentifully in-   * *Satyr, and* structed, by a long Course of useful Study in   *Panegyrick upon* *Prefaces* and *Prologues*; and therefore immedi-   *Criticks.* ately resolved to try what I could discover of either, by a diligent Perusal of the most Antient Writers, and especially those who treated of the earliest Times. Here I found to my great Surprize, that although they all entred, upon Occasion, into particular Descriptions of the *True Critick*, according as they were governed by their Fears or their Hopes: yet whatever they touch'd of that kind, was with abundance of Caution, adventuring no farther than *Mythology* and *Hieroglyphick.* This, I suppose, gave ground to superficial Readers, for urging the Silence of Authors, against the Antiquity of the *True Critick*; tho' the *Types* are so apposite, and the Applications so necessary and natural, that it is not easy to conceive, how any Reader of a *Modern Eye* and *Taste* could over-look them. I shall venture from a great Number to produce a few, which I am very confident, will put this Question beyond Dispute.

It well deserves considering, that these *Antient Writers* in treating Enigmatically upon the Subject, have generally fixed upon the very *same Hieroglyph*, varying only the Story according to their Affections or their Wit. For first; *Pausanias* is of Opinion, that the Perfection of Writing correct was entirely owing to the Institution of *Criticks*; and, that he can possibly mean no other than the *True Critick*, is, I think, manifest enough from the following Description. He says, *They were a Race of Men, who delighted to nibble at the Superfluities, and Excrescencies of Books; which the Learned at length observing, took Warning of their own Accord, to lop* the *Luxuriant*, the *Rotten*, the *Dead*, the *Sapless*, and the *Overgrown Branches from their Works*. But now, all this he cunningly shades under the following Allegory; *that the* * *Nauplians in* Argia, *learned the Art of pruning their Vines, by observing, that when an* A S S *had browsed upon one of them, it thrived the better, and bore fairer Fruit*. But † *Herodotus* holding the very same *Hieroglyph*, speaks much plainer, and almost *in terminis*. He hath been so bold as to tax the *True Criticks*, of Ignorance and Malice; telling us openly, for I think nothing can be plainer, that *in the Western Part of* Libya, *there were* A S S E S *with* H O R N S: Upon which Relation ‖ *Ctesias* yet refines, mentioning the very same animal about *India*, adding, *That whereas all other* A S S E S *wanted a* Gall, *these horned ones were so redundant in that Part, that their Flesh was not to be eaten because of its extream* Bitterness.

Now, the Reason why those Antient Writers treated this Subject only by Types and Figures, was, because they durst not make open Attacks against a Party so Potent and so Terrible, as the *Criticks* of those Ages were: whose very Voice was so Dreadful, that a Legion of Authors would tremble, and drop their Pens at the Sound; For so * *Herodotus* tells us expresly in another Place, how *a vast Army of* Scythians *was put to flight in a Panick Terror, by the Braying of an* A S S. From hence it is conjectured by certain profound *Philologers*, that the great Awe and Reverence paid to a *True Critick*, by the

Side notes:
* *Lib——*
† *Lib. 4.*
‖ Vide *excerpta ex eo apud* Photium.
* *Lib. 4.*

Writers of *Britain*, have been derived to Us, from those our *Scythian* Ancestors. In short, this Dread was so universal, that in process of Time, those Authors who had a mind to publish their Sentiments more freely, in describing the *True Criticks* of their several Ages, were forced to leave off the use of the former *Hieroglyph*, as too nearly approaching the *Prototype*, and invented other Terms instead thereof that were more cautious and mystical; so † *Diodorus* speaking to the same purpose, ventures no farther than to say, That *in the Moun-* † *Lib.* *tains of* Helicon *there grows a certain* Weed, *which bears a Flower of so damned a Scent, as to poison those who offer to smell it.* Lucretius gives exactly the Same Relation,

‖ *Est etiam in magnis Heliconis montibus arbos,*
   Floris odore hominem tetro consueta necare. Lib. 6.

BUT *Ctesias*, whom we lately quoted, hath been a great deal bolder; He had been used with much severity by the *True Criticks* of his own Age, and therefore could not forbear to leave behind him, at least one deep Mark of his Vengeance against the whole Tribe. His Meaning is so near the Surface, that I wonder how it possibly came to be overlook'd by those who deny the Antiquity of the *True Criticks*. For pretending to make a Description of many strange Animals about *India*, he hath set down these remarkable Words. *Amongst the rest*, says he, *there is a* Serpent *that wants* Teeth, *and consequently cannot bite, but if its* Vomit (*to which it is much addicted*) *happens to fall upon any Thing, a certain Rottenness or Corruption ensues: These* Serpents *are generally found among the Mountains where* Jewels *grow, and they frequently emit a* poisonous Juice *whereof, whoever drinks, that Person's* Brains *flie out of his Nostrils*.

THERE was also among the *Antients* a sort of *Critick*, not distinguisht in *Specie* from the Former, but in Growth or Degree, who seem to have been only the *Tyro's* or *junior* Scholars; yet, because of their differing Employments, they are frequently mentioned as a Sect by themselves. The usual exercise of these

‖ *Near Helicon, and round the Learned Hill,*
   Grow Trees, whose Blossoms with their Odour kill.

younger Students, was to attend constantly at Theatres, and learn to Spy out the *worst Parts* of the Play, whereof they were obliged carefully to take Note, and render a rational Account, to their Tutors. Flesht at these smaller Sports, like young Wolves, they grew up in Time, to be nimble and strong enough for hunting down large Game. For it hath been observed both among Antients and Moderns, that a *True Critick* hath one Quality in common with a *Whore* and an *Alderman*, never to change his Title or his Nature; that a *Grey Critick* has been certainly a *Green* one, the Perfections and Acquirements of his Age being only the improved Talents of his Youth; like *Hemp*, which some Naturalists inform us, is bad for *Suffocations*, tho' taken but in the Seed. I esteem the Invention, or at least the Refinement of *Prologues*, to have been owing to these younger Proficients, of whom *Terence* makes frequent and honourable mention, under the Name of *Malevoli*.

Now, 'tis certain, the Institution of the *True Criticks*, was of absolute Necessity to the Commonwealth of Learning. For all Human Actions seem to be divided like *Themistocles* and his Company; One Man can *Fiddle*, and another can make *a small Town a great City*, and he that cannot do either one or the other, deserves to be kick'd out of the Creation. The avoiding of which Penalty, has doubtless given the first Birth to the Nation of *Criticks*, and withal, an Occasion for their secret Detractors to report; that a *True Critick* is a sort of Mechanick, set up with a Stock and Tools for his Trade, at as little Expence as a *Taylor*; and that there is much Analogy between the Utensils and Abilities of both: That the *Taylor's Hell* is the Type of a Critick's *Common-Place-Book*, and his Wit and Learning held forth by the *Goose*: That it requires at least as many of these, to the making up of one Scholar, as of the others to the Composition of a Man: That the Valour of both is equal, and their *Weapons* near of a Size. Much may be said in answer to these invidious Reflections; and I can positively affirm the first to be a Falshood: For, on the contrary, nothing is more certain, than that it requires greater Layings out, to be free of the *Critick's* Company, than of any other you can name. For, as to be a *true Beggar*, it will cost the richest Candidate every Groat he is worth; so, before one can

commence a *True Critick*, it will cost a man all the good Qualities of his Mind; which, perhaps, for a less Purchase, would be
thought but an indifferent Bargain.

HAVING thus amply proved the Antiquity of *Criticism*, and
described the Primitive State of it; I shall now examine the present Condition of this Empire, and shew how
well it agrees with its antient self. * A certain
Author, whose Works have many Ages since
been entirely lost, does in his fifth Book and
eighth Chapter, say of *Criticks*, that *their Writings are the Mirrors
of Learning*. This I understand in a literal Sense, and suppose our
Author must mean, that whoever designs to be a perfect Writer,
must inspect into the Books of *Criticks*, and correct his Invention there as in a Mirror. Now, whoever considers, that the
Mirrors of the Antients were made of *Brass*, and *sine Mercurio*,
may presently apply the two Principal Qualifications of a *True
Modern Critick*, and consequently, must needs conclude, that
these have always been, and must be for ever the same. For,
Brass is an Emblem of Duration, and when it is skilfully bur-
nished, will cast *Reflections* from its own *Superficies*, without any
Assistance of *Mercury* from behind. All the other Talents of a
Critick will not require a particular Mention, being included, or
easily deducible to these. However, I shall conclude with three
Maxims, which may serve both as Characteristicks to distinguish
a *True Modern Critick* from a Pretender, and will be also of admirable Use to those worthy Spirits, who engage in so useful
and honourable an Art.

> * *A Quotation after the manner of a great Author. Vide* Bently's *Dissertation, &c.*

THE first is, That *Criticism*, contrary to all other Faculties of
the Intellect, is ever held the truest and best, when it is the very
first Result of the *Critick*'s Mind: As Fowlers reckon the first
aim for the surest, and seldom fail of missing the Mark, if they
stay for a Second.

SECONDLY; The *True Criticks* are known by their Talent of
swarming about the noblest Writers, to which they are carried
meerly by Instinct, as a Rat to the best Cheese, or a Wasp to the
fairest Fruit. So, when the *King* is a Horse-back, he is sure to be
the *dirtiest* Person of the Company, and they that make their
Court best, are such as *bespatter* him most.

LASTLY; A *True Critick*, in the Perusal of a Book, is like a *Dog* at a Feast, whose Thoughts and Stomach are wholly set upon what the Guests *fling away*, and consequently, is apt to *Snarl* most, when there are the fewest *Bones*.

THUS much, I think, is sufficient to serve by way of Address to my Patrons, the *True Modern Criticks*, and may very well atone for my past Silence, as well as That which I am like to observe for the future. I hope I have deserved so well of their whole *Body*, as to meet with generous and tender Usage at their *Hands*. Supported by which Expectation, I go on boldly to pursue those Adventures already so happily begun.

SECT. IV.

A TALE of a TUB.

I HAVE now with much Pains and Study, conducted the Reader to a Period, where he must expect to hear of great Revolutions. For no sooner had Our *Learned Brother*, so often mentioned, got a warm House of his own over his Head, than he began to look big, and to take mightily upon him; insomuch, that unless the Gentle Reader out of his great Candour, will please a little to exalt his Idea, I am afraid he will henceforth hardly know the *Hero* of the Play, when he happens to meet Him; his part, his Dress, and his Mien being so much altered.

HE told his Brothers, he would have them to know, that he was their Elder, and consequently his Father's sole Heir; Nay, a while after, he would not allow them to call Him, Brother, but Mr. *PETER*; And then he must be styl'd, *Father PETER*; and sometimes, *My Lord PETER*. To support this Grandeur, which he soon began to consider, could not be maintained without a Better *Fonde* than what he was born to; After much Thought, he cast about at last, to turn *Projector* and *Virtuoso*, wherein he so well succeeded, that many famous Discoveries, Projects and Machines, which bear great Vogue and Practice at present in the World, are owing entirely to *Lord Peter*'s Invention. I will deduce the best Account I have been able to collect of the Chief amongst them, without considering much the Order they came out in; because, I think, Authors are not well agreed as to that Point.

I hope, when this Treatise of mine shall be translated into Foreign Languages, (as I may without Vanity affirm, That the Labour of collecting, the Faithfulness in recounting, and the great Usefulness of the Matter to the Publick, will amply deserve that Justice) that the worthy Members of the several *Academies* abroad, especially those of *France* and *Italy*, will favourably accept these humble Offers, for the Advancement of Universal Knowledge. I do also advertise the most Reverend Fathers the *Eastern* Missionaries, that I have purely for their Sakes, made use of such Words and Phrases, as will best admit an easie Turn

f

into any of the *Oriental* Languages, especially the *Chinese*. And so I proceed with great Content of Mind, upon reflecting, how much Emolument this whole Globe of Earth is like to reap by my Labours.

THE first Undertaking of Lord *Peter*, was to purchase a* Large Continent, lately said to have been discovered in *Terra Australis incognita*. This Tract of Land he bought at a very great Penny-worth from the Discoverers themselves, (tho' some pretended to doubt whether they had ever been there) and then retailed it into several Cantons to certain Dealers, who carried over Colonies, but were all Shipwreckt in the Voyage. Upon which, *Lord Peter* sold the said Continent to other Customers *again*, and *again*, and *again*, and *again*, with the same Success.

THE second Project I shall mention, was his † Sovereign Remedy for the *Worms*, especially those in the *Spleen*. ‖ The Patient was to eat nothing after Supper for three Nights: as soon as he went to Bed, he was carefully to lye on one Side, and when he grew weary, to turn upon the other: He must also duly confine his two Eyes to the same Object; and by no means break Wind at both Ends together, without manifest Occasion. These Prescriptions diligently observed, the *Worms* would void insensibly by Perspiration, ascending thro' the *Brain*.

A third Invention, was the Erecting of a * *Whispering-Office*, for the Publick Good and Ease of all such as are Hypochondriacal, or troubled with the Cholick; as likewise of all Eves-droppers, Physicians, Midwives, small Politicians, Friends fallen out, Repeating Poets, Lovers Happy or in Despair, Bawds, Privy-

---

* *That is Purgatory.*

† Penance *and* Absolution *are plaid upon under the Notion of a* Sovereign Remedy for the Worms, *especially in the Spleen, which by observing* Peters *Prescription would void sensibly by Perspiration ascending thro' the Brain, &c.* W. Wotton.

‖ *Here the Author ridicules the Penances of the Church of* Rome, *which may be made as easy to the Sinner as he pleases, provided he will pay for them accordingly*.

* *By his* Whispering-Office, *for the Relief of Eves-droppers, Physitians, Bawds, and Privy-counsellours, he ridicules Auricular Confession, and the Priest who takes it, is described by the Asses Head.* W. Wotton.

Counsellours, Pages, Parasites and Buffoons; In short, of all such as are in Danger of bursting with too much *Wind*. An *Asse*'s Head was placed so conveniently, that the Party affected might easily with his Mouth accost either of the Animal's Ears; which he was to apply close for a certain Space, and by a fugitive Faculty, peculiar to the Ears of that Animal, receive immediate Benefit, either by Eructation, or Expiration, or Evomition.

ANOTHER very beneficial Project of *Lord Peter*'s was an * *Office of Ensurance*, for Tobacco-Pipes, Martyrs of the Modern Zeal; Volumes of Poetry, Shadows, ———————— and Rivers: That these, nor any of these shall receive Damage by *Fire*. From whence our *Friendly Societies* may plainly find themselves, to be only Transcribers from this Original; tho' the one and the other have been of *great* Benefit to the Undertakers, as well as of *equal* to the Publick.

LORD Peter was also held the Original Author of † *Puppets* and *Raree-Shows*; the great Usefulness whereof being so generally known, I shall not enlarge farther upon this Particular.

BUT, another Discovery for which he was much renowned, was his famous Universal ‖ *Pickle*. For having remark'd how your * Common *Pickle* in use among Huswives, was of no farther Benefit than to preserve dead Flesh, and certain kinds of Vegetables; *Peter*, with great Cost as well as Art, had contrived a *Pickle* proper for Houses, Gardens, Towns, Men, Women, Children, and Cattle; wherein he could preserve them as Sound as Insects in Amber. Now, this *Pickle* to the Taste, the Smell, and the Sight, appeared exactly same, with what is in common Service for Beef, and Butter, and Herrings, (and has been often that way applied with great Success) but for its many Sove-

---

* *This I take to be the Office of* Indulgences, *the gross Abuses whereof first gave Occasion for the Reformation.*

† *I believe are the Monkeries and ridiculous Processions,* &c. *among the Papists.*

‖ *Holy Water, he calls an* Universal Pickle *to preserve Houses, Gardens, Towns, Men, Women, Children and Cattle, wherein he could preserve them as sound as Insects in Amber.* W. Wotton.

* *This is easily understood to be Holy Water, composed of the same Ingredients with many other Pickles.*

reign Virtues was a quite different Thing. For *Peter* would put in a certain Quantity of his * *Powder Pimperlim pimp*, after which it never failed of Success. The Operation was performed by *Spargefaction* in a proper Time of the Moon. The Patient who was to be *pickled*, if it were a House, would infallibly be preserved from all Spiders, Rats and Weazels; If the Party affected were a Dog, he should be exempt from Mange, and Madness, and Hunger. It also infallibly took away all Scabs and Lice, and scall'd Heads from Children, never hindring the Patient from any Duty, either at Bed or Board.

But of all *Peter*'s Rarieties, he most valued a certain Set of † *Bulls*, whose Race was by great Fortune preserved in a lineal Descent from those that guarded the *Golden Fleece*. Tho' some who pretended to observe them curiously, doubted the Breed had not been kept entirely chast; because they had degenerated from their Ancestors in some Qualities and had acquired others very extraordinary, but a Forein Mixture. The *Bulls* of *Colchos* are recorded to have *brazen Feet*; But whether it happen'd by ill Pasture and Running, by an Allay from intervention of other Parents, from stolen Intrigues; Whether a Weakness in their Progenitors had impaired the seminal Virtue; Or by a Decline necessary thro' a long Course of Time, the Originals of Nature being depraved in these latter sinful Ages of the World; Whatever was the Cause, 'tis certain that *Lord Peter*'s *Bulls* were extreamely vitiated by the Rust of Time in the Mettal of their Feet, which was now sunk into common *Lead*. However the terrible *roaring* peculiar to their Lineage, was preserved; as likewise that Faculty of breathing out *Fire* from their Nostrils; which not-

---

* *And because Holy Water differs only in Consecration from common Water, therefore he tells us that his Pickle by the Powder of* Pimperlim-pimp *receives new Virtues though it differs not in Sight nor Smell from the common Pickle, which preserves Beef, and Butter, and Herrings.* W. Wotton.

† *The Papal* Bulls *are ridicul'd by Name, So that here we are at no loss for the Authors Meaning.* W. Wotton.

Ibid. *Here the Author has kept the Name, and means the* Popes Bulls, *or rather his Fulminations and Excommunications, of Heretical Princes, all sign'd with Lead and the Seal of the Fisherman.*

withstanding, many of their Detractors took to be a Feat of Art, and to be nothing so terrible as it appeared; proceeding only from their usual Course of Dyet, which was of * *Squibs* and *Crackers.* However, they had two peculiar Marks which extreamly distinguished them from the *Bulls of Jason*, and which I have not met together in the Description of any other Monster, beside that in *Horace*;

Varias inducere plumas,
and
Atrum desinit in piscem.

For, these had *Fishes Tails*, yet upon Occasion, could *out-fly* any Bird in the Air. *Peter* put these *Bulls* upon several Employs. Sometimes he would set them a *roaring* to fright † *Naughty Boys*, and make them quiet. Sometimes he would send them out upon Errands of great Importance; where it is wonderful to recount, and perhaps the cautious Reader may think much to believe it; An *Appetitus sensibilis*, deriving itself thro' the whole Family, from their Noble Ancestors, Guardians of the *Golden-Fleece*; they continued so extremely fond of *Gold*, that if *Peter* sent them abroad, though it were only upon a Compliment; they would *Roar*, and *Spit*, and *Belch*, and *Piss*, and *Fart*, and *Snivel* out *Fire*, and keep a perpetual Coyl, till you flung them a Bit of *Gold*; but then, *Pulveris exigui jactu*, they would grow calm and quiet as Lambs. In short, whether by secret Connivance, or Encouragement from their Master, or out of their own Liquorish Affection to Gold, or both; it is certain they were no better than a sort of sturdy, swaggering Beggars; and where they could not prevail to get an Alms, would make Women miscarry, and Children fall into Fits; who, to this very Day, usually call Sprites and Hobgoblins by the Name of *Bull-Beggars*. They grew at last so very troublesome to the Neighbourhood, that some Gentlemen of the *North-West*, got a Parcel of right *English Bull-Dogs*, and baited them so terribly, that they felt it ever after.

I must needs mention one more of *Lord Peter*'s Projects, which

---

* *These are the Fulminations of the Pope threatning Hell and Damnation to those Princes who offend him.*

† *That is Kings who incurr his Displeasure.*

was very extraordinary, and discovered him to be Master of a high Reach, and profound Invention. Whenever it happened that any Rogue of *Newgate* was condemned to be hang'd, *Peter* would offer him a Pardon for a certain Sum of Money, which when the poor Caitiff had made all Shifts to scrape up and send; *His Lordship* would return a * Piece of Paper in this Form.

TO all Mayors, Sheriffs, Jaylors, Constables, Bayliffs, Hangmen, &c. Whereas we are informed that A. B. remains in the Hands of you, or any of you, under the Sentence of Death. We will and command you upon Sight hereof, to let the said Prisoner depart to his own Habitation, whether he stands condemned for Murder, Sodomy, Rape, Sacrilege, Incest, Treason, Blasphemy, &c. for which this shall be your sufficient Warrant: And if you fail hereof, G----- d----mn You and Yours to all Eternity. And so we bid you heartily Farewel.

Your most Humble

Man's Man,

Emperor Peter.

The Wretches trusting to this, lost their Lives and Money too.

I desire of those whom the *Learned* among Posterity will appoint for Commentators upon this elaborate Treatise; that they will proceed with great Caution upon certain dark points, wherein all who are not *Verè adepti*, may be in Danger to form rash and hasty Conclusions, especially in some mysterious Paragraphs, where certain *Arcana* are joyned for brevity sake, which in the Operation must be divided. And, I am certain, that future Sons of Art, will return large Thanks to my Memory, for so grateful, so useful an *Innuendo*.

It will be no difficult Part to persuade the Reader, that so many worthy Discoveries met with great Success in the World; tho' I may justly assure him that I have related much the smallest Number; My Design having been only to single out such, as will be of most Benefit for Publick Imitation, or which best served to

---

* *This is a Copy of a General Pardon sign'd* Servus Servorum.

Ibid. *Absolution in* Articulo Mortis, *and the Tax* Cameræ Apostolicæ *are jested upon in Emperor* Peter's *Letter*. W. Wotton.

give some Idea of the Reach and Wit of the Inventor. And therefore it need not be wondred, if by this Time, *Lord Peter* was become exceeding Rich. But alas, he had kept his Brain so long, and so violently upon the Rack, that at last it *shook* it self, and began to *turn round* for a little Ease. In short, what with Pride, Projects, and Knavery, poor *Peter* was grown distracted, and conceived the strangest Imaginations in the World. In the Height of his Fits (as it is usual with those who run mad out of Pride) He would call Himself * *God Almighty*, and sometimes *Monarch of the Universe*. I have seen him, (says my Author) take three old † *high-crown'd Hats*, and clap them all on his Head, three Story high, with a huge Bunch of ‖ *Keys* at his Girdle, and an *Angling Rod* in his Hand. In which Guise, whoever went to take him by the Hand in the way of Salutation, *Peter* with much Grace, like a well educated Spaniel, would present them with his * *Foot*, and if they refused his Civility, then he would raise it as high as their Chops, and give them a damn'd Kick on the Mouth, which hath ever since been call'd a *Salute*. Whoever walkt by, without paying him their Compliments, having a wonderful strong Breath, he would blow their Hats off into the Dirt. Mean time, his Affairs at home went upside down; and his two Brothers had a wretched Time; Where his first † *Boutade* was, to kick both their ‖ *Wives* one Morning out of Doors, and his own too, and in their stead, gave Orders to pick up the first three Strolers could be met with in the Streets. A while after, he nail'd up the

---

* *The Pope is not only allow'd to be the Vicar of* Christ, *but by several Divines is call'd* God upon Earth, *and other blasphemous Titles.*

† *The Triple Crown.*

‖ *The Keys of the Church.*

Ibid. *The Pope's Universal Monarchy, and his Triple Crown, and Keys, and Fisher's Ring.* W. Wotton.

* *Neither does his arrogant way of requiring men to kiss his Slipper, escape Reflexion.* Wotton.

† *This Word properly signifies a sudden Jerk, or Lash of an Horse, when you do not expect it.*

‖ *The* Celibacy *of the* Romish *Clergy is struck at in* Peter's *beating his own and Brothers Wives out of Doors.* W. Wotton.

Cellar-Door: and would not allow his Brothers a ‖ Drop of *Drink* to their Victuals. Dining one Day at an Alderman's in the City, *Peter* observed him expatiating after the Manner of his Brethren, in the Praises of his Surloyn of Beef. *Beef*, said the Sage Magistrate, *is the King of Meat; Beef comprehends in it the Quintessence of Partridge, and Quail, and Venison, and Pheasant, and Plumpudding and Custard.* When *Peter* came home, he would needs take the Fancy of cooking up this Doctrine into Use, and apply the Precept in default of a Surloyn, to his brown Loaf: *Bread*, says he, *Dear Brothers, is the Staff of Life; in which Bread is contained,* inclusivè, *the Quintessence of Beef, Mutton, Veal, Venison, Partridge, Plum-pudding, and Custard: And to render all compleat, there is intermingled a due Quantity of Water, whose Crudities are also corrected by Yeast or Barm, thro' which means it becomes a wholesome fermented Liquor, diffused thro' the* Mass *of the Bread.* Upon the Strength of these Conclusions, next Day at Dinner was the brown Loaf served up in all the Formality of a City Feast. *Come Brothers,* said *Peter, fall to, and spare not; here is excellent good* * *Mutton; or hold, now my Hand is in, I'll help you.* At which word, in much Ceremony, with Fork and Knife, he carves out two good Slices of the Loaf, and presents each on a Plate to his Brothers. The Elder of the two not suddenly entring into *Lord Peter*'s Conceit, began with very civil Language to examine the Mystery. *My Lord,* said he, *I doubt, with great Submission, there may be some Mistake. What,* says *Peter, you are pleasant; Come then, let us hear this Jest, your Head is so big with.* None in the World, *my Lord; but unless I am very much deceived, your Lordship was pleased a while ago, to let fall a Word about Mutton, and I would be glad to see it with all my Heart. How,* said *Peter,* appearing in great Surprise, *I do not comprehend this at all—* Upon which, the younger interposing,

---

‖ *The Pope's refusing the Cup to the Laity, persuading them that the Blood is contain'd in the Bread, and that the Bread is the real and entire Body of* Christ.

* Transubstantiation. Peter *turns his Bread into Mutton, and according to the Popish Doctrine of Concomitants, his Wine too, which in his way he calls,* Pauming his damn'd Crusts upon the Brothers for Mutton. *W. Wotton.*

to set the Business right; *My Lord,* said he, *My Brother, I suppose is hungry, and longs for the Mutton, your Lordship hath promised us to Dinner.* Pray, said Peter, *take me along with you, either you are both mad, or disposed to be merrier than I approve of; If* You *there, do not like your Piece, I will carve you another, tho' I should take that to be the choice Bit of the whole Shoulder. What then, my Lord,* replied the first, *it seems this is a shoulder of Mutton all this while.* Pray Sir, says Peter, *eat your Vittles and leave off your Impertinence, if you please, for I am not disposed to relish it at present*: But the other could not forbear, being over-provoked at the affected Seriousness of *Peter's* Countenance. *By* G—, *My Lord,* said he, *I can only say, that to my Eyes, and Fingers, and Teeth, and Nose, it seems to be nothing but a Crust of Bread.* Upon which, the second put in his Word: *I never saw a Piece of Mutton in my Life, so nearly resembling a Slice from a Twelve-peny Loaf. Look ye, Gentlemen,* cries *Peter* in a Rage, *to convince you, what a couple of blind, positive, ignorant, wilful Puppies you are, I will use but this plain Argument; By* G—, *it is true, good, natural Mutton as any in* Leaden-Hall *Market; and* G—, *confound you both eternally, if you offer to believe otherwise.* Such a thundring Proof as this, left no farther Room for Objection: The two Unbelievers began to gather and pocket up their Mistake as hastily as they could. *Why, truly,* said the first, *upon more mature Consideration—Ay,* says the other, interrupting him, *now I have thought better on the Thing, your Lordship seems to have a great deal of Reason. Very well,* said *Peter. Here Boy, fill me a Beer-Glass of Claret. Here's to you both with all my Heart.* The two Brethren much delighted to see him so readily appeas'd returned their most humble Thanks, and said, they would be glad to pledge His Lordship. *That you shall,* said Peter, *I am not a Person to refuse you any Thing that is reasonable; Wine moderately taken, is a Cordial; Here is a Glass apiece for you; 'Tis true natural Juice from the Grape; none of your damn'd* Vintners *Brewings.* Having spoke thus, he presented to each of them another large dry Crust, bidding them drink it off, and not be bashful, for it would do them no Hurt. The two Brothers, after having performed the usual Office in such delicate Conjunctures, of staring a sufficient Period at *Lord Peter,* and each other; and finding how Matters were like to go, resolved not to enter on a new Dispute, but let him carry the

Point as he pleased; for he was now got into one of his mad Fits, and to Argue or Expostulate further, would only serve to render him a hundred times more untractable.

I have chosen to relate this worthy Matter in all its Circumstances, because it gave a principal Occasion to that great and famous * *Rupture*, which happened about the same time among these Brethren, and was never afterwards made up. But, of That, I shall treat at large in another Section.

HOWEVER, it is certain, that *Lord Peter*, even in his lucid Intervals, was very lewdly given in his common Conversation, extream wilful and positive, and would at any time rather argue to the Death, than allow himself to be once in an Error. Besides, he had an abominable Faculty of telling huge palpable *Lies* upon all Occasions; and swearing, not only to the Truth, but cursing the whole Company to Hell, if they pretended to make the least Scruple of believing Him. One time, he swore, he had a † *Cow* at home, which gave as much Milk at a Meal, as would fill three thousand Churches; and what was yet more extraordinary, would never turn Sower. Another time, he was telling of an old *Sign-Post* that belonged to his *Father*, with Nails and Timber enough on it, to build sixteen large Men of War. Talking one Day of *Chinese* Waggons, which were made so light as to sail over Mountains: *Z----nds*, said *Peter*, *where's the Wonder of that? By G-----, I saw a * Large House of Lime and Stone travel over Sea and Land (granting that it stopt sometimes to bait) above two thousand*

---

* *By this* Rupture *is meant the* Reformation.

† *The ridiculous Multiplying of the Virgin* Mary's Milk *among the Papists, under the Allegory of a* Cow, *which gave as much Milk at a Meal, as would fill three thousand Churches*. W. Wotton.

‖ *By this* Sign-Post *is meant the* Cross *of our Blessed Saviour*.

* *The Chappel of* Loretto. *He falls here only upon the ridiculous Inventions of Popery: The Church of* Rome *intended by these Things, to gull silly, superstitious People, and rook them of their Money; that the World had been too long in Slavery, our Ancestors gloriously redeem'd us from that Yoke. The Church of* Rome *therefore ought to be expos'd, and he deserves well of Mankind that does expose it*. W. Wotton.

Ibid. *The Chappel of* Loretto, *which travell'd from the* Holy Land *to* Italy.

German *Leagues*. And that which was the good of it, he would swear desperately all the while, that he never told a Lye in his Life; And at every Word; *By G---, Gentlemen, I tell you nothing but the Truth; And the D------l broil them eternally that will not believe me.*

In short, *Peter* grew so scandalous, that all the Neighbour-hood began in plain Words to say, he was no better than a Knave. And his two Brothers long weary of his ill Usage, re-solved at last to leave him; but first, they humbly desired a Copy of their Father's *Will*, which had now lain by neglected, time out of Mind. Instead of granting this Request, he called them *damn'd Sons of Whores, Rogues, Traytors,* and the rest of the vile Names he could muster up. However, while he was abroad one Day upon his Projects, the two Youngsters watcht their Oppor-tunity, made a shift to come at the *Will*, * and took a *Copia vera*, by which they presently saw how grosly they had been abused; Their Father having left them equal Heirs, and strictly com-manded, that whatever they got, should lye in common among them all. Pursuant to which, their next Enterprise was to break open the Cellar-Door, and get a little good † *Drink* to spirit and comfort their Hearts. In copying the *Will*, they had met another Precept against Whoring, Divorce, and separate Maintenance; Upon which, their next ‖ Work was to discard their Concubines, and send for their Wives. Whilst all this was in agitation, there enters a Sollicitor from *Newgate*, desiring *Lord Peter* would please to procure a *Pardon* for a *Thief* that was to be *hanged* to morrow. But the two Brothers told him, he was a Coxcomb to seek Pardons from a Fellow, who deserv'd to be hang'd much better than his Client; and discovered all the Method of that Im-posture, in the same Form I delivered it a while ago, advising the Sollicitor to put his Friend upon obtaining * *a Pardon from the King*. In the midst of all this Clutter and Revolution, in comes

---

* *Translated the Scriptures into the vulgar Tongues.*
† *Administred the Cup to the Laity at the Communion.*
‖ *Allowed the Marriages of Priests.*
* *Directed Penitents not to trust to Pardons and Absolutions procur'd for Money, but sent them to implore the Mercy of God, from whence alone Remission is to be obtain'd.*

Peter with a File of * Dragoons at his Heels, and gathering from all Hands what was in the Wind, He and his Gang, after several Millions of Scurrilities and Curses, not very important here to repeat, by main Force, very fairly † kicks them both out of Doors, and would never let them come under his Roof from that Day to this.

---

 * *By* Peter's *Dragoons, is meant the Civil Power which those Princes, who were bigotted to the Romish Superstition, employ'd against the Reformers.*

 † *The Pope shuts all who dissent from him out of the Church.*

SECT. V.

A Digression in the Modern Kind.

WE whom the World is pleased to honor with the Title of *Modern Authors*, should never have been able to compass our great Design of an everlasting Remembrance, and never-dying Fame, if our Endeavours had not been so highly serviceable to the general Good of Mankind. This, *O Universe*, is the Adventurous Attempt of me thy Secretary;

> ————*Quemvis perferre laborem*
> *Suadet, & inducit noctes vigilare serenas.*

To this End, I have some Time since, with a World of Pains and Art, dissected the Carcass of *Humane Nature*, and read many useful Lectures upon the several Parts, both *Containing* and *Contained*; till at last it *smelt* so strong, I could preserve it no longer. Upon which, I have been at a great Expence to fit up all the Bones with exact Contexture, and in due Symmetry; so that I am ready to shew a very compleat Anatomy thereof to all curious *Gentlemen and others*. But not to Digress farther in the midst of a Digression, as I have known some Authors inclose Digressions in one another, like a Nest of Boxes; I do affirm, that having carefully cut up *Humane Nature*, I have found a very strange, new, and important Discovery; That the Publick Good of Mankind is performed by two Ways, *Instruction*, and *Diversion*. And I have farther proved in my said several Readings, (which, perhaps, the World may one day see, if I can prevail on any Friend to steal a Copy, or on certain Gentlemen of my Admirers, to be very Importunate) that, as Mankind is now disposed, he receives much greater Advantage by being *Diverted* than *Instructed*; His Epidemical Diseases being *Fastidiosity*, *Amorphy*, and *Oscitation*; whereas in the present universal Empire of Wit and Learning, there seems but little Matter left for *Instruction*. However, in Compliance with a Lesson of Great Age and Authority, I have attempted carrying the Point in all its Heights; and accordingly throughout this Divine Treatise, have skilfully kneaded up both together with a *Layer* of *Utile* and a *Layer* of *Dulce*.

WHEN I consider how exceedingly our Illustrious *Moderns* have eclipsed the weak glimmering Lights of the *Antients*, and turned them out of the Road of all fashionable Commerce, to a degree, that our choice * Town-Wits of most refined Accomplishments, are in grave Dispute, whether there have been ever any *Antients* or no: In which Point we are like to receive wonderful Satisfaction from the most useful Labours and Lucubrations of that Worthy *Modern*, Dr. *Bently*: I say, when I consider all this, I cannot but bewail, that no famous *Modern* hath ever yet attempted an universal System in a small portable Volume, of all Things that are to be Known, or Believed, or Imagined, or Practised in Life. I am, however, forced to acknowledge, that such an enterprise was thought on some Time ago by a great Philosopher of † *O. Brazile*. The Method he proposed, was by a certain curious *Receipt*, a *Nostrum*, which after his untimely Death, I found among his Papers; and do here out of my great Affection to the *Modern Learned*, present them with it, not doubting, it may one Day encourage some worthy Undertaker.

YOU take fair correct Copies, well bound in Calfs Skin, and Lettered at the Back, of all Modern Bodies of Arts and Sciences whatsoever, and in what Language you please. These you distil in balneo Mariæ, *infusing* Quintessence of Poppy Q. S. *together with three Pints of* Lethe, *to be had from the Apothecaries. You cleanse away carefully the* Sordes *and* Caput mortuum, *letting all that is volatile evaporate. You preserve only the first Running, which is again to be distilled seventeen times, till what remains will amount to about two Drams. This you keep in a Glass Viol* Hermetically *sealed, for one and twenty Days. Then you begin your Catholick Treatise, taking every Morning fasting, (first shaking the Viol) three Drops of this* Elixir, *snuffing it strongly up your Nose. It will dilate it self about the Brain (where there is any) in fourteen Minutes, and you immediately perceive in your Head an in-*

---

* *The Learned Person here meant by our Author, hath been endeavouring to annihilate so many Antient Writers, that until he is pleas'd to stop his hand it will be dangerous to affirm, whether there have been ever any Antients in the World.*

† *This is an imaginary Island, of Kin to that which is call'd the* Painters Wives Island, *placed in some unknown part of the Ocean, meerly at the Fancy of the Map-maker.*

finite Number of Abstracts, Summaries, Compendiums, Extracts, Collections, Medulla's, Excerpta quædam's, Florilegia's *and the like, all disposed into great Order, and reducible upon Paper*.

I must needs own, it was by the Assistance of this *Arcanum*, that I, tho' otherwise *impar*, have adventured upon so daring an Attempt; never atchieved or undertaken before, but by a certain Author called *Homer*, in whom, tho' otherwise a Person not without some Abilities, and *for an Ancient*, of a tolerable Genius; I have discovered many gross Errors, which are not to be forgiven his very Ashes, if by chance any of them are left. For whereas, we are assured, he design'd his Work for a * compleat Body of all Knowledge Human, Divine, Political, and Mechanick; it is manifest, he hath wholly neglected some, and been very imperfect in the rest.

* *Homerus omnes res humanas Poematis complexus est.* Xenoph. in conviv.

For, first of all, as eminent a *Cabbalist* as his Disciples would represent Him, his Account of the *Opus magnum* is extreamly poor and deficient; he seems to have read but very superficially, either *Sendivogius, Behmen,* or † *Anthroposophia Theomagica.* He is also quite mistaken about the *Sphæra Pyroplastica,* a neglect not to be attoned for; and (if the Reader will admit so severe a Censure) *Vix crederem Autorem hunc, unquam audivisse ignis vocem.* His Failings are not less prominent in several Parts of the *Mechanicks.* For, having read his Writings with the utmost Application usual among *Modern Wits,* I could never yet discover the least Direction about the Structure of that useful Instrument a *Save-all.* For want of which, if the *Moderns* had not lent their Assistance, we might yet have wandred *in the Dark.* But I have still behind, a Fault far more notorious to tax this Author with; I mean, ‖ his gross Ignorance in the *Common Laws of this Realm,* and in the Doctrine as well as Discipline of the

---

† *A Treatise written about fifty Years ago, by a* Welsh *Gentleman of* Cambridge, *his Name, as I remember, was* Vaughan, *as appears by the Answer to it, writ by the Learned Dr.* Henry Moor, *it is a Piece of the most unintelligible Fustian, that, perhaps, was ever publish'd in any Language.*

‖ *Mr.* Wotton (*to whom our Author never gives any Quarter*) *in his Comparison of Antient and Modern Learning, Numbers Divinity, Law,* &c. *among those Parts of Knowledge wherein we excel the Antients.*

Church of *England*. A Defect indeed, for which both he and all the Ancients stand most justly censured by my worthy and ingenious Friend Mr. *Wotton*, Batchelor of Divinity, in his incomparable Treatise of *Ancient and Modern Learning*; A Book never to be sufficiently valued, whether we consider the happy Turns and Flowings of the Author's Wit, the great Usefulness of his sublime Discoveries upon the Subject of *Flies* and *Spittle*, or the laborious Eloquence of his Stile. And I cannot forbear doing that Author the Justice of my publick Acknowledgments, for the great *Helps* and *Liftings* I had out of his incomparable Piece, while I was penning this Treatise.

But, besides these Omissions in *Homer* already mentioned, the curious Reader will also observe several Defects in that Author's Writings, for which he is not altogether so accountable. For whereas every Branch of Knowledge has received such wonderful Acquirements since his Age, especially within these last three Years, or thereabouts; it is almost impossible, he could be so very perfect in Modern Discoveries, as his Advocates pretend. We freely acknowledge Him to be the Inventor of the *Compass*, of *Gun-Powder*, and the *Circulation of the Blood*: But, I challenge any of his Admirers to shew me in all his Writings, a compleat Account of the *Spleen*; Does he not also leave us wholly to seek in the Art of *Political Wagering*? What can be more defective and unsatisfactory than his long Dissertation upon *Tea*? and as to his Method of *Salivation without Mercury*, so much celebrated of late, it is to my own Knowledge and Experience, a Thing very little to be relied on.

It was to supply such momentous Defects, that I have been prevailed on after long Sollicitation, to take Pen in Hand; and I dare venture to Promise, the Judicious Reader shall find nothing neglected here, that can be of Use upon any Emergency of Life. I am confident to have included and exhausted all that Human Imagination can *Rise* or *Fall* to. Particularly, I recommend to the Perusal of the Learned, certain Discoveries that are wholly untoucht by others; whereof I shall only mention among a great many more; *My New help of Smatterers*, or the *Art of being Deep-learned, and Shallow-read. A curious Invention about Mouse-Traps. An Universal Rule of Reason, or Every Man his own Carver*; Together with a most useful Engine for *catching of Owls*. All which the judicious Reader will find largely treated on, in the several Parts of this Discourse.

I hold my self obliged to give as much Light as is possible, into the Beauties and Excellencies of what I am writing, because it is become the Fashion and Humor most applauded among the first Authors of this Polite and Learned Age, when they would correct the ill Nature of Critical, or inform the Ignorance of Courteous Readers. Besides, there have been several famous Pieces lately published both in Verse and Prose; wherein, if the Writers had not been pleas'd, out of their great Humanity and Affection to the Publick, to give us a nice Detail of the *Sublime*, and the *Admirable* they contain; it is a thousand to one, whether we should ever have discovered one Grain of either. For my own particular, I cannot deny, that whatever I have said upon this Occasion, had been more proper in a Preface, and more agreeable to the Mode, which usually directs it there. But I here think fit to lay hold on that great and honourable Privilege of being the *Last Writer*; I claim an absolute Authority in Right, as the *freshest Modern*, which gives me a Despotick Power over all Authors before me. In the Strength of which Title, I do utterly disapprove and declare against that pernicious Custom, of making the Preface a Bill of Fare to the Book. For I have always lookt upon it as a high Point of Indiscretion in *Monster-mongers* and other *Retailers of strange Sights*; to hang out a fair large Picture over the Door, drawn after the Life, with a most eloquent Description underneath: This hath saved me many a Threepence, for my Curiosity was fully satisfied, and I never offered to go in, tho' often invited by the urging and attending Orator, with his last *moving* and *standing* Piece of Rhetorick; *Sir, Upon my Word, we are just going to begin.* Such is exactly the Fate, at this Time, of *Prefaces, Epistles, Advertisements, Introductions, Prolegomena's, Apparatus's, To-the-Reader's.* This Expedient was admirable at first; Our Great *Dryden* has long carried it as far as it would go, and with incredible Success. He has often said to me in Confidence, that the World would have never suspected him to be so great a Poet, if he had not assured them so frequently in his Prefaces, that it was impossible they could either doubt or

g

forget it. Perhaps it may be so; However, I much fear, his Instructions have edify'd out of their Place, and taught Men to grow Wiser in certain Points, where he never intended they should; For it is lamentable to behold, with what a lazy Scorn, many of the yawning Readers in our Age, do now a-days twirl over forty or fifty Pages of *Preface* and *Dedication*, (which is the usual *Modern* Stint) as if it were so much *Latin*. Tho' it must be also allowed on the other Hand that a very considerable Number is known to proceed *Criticks* and *Wits*, by reading nothing else. Into which two Factions, I think, all present Readers may justly be divided. Now, for my self, I profess to be of the former Sort; and therefore having the *Modern* Inclination to expatiate upon the Beauty of my own Productions, and display the bright Parts of my Discourse; I thought best to do it in the Body of the Work, where, as it now lies, it makes a very considerable Addition to the Bulk of the Volume, *a Circumstance by no means to be neglected by a skilful Writer*.

HAVING thus paid my due Deference and Acknowledgment to an establish'd Custom of our newest Authors, by *a long Digression unsought for*, and *an universal Censure unprovoked*; By forcing into the Light, with much Pains and Dexterity, my own Excellencies and other Mens Defaults, with great Justice to my self and Candor to them; I now happily resume my Subject, to the Infinite Satisfaction both of the Reader and the Author.

SECT. VI.

A TALE of a TUB.

WE left *Lord Peter* in open Rupture with his two Brethren; both for ever discarded from his House, and resigned to the wide World, with little or nothing to trust to. Which are Circumstances that render them proper Subjects for the Charity of a Writer's Pen to work on; Scenes of Misery, ever affording the fairest Harvest for great Adventures. And in this, the World may perceive the Difference between the Integrity of a generous Author, and that of a common Friend. The latter is observed to adhere close in Prosperity, but on the Decline of Fortune, to drop suddenly off. Whereas, the generous Author, just on the contrary, finds his Hero on the Dunghil, from thence by gradual Steps, raises Him to a Throne, and then immediately withdraws, expecting not so much as Thanks for his Pains: In imitation of which Example, I have placed *Lord Peter* in a Noble House, given Him a Title to wear, and Money to spend. There I shall leave Him for some Time; returning where common Charity directs me, to the Assistance of his two Brothers, at their lowest Ebb. However, I shall by no means forget my Character of an Historian, to follow the Truth, step by step, whatever happens, or where-ever it may lead me.

THE two Exiles so nearly united in Fortune and Interest, took a Lodging together; Where, at their first Leisure, they began to reflect on the numberless Misfortunes and Vexations of their Life past, and could not tell, on the sudden, to what Failure in their Conduct they ought to impute them; When, after some Recollection, they called to Mind the Copy of their Father's *Will*, which they had so happily recovered. This was immediately produced, and a firm Resolution taken between them, to alter whatever was already amiss, and reduce all their future Measures to the strictest Obedience prescribed therein. The main Body of the *Will* (as the Reader cannot easily have forgot) consisted in certain admirable Rules about the wearing of their Coats; in the Perusal whereof, the two Brothers at every Period duly comparing the Doctrine with the Practice, there was never seen a wider Difference between two Things; horrible down-right Transgressions of every Point. Upon which, they both resolved without further Delay, to fall immediately upon reducing the Whole, exactly after their Father's Model.

But, here it is good to stop the hasty Reader, ever impatient to see the End of an Adventure, before We Writers can duly prepare him for it. I am to record, that these two Brothers began to be distinguished at this Time, by certain Names. One of them desired to be called * *M A R T I N*, and the other took the Appellation of † *J A C K*. These two had lived in much Friendship and Agreement under the Tyranny of their Brother *Peter*, as it is the Talent of Fellow-Sufferers to do; Men in Misfortune, being like Men in the Dark, to whom all Colours are the same: But when they came forward into the World, and began to display themselves to each other, and to the Light, their Complexions appear'd extreamly different; which the present Posture of their Affairs gave them sudden Opportunity to discover.

But, here the severe Reader may justly tax me as a Writer of short Memory, a Deficiency to which a true *Modern* cannot but of Necessity be a little subject. Because, *Memory* being an Employment of the Mind upon things past, is a Faculty, for which the Learned, in our Illustrious Age, have no manner of Occasion, who deal entirely with *Invention*, and strike all Things out of themselves, or at least, by Collision, from each other: Upon which Account we think it highly Reasonable to produce our great Forgetfulness, as an Argument unanswerable for our great Wit. I ought in Method, to have informed the Reader about fifty Pages ago, of a Fancy *Lord Peter* took, and infused into his Brothers, to wear on their Coats what ever Trimmings came up in Fashion; never pulling off any, as they went out of the Mode, but keeping on all together; which amounted in time to a Medley, the most Antick you can possibly conceive; and this to a Degree, that upon the Time of their falling out there was hardly a Thread of the Original Coat to be seen, but an infinite Quantity of *Lace*, and *Ribbands*, and *Fringe*, and *Embroidery*, and *Points*; (I

---

* *Martin Luther.*
† *John Calvin.*

mean, only those * *tagg'd with Silver*, for the rest fell off.) Now, this material Circumstance, having been forgot in due Place; as good Fortune hath ordered, comes in very properly here, when the two Brothers are just going to reform their Vestures into the Primitive State, prescribed by their Father's *Will*.

THEY both unanimously entred upon this great Work, looking sometimes on their Coats, and sometimes on the *Will*. *Martin* laid the first Hand; at one twitch brought off a large Handful of *Points*, and with a second pull, stript away ten dozen Yards of *Fringe*. But when He had gone thus far, he demurred a while: He knew very well, there yet remained a great deal more to be done; however, the first Heat being over, his Violence began to cool, and he resolved to proceed more moderately in the rest of the Work; having already very narrowly scap'd a swinging Rent in pulling off the *Points*, which being *tagged with Silver* (as we have observed before) the judicious Workman had with much Sagacity, double sown, to preserve them from *falling*. Resolving therefore to rid his Coat of a huge Quantity of *Gold Lace*; he pickt up the Stitches with much Caution, and diligently gleaned out all the loose Threads as he went, which proved to be a Work of Time. Then he fell about the embroidered *Indian* Figures of Men, Women and Children; against which, as you have heard in its due Place, their Father's Testament was extreamly exact and severe: These, with much Dexterity and Application, were after a while, quite eradicated, or utterly defaced. For the rest, where he observed the Embroidery to be workt so close, as not to be got away without damaging the Cloth, or where it served to hide or strengthen any Flaw in the Body of the Coat, contracted by the perpetual tampering of Workmen upon it; he concluded the wisest Course was to let it remain, resolving in no Case whatsoever, that the Substance of the Stuff should suffer Injury; which he thought the best Method for serving the true Intent and Meaning of his Father's *Will*. And this is the nearest Account I have been able to collect, of *Martin*'s Proceedings upon this great Revolution.

---

* *Points tagg'd with Silver, are those Doctrines that promote the Greatness and Wealth of the Church, which have been therefore woven deepest in the Body of Popery.*

But his Brother *Jack*, whose Adventures will be so extraordinary, as to furnish a great Part in the Remainder of this Discourse; entred upon the Matter with other Thoughts, and a quite different Spirit. For, the Memory of *Lord Peter*'s Injuries, produced a Degree of Hatred and Spight, which had a much greater Share of inciting Him, than any Regards after his Father's Commands, since these appeared at best, only Secondary and Subservient to the other. However, for this Meddly of Humor, he made a Shift to find a very plausible Name, honoring it with the Title of *Zeal*; which is, perhaps, the most significant Word that hath been ever yet produced in any Language; As, I think, I have fully proved in my excellent *Analytical* Discourse upon that Subject; wherein I have deduced a *Histori-theo-physi-logical* Account of *Zeal*, shewing how it first proceeded from a *Notion* into a *Word*, and from thence in a hot Summer, ripned into a *tangible Substance*. This Work containing three large Volumes in Folio, I design very shortly to publish by the *Modern* way of *Subscription*, not doubting but the Nobility and Gentry of the Land will give me all possible Encouragement, having already had such a Taste of what I am able to perform.

I record therefore, that Brother *Jack*, brimful of this miraculous Compound, reflecting with Indignation upon *PETER*'s Tyranny, and farther provoked by the Despondency of *Martin*; prefaced his Resolutions to this purpose. *What?* said he; *A Rogue that lock'd up his Drink, turned away our Wives, cheated us of our Fortunes; paumed his damned Crusts upon us for Mutton; and at last kickt us out of Doors; must we be in His Fashions with a Pox? a Rascal, besides, that all the Street cries out against.* Having thus kindled and enflamed himself as high as possible, and by Consequence, in a delicate Temper for beginning a Reformation, he set about the Work immediately, and in three Minutes, made more Dispatch than *Martin* had done in as many Hours. For, (Courteous Reader) you are given to understand, that *Zeal* is never so highly obliged, as when you set it a *Tearing*: and *Jack*, who doated on that Quality in himself, allowed it at this Time its full Swinge. Thus it happened, that stripping down a Parcel of *Gold Lace*, a little too hastily, he rent the *main Body* of his *Coat* from Top to Bottom; and whereas his Talent was not of the happiest in *taking up a Stitch*, he knew no better way, than to dern it again with *Packthred* and a *Scewer*. But the Matter was yet infinitely worse (I record it with Tears) when he proceeded to the *Embroidery*: For, being Clumsy by Nature, and of Temper, Impatient; withal, beholding Millions of Stitches, that required the nicest Hand, and sedatest Constitution, to extricate; in a great Rage, he tore off the whole Piece, Cloth and all, and flung it into the Kennel, and furiously thus continuing his Career; *Ah, Good Brother* Martin, said he, *do as I do, for the Love of God; Strip, Tear, Pull, Rent, Flay off all, that we may appear as unlike the Rogue* Peter, *as it is possible: I would not for a hundred Pounds carry the least Mark about me, that might give Occasion to the Neighbours, of suspecting I was related to such a Rascal.* But *Martin*, who at this Time happened to be extremely flegmatick and sedate, *begged his Brother of all Love, not to damage his Coat by any Means; for he never would get such another*: Desired him *to consider, that it was not their Business to form their Actions by any Reflection upon* Peter's, *but by observing the Rules prescribed in their Father's* Will. That *he should remember,* Peter *was still their Brother, whatever Faults or Injuries he had committed; and therefore they should by all means avoid such a Thought, as that of taking Measures for Good and Evil, from no other Rule, than of Opposition to him.* That *it was true, the Testament of their good Father was very exact in what related to the wearing of their* Coats; *yet was it no less penal and strict in prescribing Agreement, and Friendship, and Affection between them. And therefore, if straining a Point were at all dispensable, it would certainly be so, rather to the Advance of Unity, than Increase of Contradiction.*

MARTIN had still proceeded as gravely as he began; and doubtless, would have delivered an admirable Lecture of Morality, which might have exceedingly contributed to my Reader's *Repose, both of Body and Mind*: (the true ultimate End of *Ethicks*;) But *Jack* was already gone a Flight-shot beyond his Patience. And as in Scholastick Disputes, nothing serves to rouze the Spleen of him that *Opposes*, so much as a kind of Pedantick affected Calmness in the *Respondent*; Disputants being for the most part like unequal Scales, where the *Gravity* of one Side advances the *Lightness* of the Other, and causes it to fly up and kick the Beam; So it happened here, that the *Weight* of *Martin's*

Arguments exalted *Jack's Levity*, and made him fly out and spurn against his Brother's Moderation. In short, *Martin's Patience* put *Jack* in a *Rage*; but that which most afflicted him was, to observe his Brother's Coat so well reduced into the State of Innocence; while his own was either wholly rent to his Shirt; or those Places which had scaped his cruel Clutches, were still in *Peter's* Livery. So that he looked like a drunken *Beau*, half rifled by *Bullies*; Or like a fresh Tenant of *Newgate*, when he has refused the Payment of *Garnish*; Or like a discovered *Shoplifter*, left to the Mercy of *Exchange-Women*; Or like a *Bawd* in her old Velvet-Petticoat, resign'd into the secular Hands of the *Mobile*. Like any, or like all of these, a Meddley of *Rags*, and *Lace*, and *Rents*, and *Fringes*, unfortunate *Jack* did now appear: He would have been extremely glad to see his Coat in the Condition of *Martin's*, but infinitely gladder to find that of *Martin's* in the same Predicament with his. However, since neither of these was likely to come to pass, he thought fit to lend the whole Business another Turn, and to dress up Necessity into a Virtue. Therefore, after as many of the *Fox's* Arguments, as he could muster up, for bringing *Martin* to *Reason*, as he called it; or, as he meant it, into his own ragged, bobtail'd Condition; and observing he said all to little purpose; what, alas, was left for the forlorn *Jack* to do, but after a Million of Scurrilities against his Brother, to run mad with Spleen, and Spight, and Contradiction. To be short, here began a mortal Breach between these two. *Jack* went immediately to *New Lodgings*, and in a few Days it was for certain reported, that he had run out of his Wits. In a short time after, he appeared abroad, and confirmed the Report, by falling into the oddest Whimsies that ever a sick Brain conceived.

AND now the little Boys in the Streets began to salute him with several Names. Sometimes they would call Him, * *Jack the Bald*; sometimes, † *Jack with a Lanthorn*; sometimes, ‖ *Dutch Jack*; sometimes, * *French Hugh*; sometimes, † *Tom the Beggar*;

---

* *That is* Calvin, *from* Calvus, *Bald.*

† *All those who pretend to Inward Light.*

‖ Jack *of* Leyden, *who gave Rise to the* Anabaptists.

* *The* Hugonots.

† *The* Gueuses, *by which Name some Protestants in* Flanders *were call'd.*

and sometimes, || *Knocking Jack of the North.* And it was under one, or some, or all of these Appellations (which I leave the Learned Reader to determine) that he hath given Rise to the most Illustrious and Epidemick Sect of *Æolists*, who with honourable Commemoration, do still acknowledge the Renowned *J A C K* for their Author and Founder. Of whose Original, as well as Principles, I am now advancing to gratify the World with a very particular Account.

————*Mellæo contingens cuncta Lepore.*

|| John Knox, *the Reformer of* Scotland.

SECT. VII.

A Digression in Praise of Digressions.

I HAVE sometimes *heard* of an *Iliad* in a *Nut-shell*; but it hath been my Fortune to have much oftner *seen* a *Nut-shell* in an *Iliad*. There is no doubt, that Human Life has received most wonderful Advantages from both; but to which of the two the World is chiefly indebted, I shall leave among the Curious, as a Problem worthy of their utmost Enquiry. For the Invention of the latter, I think the Commonwealth of Learning is chiefly obliged to the great *Modern* Improvement of *Digressions*: The late Refinements in Knowledge, running parallel to those of Dyet in our Nation, which among Men of a judicious Taste, are drest up in various Compounds, consisting in *Soups* and *Ollio's*, *Fricassées* and *Ragousts*.

'Tis true, there is a sort of morose, detracting, ill-bred People, who pretend utterly to disrelish these polite Innovations: And as to the Similitude from Dyet, they allow the Parallel, but are so bold to pronounce the Example it self, a Corruption and Degeneracy of Taste. They tell us, that the Fashion of jumbling fifty Things together in a Dish, was at first introduced in Compliance to a depraved and *debauched Appetite*, as well as to a *crazy Constitution*; And to see a Man hunting thro' an *Ollio*, after the *Head* and *Brains* of a *Goose*, a *Wigeon*, or a *Woodcock*, is a Sign, he wants a Stomach and Digestion for more substantial Victuals. Farther, they affirm, that *Digressions* in a Book, are like *Forein Troops* in a *State*, which argue the Nation to want a *Heart* and *Hands* of its own, and often, either *subdue* the *Natives*, or drive them into the most *unfruitful Corners*.

But, after all that can be objected by these supercilious Censors; 'tis manifest, the Society of Writers would quickly be reduced to a very inconsiderable Number, if Men were put upon making Books, with the fatal Confinement of delivering nothing beyond what is to the Purpose. 'Tis acknowledged, that were the Case the same among Us, as with the *Greeks* and *Romans*, when Learning was in its *Cradle*, to be reared and fed, and cloathed by *Invention*; it would be an easy Task to fill up Volumes upon particular Occasions, without farther exspatiating from the Subject, than by moderate Excursions, helping to advance or clear the main Design. But with *Knowledge*, it has fared as with a numerous Army, encamped in a fruitful Country; which for a few Days maintains it self by the Product of the Soyl it is on; Till Provisions being spent, they send to forrage many a Mile, among Friends or Enemies it matters not. Mean while, the neighbouring Fields trampled and beaten down, become barren and dry, affording no Sustenance but Clouds of Dust.

THE whole Course of Things, being thus entirely changed between *Us* and the *Antients*; and the *Moderns* wisely sensible of it, we of this Age have discovered a shorter, and more prudent Method, to become *Scholars* and *Wits*, without the Fatigue of *Reading* or of *Thinking*. The most accomplisht Way of using Books at present, is twofold: Either first, to serve them as some Men do *Lords*, learn their *Titles* exactly, and then brag of their Acquaintance. Or Secondly, which is indeed the choicer, the profounder, and politer Method, to get a thorough Insight into the *Index*, by which the whole Book is governed and turned, like *Fishes* by the *Tail*. For, to enter the Palace of Learning at the *great Gate*, requires an Expence of Time and Forms; therefore Men of much Haste and little Ceremony, are content to get in by the *Back-Door*. For, the Arts are all in a *flying* March, and therefore more easily subdued by attacking them in the *Rear*. Thus Physicians discover the State of the whole Body, by consulting only what comes from *Behind*. Thus Men catch Knowledge by throwing their *Wit* on the *Posteriors* of a Book, as Boys do Sparrows with flinging *Salt* upon their *Tails*. Thus Human Life is best understood by the wise man's Rule of *Regarding the End*. Thus are the Sciences found like *Hercules*'s Oxen, by *tracing them Backwards*. Thus are *old Sciences* unravelled like *old Stockings*, by beginning at the *Foot*.

BESIDES all this, the Army of the Sciences hath been of late with a world of Martial Discipline, drawn into its *close Order*, so that a View, or a Muster may be taken of it with abundance of Expedition. For this great Blessing we are wholly indebted to

Systems and *Abstracts*, in which the *Modern* Fathers of Learning, like prudent Usurers, spent their Sweat for the Ease of Us their Children. For *Labor* is the Seed of *Idleness*, and it is the peculiar Happiness of our Noble Age to gather the *Fruit*.

Now the Method of growing Wise, Learned, and *Sublime*, having become so regular an Affair, and so established in all its Forms; the Number of Writers must needs have encreased accordingly, and to a Pitch that has made it of absolute Necessity for them to interfere continually with each other. Besides, it is reckoned, that there is not at this present, a sufficient Quantity of new Matter left in Nature, to furnish and adorn any one particular Subject to the Extent of a Volume. This I am told by a very skillful *Computer*, who hath given a full Demonstration of it from Rules of *Arithmetick*.

THIS, perhaps, may be objected against, by those, who maintain the Infinity of Matter, and therefore, will not allow that any *Species* of it can be exhausted. For Answer to which, let us examine the noblest Branch of *Modern* Wit or Invention, planted and cultivated by the present Age, and, which of all others, hath born the most, and the fairest Fruit. For tho' some Remains of it were left us by the *Antients*, yet have not any of those, as I remember, been translated or compiled into Systems for *Modern* Use. Therefore We may affirm, to our own Honor, that it has in some sort, been both invented, and brought to a Perfection by the same Hands. What I mean, is that highly celebrated Talent among the *Modern* Wits, of deducing Similitudes, Allusions, and Applications, very Surprizing, Agreeable, and Apposite, from the *Pudenda* of either Sex, together with *their proper Uses*. And truly, having observed how little Invention bears any Vogue, besides what is derived into these *Channels*, I have sometimes had a Thought, That the happy Genius of our Age and Country, was

* Ctesiæ fragm. apud Photium. prophetically held forth by that antient *typical Description of the *Indian* Pygmies; *whose Stature did not exceed above two Foot; Sed quorum pudenda crassa, & ad talos usque pertingentia.* Now, I have been very curious to inspect the late Productions, wherein the Beauties of this kind have most prominently appeared. And altho' this *Vein* hath bled so freely, and all Endeavours have been used in the Power of Human

Breath, to dilate, extend, and keep it open: Like the Scythians,
              * *who had a Custom, and an Instrument, to blow up*
* *Herodot. L. 4.* *the Privities of their Mares, that they might yield the*
more Milk; Yet I am under an Apprehension, it is near growing
dry, and past all Recovery; And that either some new *Fonde* of
Wit should, if possible, be provided, or else that we must e'en be
content with Repetition here, as well as upon all other Occasions.

THIS will stand as an uncontestable Argument, that our *Modern* Wits are not to reckon upon the Infinity of Matter, for a
constant Supply. What remains therefore, but that our last Recourse must be had to large *Indexes*, and little *Compendiums*;
Quotations must be plentifully gathered, and bookt in Alphabet;
To this End, tho' Authors need be little consulted, yet *Criticks*,
and *Commentators*, and *Lexicons* carefully must. But above all,
those judicious Collectors of *bright Parts*, and *Flowers*, and *Observanda's*, are to be nicely dwelt on; by some called the *Sieves* and
Boulters of Learning; tho' it is left undetermined, whether they
dealt in *Pearls* or *Meal*; and consequently, whether we are more
to value that which *passed thro'*, or what *staid behind*.

BY these Methods, in a few Weeks, there starts up many a
Writer, capable of managing the profoundest, and most uni-
versal Subjects. For, what tho' his *Head* be empty, provided his
Common-place-Book be full; And if you will bate him but the
Circumstances of *Method*, and *Style*, and *Grammar*, and *Invention*;
allow him but the common Priviledges of transcribing from
others, and digressing from himself, as often as he shall see Occasion; He will desire no more Ingredients towards fitting up a
Treatise, that shall make a very comely Figure on a Bookseller's
Shelf, there to be preserved neat and clean, for a long Eternity,
adorn'd with the Heraldry of its Title, fairly inscribed on a
Label; never to be thumb'd or greas'd by Students, nor bound to
everlasting Chains of Darkness in a Library: But when the Ful-
ness of time is come, shall haply undergo the Tryal of Purgatory, in order *to ascend the Sky*.

WITHOUT these Allowances, how is it possible, we *Modern*
Wits should ever have an Opportunity to introduce our Collections listed under so many thousand Heads of a different Nature?
for want of which, the Learned World would be deprived of

infinite Delight, as well as Instruction, and we our selves buried beyond Redress in an inglorious and undistinguisht Oblivion.

FROM such Elements as these, I am alive to behold the Day, wherein the Corporation of Authors can out-vie all its Brethren in the *Guild*. A Happiness derived to us with a great many others, from our *Scythian* Ancestors; among whom, the Number of *Pens* was so infinite, that the * *Grecian* Eloquence had no other way of expressing it, than by saying, *That in the Regions, far to the North, it was hardly possible for a Man to travel, the very Air was so replete with* Feathers.

* *Herodot.* L. 4.

THE Necessity of this Digression, will easily excuse the Length; and I have chosen for it as proper a Place as I could readily find. If the judicious Reader can assign a fitter, I do here empower him to remove it into any other Corner he please. And so I return with great Alacrity to pursue a more important Concern.

SECT. VIII.

A TALE of a TUB.

THE Learned * *Æolists*, maintain the Original Cause of all Things to be *Wind*, from which Principle this whole Universe was at first produced, and into which it must at last be resolved; that the same Breath which had kindled, and blew *up* the Flame of Nature, should one Day blow it *out*.

>*Quod procul à nobis flectat Fortuna gubernans.*

THIS is what the *Adepti* understand by their *Anima Mundi*; that is to say, the *Spirit*, or *Breath*, or *Wind* of the World: Or Examine the whole System by the Particulars of Nature, and you will find it not to be disputed. For, whether you please to call the *Forma informans* of Man, by the Name of *Spiritus*, *Animus*, *Afflatus*, or *Anima*; What are all these but several Appellations for *Wind*? which is the ruling *Element* in every Compound, and into which they all resolve upon their Corruption. Farther, what is Life itself, but as it is commonly call'd, the *Breath* of our Nostrils? Whence it is very justly observed by Naturalists, that *Wind* still continues of great Emolument in *certain Mysteries* not to be named, giving Occasion for those happy Epithets of *Turgidus*, and *Inflatus*, apply'd either to the *Emittent*, or *Recipient* Organs.

BY what I have gathered out of antient Records, I find the *Compass* of their Doctrine took in two and thirty Points, wherein it would be tedious to be very particular. However, a few of their most important Precepts, deducible from it, are by no means to be omitted; among which the following Maxim was of much Weight; That since *Wind* had the Master-Share, as well as Operation in every Compound, by Consequence, those Beings must be of chief Excellence, wherein that *Primordium* appears most prominently to abound; and therefore, *Man* is in highest Perfection of all created Things, as having by the great Bounty of Philosophers, been endued with three distinct *Anima's* or

---

* *All Pretenders to Inspiration whatsoever.*

Winds, to which the Sage *Æolists*, with much Liberality, have added a fourth of equal Necessity, as well as Ornament with the other three; by this *quartum Principium*, taking in the four Corners of the World; which gave Occasion to that Renowned *Cabbalist*, * *Bumbastus*, of placing the Body of Man, in due position to the four *Cardinal* Points.

IN Consequence of this, their next Principle was, that *Man* brings with him into the World a peculiar Portion or Grain of *Wind*, which may be called a *Quinta essentia*, extracted from the other four. This *Quintessence* is of Catholick Use upon all Emergencies of Life, is improvable into all Arts and Sciences, and may be wonderfully refined, as well as enlarged by certain Methods in Education. This, when *blown* up to its Perfection, ought not to be covetously hoarded up, stifled, or hid under a Bushel, but freely communicated to Mankind. Upon these Reasons, and others of equal Weight, the Wise *Æolists*, affirm the Gift of BELCHING, to be the noblest Act of a Rational Creature. To cultivate which Art, and render it more serviceable to Mankind, they made Use of several Methods. At certain Seasons of the Year, you might behold the Priests amongst them in vast Numbers, with their † *Mouths gaping wide against a Storm*. At other times were to be seen several Hundreds link'd together in a circular Chain, with every Man a Pair of Bellows applied to his Neighbour's Breech, by which they blew up each other to the Shape and Size of a *Tun*; and for that Reason, with great Propriety of Speech, did usually call their Bodies, their *Vessels*. When, by these and the like Performances, they were grown sufficiently replete, they would immediately depart, and disembogue for the Publick Good, a plentiful Share of their Acquirements into their Disciples Chaps. For we must here observe, that all Learning was esteemed among them to be compounded from the same Principle. Because, First, it is generally affirmed, or confess'd that Learning *puffeth Men up*: And Secondly, they

---

* *This is one of the Names of* Paracelsus; *He was call'd* Christophorus, Theophrastus, Paracelsus, Bumbastus.

† *This is meant of those Seditious Preachers, who blow up the Seeds of Rebellion*, &c.

proved it by the following Syllogism; *Words are but Wind; and Learning is nothing but Words*; Ergo, *Learning is nothing but Wind*. For this Reason, the Philosophers among them, did in their Schools, deliver to their Pupils, all their Doctrines and Opinions by *Eructation*, wherein they had acquired a wonderful Eloquence, and of incredible Variety. But the great Characteristick, by which their chief Sages were best distinguished, was a certain Position of Countenance, which gave undoubted Intelligence to what Degree or Proportion, the Spirit agitated the inward Mass. For, after certain Gripings, the *Wind* and Vapours issuing forth; having first by their Turbulence and Convulsions within, caused an Earthquake in Man's little World; distorted the Mouth, bloated the Cheeks, and gave the Eyes a terrible kind of *Relievo*. At which Junctures, all their *Belches* were received for Sacred, the Sourer the better, and swallowed with infinite Consolation by their meager Devotes. And to render these yet more compleat, because the Breath of Man's Life is in his Nostrils, therefore, the choicest, most edifying, and most enlivening *Belches*, were very wisely conveyed thro' that Vehicle, to give them a Tincture as they passed.

THEIR Gods were the four *Winds*, whom they worshipped, as the Spirits that pervade and enliven the Universe, and as those from whom alone all *Inspiration* can properly be said to proceed. However, the Chief of these, to whom they performed the Adoration of *Latria*, was the *Almighty-North*. An antient Deity, whom the Inhabitants of *Megalopolis* in Greece, had likewise in highest Reverence. * *Omnium Deorum Boream maxime celebrant*. This God, tho' endued with   * *Pausan*. L.8. Ubiquity, was yet supposed by the profounder *Æolists*, to possess one peculiar Habitation, or (to speak in Form) a *Cælum Empyræum*, wherein he was more intimately present. This was situated in a certain Region, well known to the Antient *Greeks*, by them called, Σκοτία, or the *Land of Darkness*. And altho' many Controversies have arisen upon that Matter; yet so much is undisputed, that from a Region of the *like Denomination*, the most refined *Æolists* have borrowed their Original, from whence, in every Age, the zealous among their Priesthood, have brought over their choicest *Inspiration*, fetching it with their own Hands,

h

from the Fountain Head, in certain *Bladders*, and disploding it among the Sectaries in all Nations, who did, and do, and ever will, daily Gasp and Pant after it.

Now, their Mysteries and Rites were performed in this Manner. 'Tis well known among the Learned, that the Virtuoso's of former Ages, had a Contrivance for carrying and preserving *Winds* in Casks or Barrels, which was of great Assistance upon long Sea Voyages; and the Loss of so useful an Art at present, is very much to be lamented, tho' I know not how, with great Negligence omitted by * *Pancirollus*. It was an Invention ascribed to *Æolus* himself, from whom this Sect is denominated, and who in Honour of their Founder's Memory, have to this Day preserved great Numbers of those *Barrels*, whereof they fix one in each of their Temples, first beating out the Top. Into this *Barrel*, upon Solemn Days, the Priest enters; where, having before duly prepared himself by the methods already described, a secret Funnel is also convey'd from his Posteriors, to the Bottom of the Barrel, which admits new Supplies of Inspiration from a *Northern* Chink or Crany. Whereupon, you behold him swell immediately to the Shape and Size of his *Vessel*. In this Posture he disembogues whole Tempests upon his Auditory, as the Spirit from beneath gives him Utterance; which issuing *ex adytis*, and *penetralibus*, is not performed without much Pain and Gripings. And the *Wind* in breaking forth, † deals with his Face, as it does with that of the Sea; first *blackning*, then *wrinkling*, and at last, *bursting it into a Foam*. It is in this Guise, the Sacred *Æolist* delivers his oracular *Belches* to his panting Disciples; Of whom, some are greedily gaping after the sanctified Breath; others are all the while hymning out the Praises of the *Winds*; and gently wafted to and fro by their own Humming, do thus represent the soft Breezes of their Deities appeased.

It is from this Custom of the Priests, that some Authors maintain these *Æolists*, to have been very antient in the World.

---

* *An Author who writ* De Artibus Perditis, &c. *of Arts lost, and of Arts invented.*

† *This is an exact Description of the Changes made in the Face by Enthusiastick Preachers.*

Because, the Delivery of their Mysteries, which I have just now mention'd, appears exactly the same with that of other antient Oracles, whose Inspirations were owing to certain subterraneous *Effluviums* of *Wind*, delivered with the *same* Pain to the Priest, and much about the *same* Influence on the People. It is true indeed, that these were frequently managed and directed by *Female* Officers, whose Organs were understood to be better disposed for the Admission of those Oracular *Gusts*, as entring and passing up thro' a Receptacle of greater Capacity, and causing also a Pruriency by the Way, such as with due Management, hath been refined from a Carnal, into a Spiritual Extasie. And to strengthen this profound Conjecture, it is farther insisted, that this Custom of * *Female* Priests is kept up still in certain refined Colleges of our *Modern Æolists*, who are agreed to receive their Inspiration, derived thro' the Receptacle aforesaid, like their Ancestors, the *Sibyls*.

AND, whereas the mind of Man, when he gives the Spur and Bridle to his Thoughts, doth never stop, but naturally sallies out into both extreams of High and Low, of Good and Evil; His first Flight of Fancy, commonly transports Him to Idea's of what is most Perfect, finished, and exalted; till having soared out of his own Reach and Sight, not well perceiving how near the Frontiers of Height and Depth, border upon each other; With the same Course and Wing, he falls down plum into the lowest Bottom of Things; like one who travels the *East* into the *West*; or like a strait Line drawn by its own Length into a Circle. Whether a Tincture of Malice in our Natures, makes us fond of furnishing every bright Idea with its Reverse; Or, whether Reason reflecting upon the Sum of Things, can, like the Sun, serve only to enlighten one half of the Globe, leaving the other half, by Necessity, under Shade and Darkness: Or, whether Fancy, flying up to the imagination of what is Highest and Best, becomes over-shot, and spent, and weary, and suddenly falls like a dead Bird of Paradise, to the Ground. Or, whether after all these *Metaphysical* Conjectures, I have not entirely missed the true Reason; The Proposition, however, which hath stood me

---

* *Quakers who suffer their Women to preach and pray.*

in so much Circumstance, is altogether true; That, as the most unciviliz'd Parts of Mankind, have some way or other, climbed up into the Conception of a *God*, or Supream Power, so they have seldom forgot to provide their Fears with certain ghastly Notions, which instead of better, have served them pretty tolerably for a *Devil*. And this Proceeding seems to be natural enough; For it is with Men, whose Imaginations are lifted up very high, after the same Rate, as with those, whose Bodies are so; that, as they are delighted with the Advantage of a nearer Contemplation upwards, so they are equally terrified with the dismal Prospect of the Precipice below. Thus, in the Choice of a *Devil*, it hath been the usual Method of Mankind, to single out some Being, either in Act, or in Vision, which was in most Antipathy to the God they had framed. Thus also the Sect of *Æolists*, possessed themselves with a Dread, and Horror, and Hatred of two Malignant Natures, betwixt whom, and the Deities they adored, perpetual Enmity was established. The first of these, was the * *Camelion* sworn Foe to *Inspiration*, who in Scorn, devoured large Influences of their God; without refunding the smallest Blast by *Eructation*. The other was a huge terrible Monster, called *Moulinavent*, who with four strong Arms, waged eternal Battel with all their Divinities, dextrously turning to avoid their Blows, and repay them with Interest.

THUS furnisht, and set out with *Gods*, as well as *Devils*, was the renowned Sect of *Æolists*; which makes at this Day so illustrious a Figure in the World, and whereof, that Polite Nation of *Laplanders*, are beyond all Doubt, a most Authentick Branch; Of whom, I therefore cannot, without Injustice, here omit to make honourable Mention; since they appear to be so closely allied in Point of Interest, as well as Inclinations, with their Brother *Æolists* among Us, as not only to buy their *Winds* by wholesale from the *same* Merchants, but also to retail them after the *same* Rate and Method, and to Customers much alike.

Now, whether the System here delivered, was wholly com-

---

* *I do not well understand what the Author aims at here, any more than by the terrible Monster, mention'd in the following Lines, called* Moulinavent, *which is the* French *Word for a* Windmill.

piled by *Jack*, or, as some Writers believe, rather copied from the Original at *Delphos*, with certain Additions and Emendations suited to Times and Circumstances, I shall not absolutely determine. This I may affirm, that *Jack* gave it at least a new Turn, and formed it into the same Dress and Model, as it lies deduced by me.

I have long sought after this Opportunity, of doing Justice to a Society of Men, for whom I have a peculiar Honour, and whose Opinions, as well as Practices, have been extreamly misrepresented, and traduced by the Malice or Ignorance of their Adversaries. For, I think it one of the greatest, and best of human Actions, to remove Prejudices, and place Things in their truest and fairest Light; which I therefore boldly undertake without any Regards of my own, beside the Conscience, the Honour, and the Thanks.

SECT. IX.

A Digression concerning the Original, the Use and Improvement of Madness *in a Commonwealth.*

NOR shall it any ways detract from the just Reputation of this famous Sect, that its Rise and Institution are owing to such an Author as I have described *Jack* to be; A Person whose Intellectuals were overturned, and his Brain shaken out of its Natural Position; which we commonly suppose to be a Distemper, and call by the Name of *Madness* or *Phrenzy*. For, if we take a Survey of the greatest Actions that have been performed in the World, under the Influence of Single Men; which are, *The Establishment of New Empires by Conquest: The Advance and Progress of New Schemes in Philosophy; and the contriving, as well as the propagating of New Religions*: We shall find the Authors of them all, to have been Persons, whose natural Reason hath admitted great Revolutions from their Dyet, their Education, the Prevalency of some certain Temper, together with the particular Influence of Air and Climate. Besides, there is something Individual in human Minds, that easily kindles at the accidental Approach and Collision of certain Circumstances, which tho' of paltry and mean Appearance, do often flame out into the greatest Emergencies of Life. For great Turns are not always given by strong Hands, but by lucky Adaption, and at proper Seasons; and it is of no import, where the Fire was kindled, if the Vapor has once got up into the Brain. For the *upper Region* of Man, is furnished like the *middle Region* of the Air; The Materials are formed from Causes of the widest Difference, yet produce at last the same Substance and Effect. Mists arise from the Earth, Steams from Dunghils, Exhalations from the Sea, and Smoak from Fire; yet all Clouds are the same in Composition, as well as Consequences: and the Fumes issuing from a Jakes, will furnish as comely and useful a Vapor, as Incense from an Altar. Thus far, I suppose, will easily be granted me; and then it will follow, that as the Face of Nature never produces Rain, but when it is overcast and disturbed, so Human Understanding, seated in the Brain, must be troubled and overspread by Vapours, ascending from the lower Faculties, to water the Invention, and render it fruitful. Now, altho' these Vapours (as it hath been already said) are of as various Original, as those of the Skies, yet the Crop they produce, differs both in Kind and Degree, meerly according to the Soil. I will produce two Instances to prove and Explain what I am now advancing.

    * A certain Great Prince raised a mighty Army, filled his Coffers with infinite Treasures, provided an invincible Fleet, and all this, without giving the least Part of his Design to his greatest Ministers, or his nearest Favourites. Immediately the whole World was alarmed; the neighbouring Crowns, in trembling Expectation, towards what Point the Storm would burst; the small Politicians, every where forming profound Conjectures. Some believed he had laid a Scheme for Universal Monarchy: Others, after much Insight, determined the Matter to be a Project for pulling down the *Pope*, and setting up the *Reformed* Religion, which had once been his own. Some, again, of a deeper Sagacity, sent him into *Asia* to subdue the *Turk*, and recover *Palestine*. In the midst of all these Projects and Preparations; a certain † *State-Surgeon*, gathering the Nature of the Disease by these Symptoms, attempted the Cure, at one Blow performed the Operation, broke the Bag, and out flew the *Vapour*; nor did any thing want to render it a compleat Remedy, only, that the Prince unfortunately happened to Die in the Performance. Now, is the Reader exceeding curious to learn, from whence this *Vapour* took its Rise, which had so long set the Nations at a Gaze? What secret Wheel, what hidden Spring could put into Motion so wonderful an Engine? It was afterwards discovered, that the Movement of this whole Machine had been directed by an absent *Female*, whose Eyes had raised a Protuberancy, and before Emission, she was removed into an Enemy's Country. What should an unhappy Prince do in such ticklish Circumstances as these? He tried in vain the Poet's never-failing Receipt of *Corpora quæque*; For,

> *Idque petit corpus mens unde est saucia amore;*
> *Unde feritur, eo tendit, gestitq; coire.* Lucr.

---

    * *This was* Harry *the Great of* France.
    † Ravillac, *who stabb'd* Henry *the Great in his Coach.*

HAVING to no purpose used all peaceable Endeavours, the collected part of the *Semen*, raised and enflamed, became adust, converted to Choler, turned head upon the spinal Duct, and ascended to the Brain. The very same Principle that influences a *Bully* to break the Windows of a Whore, who has jilted him, naturally stirs up a Great Prince to raise mighty Armies, and dream of nothing but Sieges, Battles, and Victories.

———*Teterrima belli*
   Causa———

THE other * Instance is, what I have read somewhere, in a very antient Author, of a mighty King, who for the space of above thirty Years, amused himself to take and lose Towns; beat Armies, and be beaten; drive Princes out of their Dominions; fright Children from their Bread and Butter; burn, lay waste, plunder, dragoon, massacre Subject and Stranger, Friend and Foe, Male and Female. 'Tis recorded, that the Philosophers of each Country were in grave Dispute, upon Causes Natural, Moral, and Political, to find out where they should assign an original Solution of this *Phænomenon*. At last the *Vapour* or *Spirit*, which animated the Hero's Brain, being in perpetual Circulation, seized upon that Region of the Human Body, so renown'd for furnishing the † *Zibeta Occidentalis*, and gathering there into a Tumor, left the rest of the World for that Time in Peace. Of such mighty Consequence it is, where those Exhalations fix; and of so little, from whence they proceed. The same Spirits which in their superior Progress would conquer a Kingdom, descending upon the *Anus*, conclude in a *Fistula*.

LET us next examine the great Introducers of new Schemes in Philosophy, and search till we can find, from what Faculty of the Soul the Disposition arises in mortal Man, of taking it into his Head, to advance new Systems with such an eager Zeal, in

---

* *This is meant of the Present* French *King.*

† Paracelsus, *who was so famous for Chymistry, try'd an Experiment upon human Excrement, to make a Perfume of it, which when he had brought to Perfection, he called* Zibeta Occidentalis, *or* Western-Civet, *the back Parts of Man (according to his Division mention'd by the Author,* page [96].) *being the* West.

things agreed on all hands impossible to be known: from what Seeds this Disposition springs, and to what Quality of human Nature these Grand Innovators have been indebted for their Number of Disciples. Because, it is plain, that several of the chief among them, both *Antient* and *Modern*, were usually mistaken by their Adversaries, and indeed, by all, except their own Followers, to have been Persons Crazed, or out of their Wits, having generally proceeded in the common Course of their Words and Actions, by a Method very different from the vulgar Dictates of *unrefined* Reason: agreeing for the most Part in their several Models, with their present undoubted Successors in the *Academy* of *Modern Bedlam* (whose Merits and Principles I shall farther examine in due Place.) Of this Kind were *Epicurus, Diogenes, Apollonius, Lucretius, Paracelsus, Des Cartes*, and others; who, if they were now in the World, tied fast, and separate from their Followers, would in this our undistinguishing Age, incur manifest Danger of *Phlebotomy*, and *Whips*, and *Chains*, and *dark Chambers*, and *Straw*. For, what Man in the natural State, or Course of Thinking, did ever conceive it in his Power, to reduce the Notions of all Mankind, exactly to the same Length, and Breadth, and Heighth of his own? Yet this is the first humble and civil Design of all Innovators in the Empire of Reason. *Epicurus* modestly hoped, that one Time or other, a certain Fortuitous Concourse of all Mens Opinions, after perpetual Justlings, the Sharp with the Smooth, the Light and the Heavy, the Round and the Square, would by certain *Clinamina*, unite in the Notions of *Atoms* and *Void*, as these did in the Originals of all Things. *Cartesius* reckoned to see before he died, the Sentiments of all Philosophers, like so many lesser Stars in his *Romantick* System, rapt and drawn within his own *Vortex*. Now, I would gladly be informed, how it is possible to account for such Imaginations as these in particular Men, without Recourse to my *Phænomenon* of *Vapours*, ascending from the lower Faculties to over-shadow the Brain, and thence distilling into Conceptions, for which the Narrowness of our Mother-Tongue has not yet assigned any other Name, besides that of *Madness* or *Phrenzy*. Let us therefore now conjecture how it comes to pass, that none of these great Prescribers, do ever fail providing themselves and their Notions, with a Number of implicite Disciples. And, I think, the Reason is easie to be assigned: For, there is a peculiar *String* in the Harmony of Human Understanding, which in several individuals is exactly of the same Tuning. This, if you can dexterously screw up to its right Key, and then strike gently upon it; Whenever you have the Good Fortune to light among those of the same Pitch, they will by a secret necessary Sympathy, strike exactly at the same time. And in this one Circumstance, lies all the Skill or Luck of the Matter; for if you chance to jar the String among those who are either above or below your own Height, instead of subscribing to your Doctrine, they will tie you fast, call you Mad, and feed you with Bread and Water. It is therefore a Point of the nicest Conduct to distinguish and adapt this noble Talent, with respect to the Differences of Persons and of Times. *Cicero* understood this very well, when writing to a Friend in *England*, with a Caution, among other Matters, to beware of being cheated by our *Hackney-Coachmen* (who, it seems, in those days, were as arrant Rascals as they are now) has these remarkable

* Epist. ad Words. * *Est quod gaudeas te in ista loca venisse, ubi*
Fam. Trebatio. *aliquid sapere viderere.* For, to speak a bold Truth, it is a fatal Miscarriage, so ill to order Affairs, as to pass for a *Fool* in one Company, when in another you might be treated as a *Philosopher*. Which I desire *some certain Gentlemen of my Acquaintance*, to lay up in their Hearts, as a very seasonable *Innuendo*.

THIS, indeed, was the Fatal Mistake of that worthy Gentleman, my most ingenious Friend, Mr. *Wotton*: A Person, in appearance ordain'd for great Designs, as well as Performances; whether you will consider his *Notions* or his *Looks*. Surely, no Man ever advanced into the Publick, with fitter Qualifications of Body and Mind, for the Propagation of a new Religion. Oh, had those happy Talents misapplied to vain Philosophy, been turned into their proper Channels of *Dreams* and *Visions*, where *Distortion* of Mind and Countenance, are of such Sovereign Use; the base detracting World would not then have dared to report, that something is amiss, that his Brain hath undergone an unlucky Shake; which even his Brother *Modernists* themselves, like Ungrates, do whisper so loud, that it reaches up to the very *Garrat* I am writing in.

LASTLY, Whosoever pleases to look into the Fountains of *Enthusiasm*, from whence, in all Ages, have eternally proceeded such fatning Streams, will find the Spring Head to have been as *troubled* and *muddy* as the Current; Of such great Emolument, is a Tincture of this *Vapour*, which the World calls *Madness*, that without its Help, the World would not only be deprived of those two great Blessings, *Conquests* and *Systems*, but even all Mankind would unhappily be reduced to the same Belief in Things Invisible. Now, the former *Postulatum* being held, that it is of no Import from what Originals this *Vapour* proceeds, but either in what *Angles* it strikes and spreads over the Understanding, or upon what *Species* of Brain it ascends; It will be a very delicate Point, to cut the Feather, and divide the several Reasons to a Nice and Curious Reader, how this numerical Difference in the Brain, can produce Effects of so vast a Difference from the same *Vapour*, as to be the sole Point of Individuation between *Alexander the Great*, *Jack of Leyden*, and Monsieur *Des Cartes*. The present Argument is the most abstracted that ever I engaged in, it strains my Faculties to their highest Stretch; and I desire the Reader to attend with utmost Perpensity; For, I now proceed to unravel this knotty Point.

†THERE is in Mankind a certain * * * * *

* * * * * * * * * *

* * * * * * * * * *

* * * * * * * *   *Hic multa*

* * * * * * * *   *desiderantur.*

* * * * * * * * * *

* * * And this I take to be a clear Solution of the Matter.

HAVING therefore so narrowly past thro' this intricate Difficulty, the Reader will, I am sure, agree with me in the Conclusion; that if the *Moderns* mean by *Madness*, only a Disturbance or Transposition of the Brain, by Force of certain *Vapours* issuing

---

†*Here is another Defect in the Manuscript, but I think the Author did wisely, and that the Matter which thus strained his Faculties, was not worth a Solution; and it were well if all Metaphysical Cobweb Problems were no otherwise answered.*

up from the lower Faculties; Then has this *Madness* been the Parent of all those mighty Revolutions, that have happened in *Empire*, in *Philosophy*, and in *Religion*. For, the Brain, in its natural Position and State of Serenity, disposeth its Owner to pass his Life in the common Forms, without any Thought of subduing Multitudes to his own *Power*, his *Reasons* or his *Visions*; and the more he shapes his Understanding by the Pattern of Human Learning, the less he is inclined to form Parties after his particular Notions; because that instructs him in his private Infirmities, as well as in the stubborn Ignorance of the People. But when a Man's Fancy gets *astride* on his Reason, when Imagination is at Cuffs with the Senses, and common Understanding, as well as common Sense, is Kickt out of Doors; the first Proselyte he makes, is Himself, and when that is once compass'd, the Difficulty is not so great in bringing over others; A strong Delusion always operating from *without*, as vigorously as from *within*. For, Cant and Vision are to the Ear and the Eye, the same that Tickling is to the Touch. Those Entertainments and Pleasures we most value in Life, are such as *Dupe* and play the Wag with the Senses. For, if we take an Examination of what is generally understood by *Happiness*, as it has Respect, either to the Understanding or the Senses, we shall find all its Properties and Adjuncts will herd under this short Definition: That, *it is a perpetual Possession of being well Deceived*. And first, with Relation to the Mind or Understanding; 'tis manifest, what mighty Advantages Fiction has over Truth; and the Reason is just at our Elbow; because Imagination can build nobler Scenes, and produce more wonderful Revolutions than Fortune or Nature will be at Expence to furnish. Nor is Mankind so much to blame in his Choice, thus determining him, if we consider that the Debate meerly lies between *Things past*, and *Things conceived*; and so the Question is only this; Whether Things that have Place in the *Imagination*, may not as properly be said to *Exist*, as those that are seated in the *Memory*; which may be justly held in the Affirmative, and very much to the Advantage of the former, since This is acknowledged to be the *Womb* of Things, and the other allowed to be no more than the *Grave*. Again, if we take this Definition of Happiness, and examine it with Reference to the

Senses, it will be acknowledged wonderfully adapt. How fade and insipid do all Objects accost us that are not convey'd in the Vehicle of *Delusion*? How shrunk is every Thing, as it appears in the Glass of Nature? So, that if it were not for the Assistance of Artificial *Mediums*, false Lights, refracted Angles, Varnish, and Tinsel; there would be a mighty Level in the Felicity and Enjoyments of Mortal Men. If this were seriously considered by the World, as I have a certain Reason to suspect it hardly will; Men would no longer reckon among their high Points of Wisdom, the Art of exposing weak Sides, and publishing Infirmities; an Employment in my Opinion, neither better nor worse than that of *Unmasking*, which I think, has never been allowed fair Usage, either in the *World* or the *Play-House*.

In the Proportion that Credulity is a more peaceful Possession of the Mind, than Curiosity, so far preferable is that Wisdom, which converses about the Surface, to that pretended Philosophy which enters into the Depth of Things, and then comes gravely back with Informations and Discoveries, that in the inside they are good for nothing. The two Senses, to which all Objects first address themselves, are the Sight and the Touch; These never examine farther than the Colour, the Shape, the Size, and whatever other Qualities dwell, or are drawn by Art upon the Outward of Bodies; and then comes Reason officiously, with Tools for cutting, and opening, and mangling, and piercing, offering to demonstrate, that they are not of the same consistence quite thro'. Now, I take all this to be the last Degree of perverting Nature; one of whose Eternal Laws it is, to put her best Furniture forward. And therefore, in order to save the Charges of all such expensive Anatomy for the Time to come; I do here think fit to inform the Reader, that in such Conclusions as these, Reason is certainly in the Right; and that in most Corporeal Beings, which have fallen under my Cognizance, the *Outside* hath been infinitely preferable to the *In*: Whereof I have been farther convinced from some late Experiments. Last Week I saw a Woman *flay'd*, and you will hardly believe, how much it altered her Person for the worse. Yesterday I ordered the Carcass of a *Beau* to be stript in my Presence; when we were all amazed to find so many unsuspected Faults under one Suit of Cloaths:

Then I laid open his *Brain*, his *Heart*, and his *Spleen*; But, I plainly perceived at every Operation, that the farther we proceeded, we found the Defects encrease upon us in Number and Bulk: from all which, I justly formed this Conclusion to my self; That whatever Philosopher or Projector can find out an Art to sodder and patch up the Flaws and Imperfections of Nature, will deserve much better of Mankind, and teach us a more useful Science, than that so much in present Esteem, of widening and exposing them (like him who held *Anatomy* to be the ultimate End of *Physick*.) And he, whose Fortunes and Dispositions have placed him in a convenient Station to enjoy the Fruits of this noble Art; He that can with *Epicurus* content his Ideas with the *Films* and *Images* that fly off upon his Senses from the *Superficies* of Things; Such a Man truly wise, creams off Nature, leaving the Sower and the Dregs, for Philosophy and Reason to lap up. This is the sublime and refined Point of Felicity, called, *the Possession of being well deceived*; The Serene Peaceful State of being a Fool among Knaves.

BUT to return to *Madness*. It is certain, that according to the System I have above deduced; every *Species* thereof proceeds from a Redundancy of *Vapour*; therefore, as some Kinds of *Phrenzy* give double Strength to the Sinews, so there are of other *Species*, which add Vigor, and Life, and Spirit to the Brain: Now, it usually happens, that these active Spirits, getting Possession of the Brain, resemble those that haunt other waste and empty Dwellings, which for want of Business, either vanish, and carry away a Piece of the House, or else stay at home and fling it all out of the Windows. By which are mystically display'd the two principal Branches of *Madness*, and which some Philosophers not considering so well as I, have mistook to be different in their Causes, over-hastily assigning the first to Deficiency, and the other to Redundance.

I think it therefore manifest, from what I have here advanced, that the main Point of Skill and Address, is to furnish Employment for this Redundancy of *Vapour*, and prudently to adjust the Seasons of it; by which means it may certainly become of Cardinal and Catholick Emolument in a Commonwealth. Thus one Man chusing a proper Juncture, leaps into a Gulph, from thence proceeds a Hero, and is called the Saver of his Country; Another atchieves the same Enterprise, but unluckily timing it, has left the Brand of *Madness*, fixt as a Reproach upon his Memory; Upon so nice a Distinction are we taught to repeat the Name of *Curtius* with Reverence and Love; that of *Empedocles*, with Hatred and Contempt. Thus, also it is usually conceived, that the Elder *Brutus* only personated the *Fool* and *Madman*, for the Good of the Publick: but this was nothing else, than a Redundancy of the same *Vapor*, long misapplied, called by the *Latins*, * *Ingenium par negotiis*: Or, (to translate it as nearly as I can) a sort of *Phrenzy*, never in its right * *Tacit.* Element, till you take it up in Business of the State.

Upon all which, and many other Reasons of equal Weight, though not equally curious; I do here gladly embrace an Opportunity I have long sought for, of Recommending it as a very noble Undertaking, to Sir *Edward Seymour*, Sir *Christopher Musgrave*, Sir *John Bowls*, *John How*, Esq; and other Patriots concerned, that they would move for Leave to bring in a Bill, for appointing Commissioners to Inspect into *Bedlam*, and the Parts adjacent; who shall be empowered to *send for Persons, Papers, and Records*: to examine into the Merits and Qualifications of every Student and Professor; to observe with utmost Exactness their several Dispositions and Behaviour; by which means, duly distinguishing and adapting their Talents, they might produce admirable Instruments for the several Offices in a State, * * * * * * † *Civil* and *Military*; proceeding in such Methods as I shall here humbly propose. And, I hope the Gentle Reader will give some Allowance to my great Solicitudes in this important Affair, upon Account of that high Esteem I have ever born that honourable Society, whereof I had some Time the Happiness to be an unworthy Member.

Is any Student tearing his Straw in piece-meal, Swearing and Blaspheming, biting his Grate, foaming at the Mouth, and emptying his Pispot in the Spectator's Faces? Let the Right Worshipful, the *Commissioners of Inspection*, give him a Regiment of Dragoons, and send him into *Flanders* among the *Rest*. Is another eternally talking, sputtering, gaping, bawling, in a Sound without Period or Article? What wonderful Talents are here mislaid! Let him be furnished immediately with a green Bag and Papers, and * *three Pence* in his Pocket, and away with Him to *Westminster-Hall*. You will find a Third, gravely taking the Dimensions of his Kennel; A Person of Foresight and Insight, tho' kept quite in the Dark; for why, like *Moses*, *Ecce* * *cornuta erat ejus facies*. He walks duly in one Pace, intreats your Penny with due Gravity and Ceremony; talks much of hard Times, and Taxes, and the *Whore of Babylon*; Bars up the woodden Window of his Cell constantly at eight a Clock: Dreams of *Fire*, and *Shop-lifters*, and *Court-Customers*, and *Priviledg'd Places*. Now, what a Figure would all these Acquirements amount to, if the Owner were sent into the *City* among his Brethren! Behold a Fourth, in much and deep Conversation with himself, biting his Thumbs at proper Junctures; His Countenance chequered with Business and Design; sometimes walking very fast, with his Eyes nailed to a Paper that he holds in his Hands: A great Saver of Time, somewhat thick of Hearing, very short of Sight, but more of Memory. A Man ever in Haste, a great Hatcher and Breeder of Business, and excellent at the Famous Art of *whispering Nothing*. A huge Idolater of Monosyllables and Procrastination; so ready to *Give* his Word to every Body, that he never *keeps* it. One that has forgot the common *Meaning* of Words, but an admirable Retainer of the *Sound*. Extreamly subject to the *Loosness*, for his *Occasions* are perpetually *calling him away*. If you approach his Grate in his familiar Intervals; *Sir*, says he, *Give me a Penny, and I'll sing you a Song: But give me the Penny first*. (Hence comes the common Saying, and commoner Practice of parting with Money for a *Song*.) What a compleat System of *Court-Skill* is here described in every Branch of it, and all utterly lost with wrong Application? Accost the Hole of another Kennel, first stopping your Nose, you will behold a surley, gloomy, nasty, slovenly Mortal, raking in his own Dung, and dabling in his Urine. The best Part of his Diet, is the

A Lawyer's Coach-hire.

---

* Cornutus, *is either Horned or Shining, and by this Term*, Moses *is described in the vulgar* Latin *of the Bible.*

Reversion of his own Ordure, which exspiring into Steams, whirls perpetually about, and at last reinfunds. His Complexion is of a dirty Yellow, with a thin scattered Beard, exactly agreeable to that of his Dyet upon its first Declination; like other Insects, who having their Birth and Education in an Excrement, from thence borrow their Colour and their Smell. The Student of this Apartment is very sparing of his Words, but somewhat over-liberal of his Breath; He holds his Hand out ready to receive your Penny, and immediately upon Receipt, withdraws to his former Occupations. Now, is it not amazing to think, the Society of *Warwick-Lane*, should have no more Concern, for the Recovery of so useful a Member, who, if one may judge from these Appearances, would become the greatest Ornament to that Illustrious Body? Another Student struts up fiercely to your Teeth, puffing with his Lips, half squeezing out his Eyes, and very graciously holds you out his Hand to kiss. The *Keeper* desires you not to be afraid of this Professor, for he will do you no Hurt: To him alone is allowed the Liberty of the Anti-Chamber, and the *Orator* of the Place gives you to understand, that this solemn Person is a *Taylor* run mad with Pride. This considerable Student is adorned with many other Qualities, upon which, at present, I shall not farther enlarge. - - - - - - - * *Heark in your Ear* - - - - - - - - I am strangely mistaken, if all his Address, his Motions, and his Airs, would not then be very natural, and in their proper Element.

I shall not descend so minutely, as to insist upon the vast Number of *Beaux*, *Fidlers*, *Poets*, and *Politicians*, that the World might recover by such a Reformation; But what is more material, besides the clear Gain redounding to the Commonwealth, by so large an Acquisition of Persons to employ, whose Talents and Acquirements, if I may be so bold to affirm it, are now buried, or at least misapplied: It would be a mighty Advantage accruing to the Publick from this Enquiry, that all these would very much excel, and arrive at great Perfection in their several Kinds; which, I think, is manifest from what I have already

---

* *I cannot conjecture what the Author means here, or how this Chasm could be fill'd, tho' it is capable of more than one Interpretation.*

i

shewn; and shall inforce by this one plain Instance; That even, I my self, the Author of these momentous Truths, am a Person, whose Imaginations are hard-mouth'd, and exceedingly disposed to run away with his *Reason*, which I have observed from long Experience, to be a very light Rider, and easily shook off; upon which Account, my Friends will never trust me alone, without a solemn Promise, to vent my Speculations in this, or the like manner, for the universal Benefit of Human kind; which, perhaps, the gentle, courteous, and candid Reader, brimful of that *Modern* Charity and Tenderness, usually annexed to his *Office*, will be very hardly persuaded to believe.

SECT. X.

A TALE of a TUB.

IT is an unanswerable Argument of a very refined Age, the wonderful Civilities that have passed of late Years, between the Nation of *Authors*, and that of *Readers*. There can hardly pop out * a *Play*, a *Pamphlet*, or a *Poem*, without a Preface full of Acknowledgements to the World, for the general Reception and Applause they have given it, which the Lord knows where, or when, or how, or from whom it received. In due Deference to so laudable a Custom, I do here return my humble Thanks to *His Majesty*, and both Houses of *Parliament*; To the *Lords* of the King's most honourable Privy-Council, to the Reverend the *Judges*: To the *Clergy*, and *Gentry*, and *Yeomantry* of this Land: But in a more especial manner, to my worthy Brethren and Friends at *Will's Coffee-House*, and *Gresham-College*, and *Warwick-Lane*, and *Moor-Fields*, and *Scotland-Yard*, and *Westminster-Hall*, and *Guild-Hall*; In short, to all Inhabitants and Retainers whatsoever, either in Court, or Church, or Camp, or City, or Country; for their generous and universal Acceptance of this Divine Treatise. I accept their Approbation, and good Opinion with extream Gratitude, and to the utmost of my poor Capacity, shall take hold of all Opportunities to return the Obligation.

I am also happy, that Fate has flung me into so blessed an Age for the mutual Felicity of *Booksellers* and *Authors*, whom I may safely affirm to be at this Day the two only satisfied Parties in *England*. Ask an *Author* how his last Piece hath succeeded; *Why, truly he thanks his Stars, the World has been very favourable, and he has not the least Reason to complain: And yet, By G—, He writ it in a Week at Bits and Starts, when he could steal an Hour from his urgent Affairs*; as it is a hundred to one, you may see farther in the Preface, to which he refers you; and for the rest, to the Bookseller. There you go as a Customer, and make the same Question: *He blesses his God, the* Thing *takes wonderfully, he is just*

---

* *This is literally true, as we may observe in the Prefaces to most Plays, Poems, &c.*

Printing a Second Edition, and has but three left in his Shop. You beat down the Price: *Sir, we shall not differ* ; and in hopes of your Custom another Time, lets you have it as reasonable as you please; *And, pray send as many of your Acquaintance as you will, I shall upon your Account furnish them all at the same Rate.*

Now, it is not well enough consider'd, to what Accidents and Occasions the World is indebted for the greatest Part of those noble Writings, which hourly start up to entertain it. If it were not for a *rainy Day, a drunken Vigil, a Fit of the Spleen, a Course of Physick, a sleepy Sunday, an ill Run at Dice, a long Taylor's Bill, a Beggar's Purse, a factious Head, a hot Sun, costive Dyet, Want of Books, and a just Contempt of Learning.* But for these Events, I say, and some Others too long to recite, (especially *a prudent Neglect of taking Brimstone inwardly,*) I doubt, the Number of *Authors,* and of *Writings* would dwindle away to a Degree most woful to behold. To confirm this Opinion, hear the Words of the famous *Troglodyte* Philosopher: '*Tis certain* (said he) *some Grains of Folly are of course annexed, as Part of the Composition of Human Nature, only the Choice is left us, whether we please to wear them* Inlaid *or* Embossed; *And we need not go very far to seek how that is usually determined, when we remember, it is with Human Faculties as with Liquors, the lightest will be ever at the Top.*

THERE is in this famous Island of *Britain* a certain paultry *Scribbler,* very voluminous, whose Character the Reader cannot wholly be a Stranger to. He deals in a pernicious Kind of Writings, called *Second Parts,* and usually passes under the Name of *The Author of the First.* I easily foresee, that as soon as I lay down my Pen, this nimble *Operator* will have stole it, and treat me as inhumanly as he hath already done Dr. *Blackmore, L'Estrange,* and many others who shall here be nameless, I therefore fly for Justice and Relief, into the Hands of that great *Rectifier of Saddles,* and *Lover of Mankind,* Dr. *Bently,* begging he will take this enormous Grievance into his most *Modern* Consideration: And if it should so happen, that the *Furniture of an Ass,* in the Shape of a *Second Part,* must for my Sins be clapt, by a Mistake upon my Back, that he will immediately please, in the Presence of the World, to lighten me of the Burthen, and take it home to *his own House,* till the *true Beast* thinks fit to call for it.

In the mean time I do here give this publick Notice, that my Resolutions are, to circumscribe within this Discourse the whole Stock of Matter I have been so many Years providing. Since my *Vein* is once opened, I am content to exhaust it all at a Running, for the peculiar Advantage of my dear Country, and for the universal Benefit of Mankind. Therefore hospitably considering the Number of my Guests, they shall have my whole Entertainment at a Meal; And I scorn to set up the *Leavings* in the Cupboard. What the *Guests* cannot eat may be given to the *Poor*, and the * *Dogs* under the Table may gnaw the *Bones*; This I understand for a more generous Proceeding, than to turn the Company's Stomachs, by inviting them again to morrow to a scurvy Meal of *Scraps*.

If the Reader fairly considers the Strength of what I have advanced in the foregoing Section, I am convinced it will produce a wonderful Revolution in his Notions and Opinions; And he will be abundantly better prepared to receive and to relish the concluding Part of this miraculous Treatise. Readers may be divided into three Classes, the *Superficial*, the *Ignorant*, and the *Learned*: And I have with much Felicity fitted my Pen to the Genius and Advantage of each. The *Superficial* Reader will be strangely provoked to *Laughter*; which clears the Breast and the Lungs, is Soverain against the *Spleen*, and the most innocent of all *Diureticks*. The *Ignorant* Reader (between whom and the former, the Distinction is extreamly nice) will find himself disposed to *Stare*; which is an admirable Remedy for ill Eyes, serves to raise and enliven the Spirits, and wonderfully helps *Perspiration*. But the Reader truly *Learned*, chiefly for whose Benefit I wake, when others sleep, and sleep when others wake, will here find sufficient Matter to employ his Speculations for the rest of his Life. It were much to be wisht, and I do here humbly propose for an Experiment, that every Prince in *Christendom* will take seven of the *deepest Scholars* in his Dominions, and shut them up close for *seven* Years, in *seven* Chambers, with a Command to write *seven* ample Commentaries on this comprehensive Discourse. I

---

* *By* Dogs, *the Author means common injudicious Criticks, as he explains it himself before in his* Digression upon Criticks, *Page* [64].

shall venture to affirm, that whatever Difference may be found
in their several Conjectures, they will be all, without the least
Distortion, manifestly deduceable from the Text. Mean time, it
is my earnest Request, that so useful an Undertaking may be
entered upon (if their Majesties please) with all convenient
speed; because I have a strong Inclination, before I leave the
World, to taste a Blessing, which we *mysterious* Writers can seldom reach, till we have got into our Graves. Whether it is, that
Fame being a Fruit grafted on the Body, can hardly grow, and
much less ripen, till the *Stock* is in the Earth: Or, whether she be
a Bird of Prey, and is lured among the rest, to pursue after the
Scent of a *Carcass*: Or, whether she conceives, her Trumpet
sounds best and farthest, when she stands on a *Tomb*, by the
Advantage of a rising Ground, and the Echo of a hollow Vault.

'TIS true, indeed, the Republick of *dark* Authors, after they
once found out this excellent Expedient of *Dying*, have been
peculiarly happy in the Variety, as well as Extent of their Reputation. For, *Night* being the universal Mother of Things, wise
Philosophers hold all Writings to be *fruitful* in the Proportion
they are *dark*; And therefore, the * *true illuminated*
(that is to say, the *Darkest* of all) have met with
such numberless Commentators, whose *Scholias-
tick* Midwifry hath deliver'd them of Meanings, that the Authors
themselves, perhaps, never conceived, and yet may very justly
be allowed the Lawful Parents of them: * The Words of such
Writers being like Seed, which, however scattered at random,
when they light upon a fruitful Ground, will multiply far beyond
either the Hopes or Imagination of the Sower.

AND therefore in order to promote so useful a Work, I will
here take Leave to glance a few *Innuendo*'s, that may be of great
Assistance to those sublime Spirits, who shall be appointed to
labor in a universal Comment upon this wonderful Discourse.
And First, † I have couched a very profound Mystery in the

* A Name of the Rosycrucians.

---

* *Nothing is more frequent than for Commentators to force Interpretation, which the Author never meant.*

† *This is what the* Cabbalists *among the* Jews *have done with the*
Bible, *and pretend to find wonderful Mysteries by it.*

Number of O's multiply'd by *Seven*, and divided by *Nine*. Also, if a devout Brother of the *Rosy Cross* will pray fervently for sixty three Mornings, with a lively Faith, and then transpose certain Letters and Syllables according to Prescription, in the second and fifth Section; they will certainly reveal into a full Receit of the *Opus Magnum*. Lastly, Whoever will be at the Pains to calculate the whole Number of each Letter in this Treatise, and sum up the Difference exactly between the several Numbers, assigning the true natural Cause for every such Difference; the Discoveries in the Product, will plentifully reward his Labour. But then he must beware of † *Bythus* and *Sigè*, and be sure not to forget the Qualities of *Acamoth; A cujus lacrymis humecta prodit Substantia, à risu lucida, à tristitiâ solida, & à timore mobilis*, wherein * *Eugenius Philalethes* hath committed an unpardonable Mistake.

* *Vid. Anima magica abscondita*

---

† *I was told by an Eminent Divine, whom I consulted on this Point, that these two Barbarous Words, with that of* Acamoth *and its Qualities, as here set down, are quoted from* Irenæus. *This he discover'd by searching that Antient Writer for another Quotation of our Author, which he has placed in the Title Page, and refers to the Book and Chapter; the Curious were very Inquisitive, whether those Barbarous Words,* Basima Eacabasa, &c. *are really in* Irenæus, *and upon enquiry 'twas found they were a sort of Cant or Jargon of certain Hereticks, and therefore very properly prefix'd to such a Book as this of our Author.*

* *To the abovementioned Treatise, called* Anthroposophia Theomagica, *there is another annexed, called* Anima Magica Abscondita, *written by the same Author* Vaughan, *under the Name of* Eugenius Philalethes, *but in neither of those Treatises is there any mention of* Acamoth *or its Qualities, so that this is nothing but Amusement, and a Ridicule of dark, unintelligible Writers; only the Words,* A cujus lacrymis, &c. *are as we have said, transcribed from* Irenæus, *tho' I know not from what part. I believe one of the Authors Designs was to set curious Men a hunting thro' Indexes, and enquiring for Books out of the common Road.*

SECT. XI.

A TALE of a TUB.

AFTER so wide a Compass as I have wandred, I do now gladly overtake, and close in with my Subject, and shall henceforth hold on with it an even Pace to the End of my Journey, except some beautiful Prospect appears within sight of my Way; whereof, tho' at present I have neither Warning nor Expectation, yet upon such an Accident, come when it will, I shall beg my Readers Favour and Company, allowing me to conduct him thro' it along with my self. For in *Writing*, it is as in *Travelling*: If a Man is in haste to be at home, (which I acknowledge to be none of my Case, having never so little Business, as when I am there) if his *Horse* be tired with long Riding, and ill Ways, or be naturally a Jade, I advise him clearly to make the straitest and the commonest Road, be it ever so dirty; But, then surely, we must own such a man to be a scurvy Companion at best; He *spatters* himself and his Fellow-Travellers at every Step: All their Thoughts, and Wishes, and Conversation turn entirely upon the Subject of their Journey's End; and at every Splash, and Plunge, and Stumble, they heartily wish one another at the Devil.

ON the other side, when a Traveller and his *Horse* are in Heart and Plight, when his Purse is full, and the Day before him; he takes the Road only where it is clean or convenient; entertains his Company there as agreeably as he can; but upon the first Occasion, carries them along with him to every delightful Scene in View, whether of Art, of Nature, or of both; and if they chance to refuse out of Stupidity or Weariness; let them jog on by themselves, and be d——n'd; He'll overtake them at the next Town; at which arriving, he Rides furiously thro', the Men, Women, and Children run out to gaze, a hundred * *noisy Curs* run *barking* after him, of which, if he honors the boldest with a *Lash of his Whip*, it is rather out of Sport than Revenge: But should some *sourer*

---

* *By these are meant what the Author calls*, The True Criticks, *Page* [64].

Mungrel dare too near an Approach, he receives a *Salute* on the Chaps by an accidental Stroak from the Courser's Heels, (nor is any Ground lost by the Blow) which sends him yelping and limping home.

I now proceed to sum up the singular Adventures of my renowned *Jack*; the State of whose Dispositions and Fortunes, the careful Reader does, no doubt, most exactly remember, as I last parted with them in the Conclusion of a former Section. Therefore, his next Care must be from two of the foregoing, to extract a Scheme of Notions, that may best fit his Understanding for a true Relish of what is to ensue.

JACK had not only calculated the first Revolutions of his Brain so prudently, as to give Rise to that Epidemick Sect of *Æolists*, but succeeding also into a new and strange Variety of Conceptions, the Fruitfulness of his Imagination led him into certain Notions, which, altho' in Appearance very unaccountable, were not without their Mysteries and their Meanings, nor wanted Followers to countenance and improve them. I shall therefore be extreamly careful and exact in recounting such material Passages of this Nature, as I have been able to collect, either from undoubted Tradition, or indefatigable Reading; and shall describe them as graphically as it is possible, and as far as Notions of that Height and Latitude can be brought within the Compass of a Pen. Nor do I at all question, but they will furnish Plenty of noble Matter for such, whose converting Imaginations dispose them to reduce all Things into *Types*; who can make *Shadows*, no thanks to the Sun; and then mold them into Substances, no thanks to Philosophy; whose peculiar Talent lies in fixing Tropes and Allegories to the *Letter*, and refining what is Literal into Figure and Mystery.

JACK had provided a fair Copy of his Father's *Will*, engrossed in Form upon a large Skin of Parchment; and resolving to act the Part of a most dutiful Son, he became the fondest Creature of it imaginable. For, altho', as I have often told the Reader, it consisted wholly in certain plain, easy Directions about the management and wearing of their Coats, with Legacies and Penalties, in case of Obedience or Neglect; yet he began to entertain a Fancy, that the Matter was *deeper* and *darker*, and therefore must needs have a great deal more of Mystery at the Bottom. *Gentlemen*, said he, *I will prove this very Skin of Parchment to be Meat, Drink, and Cloth, to be the Philosopher's Stone, and the Universal Medicine.* * In consequence of which Raptures, he resolved to make use of it in the most necessary, as well as the most paltry Occasions of Life. He had a Way of working it into any Shape he pleased; so that it served him for a Night-cap when he went to Bed, and for an Umbrello in rainy Weather. He would lap a Piece of it about a sore Toe, or when he had Fits, burn two Inches under his Nose; or if any Thing lay heavy on his Stomach, scrape off, and swallow as much of the Powder as would lie on a silver Penny, they were all infallible Remedies. With Analogy to these Refinements, his common Talk and Conversation, † ran wholly in the Phrase of his Will, and he circumscribed the utmost of his Eloquence within that Compass, not daring to let slip a Syllable without Authority from thence. Once at a strange House, he was suddenly taken short, upon an urgent Juncture, whereon it may not be allowed too particularly to dilate; and being not able to call to mind, with that Suddenness, the Occasion required, an Authentick Phrase for demanding the Way to the Backside; he chose rather as the more prudent Course, to incur the Penalty in such Cases usually annexed. Neither was it possible for the united Rhetorick of Mankind to prevail with him to make himself clean again: Because having consulted the Will upon this Emergency, he met with a ‖ Passage near the Bottom (whether foisted in by the Transcriber, is not known) which seemed to forbid it.

HE made it a Part of his Religion, never to say * Grace to his

---

* *The Author here lashes those Pretenders to Purity, who place so much Merit in using Scripture Phrases on all Occasions.*

† *The Protestant Dissenters use Scripture Phrases in their serious Discourses, and Composures more than the Church of England-Men, accordingly Jack is introduced making his common Talk and Conversation to run wholly in the Phrase of his WILL.* W. Wotton.

‖ *I cannot guess the Author's meaning here, which I would be very glad to know, because it seems to be of Importance.*

* *The slovenly way of Receiving the Sacrament among the Fanaticks.*

Meat, nor could all the World persuade him, as the common Phrase is, to * eat his Victuals *like a Christian*.

HE bore a strange kind of Appetite to † *Snap-Dragon*, and to the livid Snuffs of a burning Candle, which he would catch and swallow with an Agility, wonderful to conceive; and by this Procedure, maintained a perpetual Flame in his Belly, which issuing in a glowing Steam from both his Eyes, as well as his Nostrils, and his Mouth; made his Head appear in a dark Night, like the Scull of an Ass, wherein a roguish Boy hath conveyed a Farthing Candle, *to the Terror of His Majesty's Liege Subjects*. Therefore, he made use of no other Expedient to light himself home, but was wont to say, That *a Wise Man was his own Lanthorn*.

HE would shut his Eyes as he walked along the Streets, and if he happened to bounce his Head against a Post, or fall into the Kennel (as he seldom missed either to do one or both) he would tell the gibing Prentices, who looked on, that *he submitted with entire Resignation, as to a Trip, or a Blow of Fate, with whom he found, by long Experience, how vain it was either to wrestle or to cuff; and whoever durst undertake to do either, would be sure to come off with a swinging Fall, or a bloody Nose. It was ordained,* said he, *some few Days before the Creation, that my Nose and this very Post should have a Rencounter; and therefore, Nature thought fit to send us both into the World in the same Age, and to make us Country-men and Fellow-Citizens. Now, had my Eyes been open, it is very likely, the Business might have been a great deal worse; For, how many a confounded Slip is daily got by Man, with all his Foresight about him? Besides, the Eyes of the Understanding see best, when those of the Senses are out of the way; and therefore, blind Men are observed to tread their Steps with much more Caution, and Conduct, and Judgment, than those who rely with too much Confidence, upon the Virtue of the visual Nerve, which every little Accident shakes out of Order, and a Drop, or a Film, can*

---

* *This is a common Phrase to express Eating cleanlily, and is meant for an Invective against that undecent Manner among some People in Receiving the Sacrament, so in the Lines before, which is to be understood of the Dissenters refusing to kneel at the Sacrament.*

† *I cannot well find the Author's meaning here, unless it be the hot, untimely, blind Zeal of Enthusiasts.*

wholly disconcert; like a Lanthorn among a Pack of roaring Bullies,
when they scower the Streets; exposing its Owner, and it self, to outward
Kicks and Buffets, which both might have escaped, if the Vanity of
Appearing would have suffered them to walk in the Dark. But, farther,
if we examine the Conduct *of these boasted Lights, it will prove yet a*
great deal worse than their Fortune *: 'Tis true, I have broke my Nose*
against this Post, because Fortune either forgot, or did not think it con-
venient to twitch me by the Elbow, and give me notice to avoid it. But, let
not this encourage either the present Age or Posterity, to trust their
Noses into the keeping of their Eyes, *which may prove the fairest Way*
of losing them for good and all. For, O ye Eyes, Ye blind Guides; miser-
able Guardians are Ye of our frail Noses; Ye, I say, who fasten upon
the first Precipice in view, and then tow our wretched willing Bodies after
You, to the very Brink of Destruction: But, alas, that Brink is rotten,
our Feet slip, and we tumble down prone into a Gulph, without one
hospitable Shrub in the Way to break the Fall; a Fall, to which not any

* *Vide* Don *Nose of mortal Make is equal, except that of the Gian,*
Quixot. * *Laurcalco, who was Lord of the* Silver Bridge.
Most properly, therefore, O Eyes, and with great Justice, may You be
compared to those foolish Lights, which conduct Men thro' Dirt and
Darkness, till they fall into a deep Pit, or a noisom Bog.

This I have produced, as a Scantling of *Jack*'s great Eloquence, and the Force of his Reasoning upon such abstruse
Matters.

He was besides, a Person of great Design and Improvement
in Affairs of *Devotion*, having introduced a new Deity, who hath
since met with a vast Number of Worshippers; by some called
Babel, by others, *Chaos*; who had an antient Temple of *Gothick*
Structure upon *Salisbury* Plain; famous for its Shrine, and Cele-
bration by Pilgrims.

* When he had some Roguish Trick to play, he would down
with his Knees, up with his Eyes, and fall to Prayers, tho' in the
midst of the Kennel. Then it was that those who understood his
Pranks, would be sure to get far enough out of his Way; And

* *The Villanies and Cruelties committed by Enthusiasts and Phanatick*
among us, were all performed under the Disguise of Religion and long
Prayers.

whenever Curiosity attracted Strangers to Laugh, or to Listen; he would of a sudden, with one Hand out with his *Gear*, and piss full in their Eyes, and with the other, all to-bespatter them with Mud.

* In Winter he went always loose and unbuttoned, and clad as thin as possible, to let *in* the ambient Heat; and in Summer, lapt himself close and thick to keep it *out*.

† In all Revolutions of Government, he would make his Court for the Office of *Hangman* General; and in the Exercise of that Dignity, wherein he was very dextrous, would make use of no other *Vizard* than a long *Prayer*.

He had a Tongue so Musculous and Subtil, that he could twist it up into his Nose, and deliver a strange Kind of Speech from thence. He was also the first in these Kingdoms, who began to improve the *Spanish* Accomplishment of *Braying*; and having large Ears, perpetually exposed and arrect, he carried his Art to such a Perfection, that it was a Point of great Difficulty to distinguish either by the View or the Sound, between the *Original* and the *Copy*.

He was troubled with a Disease, reverse to that called the Stinging of the *Tarantula*; and would * run Dog-mad, at the Noise of *Musick*, especially a *Pair of Bag-Pipes*. But he would cure himself again, by taking two or three Turns in *Westminster-Hall*, or *Billingsgate*, or in a *Boarding-School*, or the *Royal-Exchange*, or a *State Coffee-House*.

He was a Person that † *feared* no *Colours*, but mortally *hated* all, and upon that Account, bore a cruel Aversion to *Painters*, insomuch, that in his Paroxysms, as he walked the Streets, he would have his Pockets loaden with Stones, to pelt at the *Signs*.

---

* *They affect Differences in Habit and Behaviour.*

† *They are severe Persecutors, and all in a Form of Cant and Devotion.*

‖ Cromwell *and his Confederates went, as they called it,* to seek God, *when they resolved to murther the King.*

* *This is to expose our Dissenters Aversion to Instrumental Musick in Churches.* W. Wotton.

† *They quarrel at the most Innocent Decency and Ornament, and defaced the Statues and Paintings on all the Churches in* England.

HAVING from this manner of Living, frequent Occasion to *wash* himself, he would often leap over Head and Ears into the Water, tho' it were in the midst of the Winter, but was always observed to come out again much *dirtier*, if possible, than he went in.

HE was the first that ever found out the Secret of contriving a * *Soporiferous* Medicine to be convey'd in at the *Ears*; It was a Compound of *Sulphur* and *Balm of Gilead*, with a little *Pilgrim's Salve*.

HE wore a large Plaister of artificial *Causticks* on his Stomach, with the Fervor of which, he could set himself a *groaning*, like the famous *Board* upon Application of a red-hot Iron.

† HE would stand in the Turning of a Street, and calling to those who passed by, would cry to One; *Worthy Sir, do me the Honour of a good Slap in the Chaps*: To another, *Honest Friend, pray favour me with a handsom Kick on the Arse: Madam, shall I entreat a small Box on the Ear, from your Ladyship's fair Hands? Noble Captain, Lend a reasonable Thwack, for the Love of God, with that Cane of yours, over these poor Shoulders*. And when he had by such earnest Sollicitations, made a shift to procure a Basting sufficient to swell up his Fancy and his Sides, He would return home extremely comforted, and full of terrible Accounts of what he had undergone for the *Publick Good. Observe this Stroak*, (said he, shewing his bare Shoulders) *a plaguy* Janisary *gave it me this very Morning at seven a Clock, as, with much ado, I was driving off the* Great Turk. *Neighbours mine, this broken Head deserves a Plaister; had poor* Jack *been tender of his Noddle, you would have seen the* Pope, *and the* French King, *long before this time of Day, among your Wives and your Ware-houses. Dear* Christians, *the* Great Mogul *was come as far as* White-Chappel, *and you may thank these poor Sides that he hath not* (God bless us) *already swallowed up Man, Woman, and Child.*

---

* *Fanatick Preaching, composed either of Hell and Damnation, or a fulsome Description of the Joys of Heaven, both in such a dirty, nauseous Style, as to be well resembled to Pilgrims Salve.*

† *The Fanaticks have always had a way of affecting to run into Persecution, and count vast Merit upon every little Hardship they suffer.*

* It was highly worth observing, the singular Effects of that Aversion, or Antipathy, which *Jack* and his Brother *Peter* seemed, even to an Affectation, to bear toward each other. *Peter* had lately done *some Rogueries*, that forced him to abscond; and he seldom ventured to stir out before Night, for fear of Bayliffs. Their Lodgings were at the two most distant Parts of the Town from each other; and whenever their Occasions, or Humors called them abroad, they would make Choice of the oddest unlikely Times, and most uncouth Rounds they could invent; that they might be sure to avoid one another: Yet after all this, it was their perpetual Fortune to meet. The Reason of which, is easy enough to apprehend: For, the Phrenzy and the Spleen of both, having the same Foundation, we may look upon them as two Pair of Compasses, equally extended, and the fixed Foot of each, remaining in the same Center; which, tho' moving contrary Ways at first, will be sure to encounter somewhere or other in the Circumference. Besides, it was among the great Misfortunes of *Jack*, to bear a huge Personal Resemblance with his Brother *Peter*. Their Humours and Dispositions were not only the same, but there was a close Analogy in their Shape, their Size and their Mien. Insomuch, as nothing was more frequent than for a Bayliff to seize *Jack* by the Shoulders, and cry, *Mr*. Peter, *You are the King's Prisoner*. Or, at other Times, for one of *Peter's* nearest Friends, to accost *Jack* with open Arms, *Dear* Peter, *I am glad to see thee, pray send me one of your best Medicines for the Worms*. This we may suppose, was a mortifying Return of those Pains and Proceedings, *Jack* had laboured in so long; And finding, how directly opposite all his Endeavours had answered to the sole End and Intention, which he had proposed to himself; How could it avoid having terrible Effects upon a Head and Heart so

* *The Papists and Fanaticks, tho' they appear the most Averse to each other, yet bear a near Resemblance in many things, as has been observed by Learned Men.*

Ibid. *The Agreement of our Dissenters and the Papists in that which Bishop* Stillingfleet *called*, The Fanaticism of the Church of *Rome*, *is ludicrously described for several Pages together by* Jack's Likeness to Peter, *and their being often mistaken for each other, and their frequent Meeting, when they least intended it.* W. Wotton.

furnished as his? However, the poor Remainders of his *Coat*
bore all the Punishment; The orient Sun never entred upon his
diurnal Progress, without missing a Piece of it. He hired a Taylor
to stitch up the Collar so close, that it was ready to choak him,
and squeezed out his Eyes at such a Rate, as one could see
nothing but the White. What little was left of the main Substance
of the Coat, he rubbed every day for two hours, against a rough-
cast Wall, in order to grind away the Remnants of *Lace* and
Embroidery; but at the same time went on with so much Violence,
that he proceeded a *Heathen Philosopher*. Yet after all he could do
of this kind, the Success continued still to disappoint his Expectation. For, as it is the Nature of Rags, to bear a kind of mock
Resemblance to Finery; there being a sort of fluttering Appearance in both, which is not to be distinguished at a Distance, in
the Dark, or by short-sighted Eyes: So, in those Junctures, it
fared with *Jack* and his Tatters, that they offered to the first View
a ridiculous Flanting, which assisting the Resemblance in Person
and Air, thwarted all his Projects of Separation, and left so near
a Similitude between them, as frequently deceived the very
Disciples and Followers of both.   *   *   *   *

*   *   *   *   *   *   *   *   *   *

         *   *   *   *   *   *   *   *

Desunt non-   *   *   *   *   *   *   *

nulla.   *   *   *   *   *   *   *

*   *   *   *   *   *   *   *   *   *

THE old *Sclavonian* Proverb said well, That *it is with* Men, *as
with* Asses; *whoever would keep them fast, may find a very good Hold
at their Ears.* Yet, I think, we may affirm, and it hath been verified
by repeated Experience, that,

Effugiet tamen hæc sceleratus vincula Proteus.

IT is good therefore, to read the Maxims of our Ancestors,
with great Allowances to Times and Persons: For, if we look
into Primitive Records, we shall find, that no Revolutions have
been so great, or so frequent, as those of human *Ears.* In former
Days, there was a curious Invention to catch and keep them;
which, I think, we may justly reckon among the *Artes perditæ*:
And how can it be otherwise, when in these latter Centuries, the

very Species is not only diminished to a very lamentable Degree, but the poor Remainder is also degenerated so far, as to mock our skilfullest *Tenure*? For, if the only slitting of one *Ear* in a Stag, hath been found sufficient to propagate the Defect thro' a whole Forest; Why should we wonder at the greatest Consequences, from so many Loppings and Mutilations, to which the *Ears* of our Fathers and our own, have been of late so much exposed? 'Tis true, indeed, that while this *Island* of ours, was under the *Dominion of Grace*, many Endeavours were made to improve the Growth of *Ears* once more among us. The Proportion of Largeness, was not only lookt upon as an Ornament of the *Outward* Man, but as a Type of Grace in the *Inward*. Besides, it is held by Naturalists, that if there be a Protuberancy of Parts in the *Superiour* Region of the Body, as in the *Ears* and *Nose*, there must be a Parity also in the *Inferior*: And therefore in that truly pious Age, the *Males* in every Assembly, according as they were gifted, appeared very forward in exposing their *Ears* to view, and the Regions about them; because * *Hip-*   * *Lib. de aëre* *pocrates* tells us, that *when the Vein behind the*   *locis & aquis.* *Ear happens to be cut, a Man becomes a Eunuch* : And the *Females* were nothing backwarder in beholding and edifying by them: Whereof those who had already *used the Means*, lookt about them with great Concern, in hopes of conceiving a suitable Offspring by such a Prospect: Others, who stood Candidates for *Benevolence*, found there a plentiful Choice, and were sure to fix upon such as discovered the largest *Ears*, that the Breed might not dwindle between them. Lastly, the devouter Sisters, who lookt upon all extraordinary Dilatations of that Member, as Protrusions of Zeal, or spiritual Excrescencies, were sure to honor every Head they sat upon, as if they had been *Marks of Grace*; but, especially, that of the Preacher, whose *Ears* were usually of the prime Magnitude; which upon that Account, he was very frequent and exact in exposing with all Advantages to the People: in his Rhetorical *Paroxysms*, turning sometimes to *hold forth* the one, and sometimes to *hold forth* the other: From which Custom, the whole Operation of Preaching is to this very Day among their Professors, styled by the Phrase of *Holding forth.*

k

Such was the Progress of the *Saints*, for advancing the Size of that Member; And it is thought, the Success would have been every way answerable, if in Process of time, a * cruel King had not arose, who raised a bloody Persecution against all *Ears*, above a certain Standard: Upon which, some were glad to hide their flourishing Sprouts in a black Border, others crept wholly under a Perewig: some were slit, others cropt, and a great Number sliced off to the Stumps. But of this, more hereafter, in my *general History of Ears*; which I design very speedily to bestow upon the Publick.

From this brief Survey of the falling State of *Ears*, in the last Age, and the small Care had to advance their antient Growth in the present, it is manifest, how little Reason we can have to rely upon a Hold so short, so weak, and so slippery; and that, whoever desires to catch Mankind fast, must have Recourse to some other Methods. Now, he that will examine Human Nature with Circumspection enough, may discover several *Handles*, whereof † *Including* the † *Six* Senses afford one apiece, beside a great Scaliger's. Number that are screw'd to the Passions, and some few riveted to the Intellect. Among these last, *Curiosity* is one, and of all others, affords the firmest Grasp: *Curiosity*, that Spur in the side, that Bridle in the Mouth, that Ring in the Nose, of a lazy, an impatient, and a grunting Reader. By this *Handle* it is, that an Author should seize upon his Readers; which as soon as he hath once compast, all Resistance and struggling are in vain; and they become his Prisoners as close as he pleases, till Weariness or Dullness force him to let go his Gripe.

And therefore, I the Author of this miraculous Treatise, having hitherto, beyond Expectation, maintained by the aforesaid *Handle*, a firm Hold upon my gentle Readers; It is with great Reluctance, that I am at length compelled to remit my Grasp; leaving them in the Perusal of what remains, to that natural *Oscitancy* inherent in the Tribe. I can only assure thee, Courteous Reader, for both our Comforts, that my Concern is altogether equal to thine, for my Unhappiness in losing, or mislaying

---

* *This was King* Charles *the Second, who at his Restauration, turned out all the Dissenting Teachers that would not conform.*

among my Papers the remaining Part of these Memoirs; which consisted of Accidents, Turns, and Adventures, both New, Agreeable, and Surprizing; and therefore, calculated in all due Points, to the delicate Taste of this our noble Age. But, alas, with my utmost Endeavours, I have been able only to retain a few of the Heads. Under which, there was a full Account, how *Peter* got a *Protection* out of the *King's-Bench*; And of a * Reconcilement between *Jack* and Him, upon a Design they had in a certain *rainy Night*, to trepan Brother *Martin* into a *Spunginghouse*, and there strip him to the Skin. How *Martin*, with much ado, shew'd them both a fair pair of Heels. How a *new Warrant* came out against *Peter*: upon which, how *Jack* left him in the lurch, *stole his Protection, and made use of it himself*. How *Jack's* Tatters came into Fashion in *Court* and *City*; How *he* † *got upon a great Horse, and eat* ‖ *Custard*. But the Particulars of all these, with several others, which have now slid out of my Memory, are lost beyond all Hopes of Recovery. For which Misfortune, leaving my Readers to condole with each other, as far as they shall find it to agree with their several Constitutions; but conjuring them by all the Friendship that hath passed between Us, from the Title-Page to this, not to proceed so far as to injure their Healths, for an Accident past Remedy; I now go on to the Ceremonial Part of an accomplish'd Writer, and therefore, by a Courtly *Modern*, least of all others to be omitted.

---

* *In the Reign of King* James *the Second, the Presbyterians by the King's Invitation, joined with the Papists, against the Church of* England, *and Address him for Repeal of the Penal-Laws and Test. The King by his Dispensing Power, gave Liberty of Conscience, which both Papists and Presbyterians made use of, but upon the Revolution, the Papists being down of Course, the Presbyterians freely continued their Assemblies, by Virtue of King* James's *Indulgence, before they had a Toleration by Law; this I believe the Author means by* Jack's *stealing* Peter's *Protection, and making use of it himself.*

† *Sir* Humphry Edwyn, *a Presbyterian, was some Years ago LordMayor of* London, *and had the Insolence to go in his Formalities to a Conventicle, with the Ensigns of his Office.*

‖ *Custard is a famous Dish at a Lord-Mayors Feast.*

THE

CONCLUSION.

GOING *too long* is a Cause of Abortion as effectual, tho' not so frequent, as *Going too short*; and holds true especially in the *Labors* of the Brain. Well fare the Heart of that Noble * *Jesuit*, who first adventur'd to confess in Print, that Books must be suited to their several Seasons, like Dress, and Dyet, and Diversions: And better fare our noble Nation, for refining upon this, among other *French* Modes. I am living fast, to see the Time, when a *Book* that misses its Tide, shall be neglected, as the *Moon* by day, or like *Mackarel* a Week after the Season. No Man hath more nicely observed our Climate, than the Bookseller who bought the Copy of this Work; He knows to a Tittle what Subjects will best go off in a *dry Year*, and which it is proper to expose foremost, when the Weatherglass is fallen to *much Rain*. When he had seen this Treatise, and consulted his *Almanack* upon it; he gave me to understand, that he had maturely considered the two Principal Things, which were the *Bulk*, and the *Subject*; and found, it would never *take*, but after a long Vacation, and then only, in case it should happen to be a hard Year for Turnips. Upon which I desired to know, *considering my urgent Necessities*, what he thought might be acceptable this Month. He lookt *Westward*, and said, *I doubt we shall have a Fit of bad Weather; However, if you could prepare some pretty little* Banter (but not in Verse) *or a small Treatise upon the ⸺ it would run like Wild-Fire. But,* if it hold up, *I have already hired an Author to write something against* Dr. Bentley, *which, I am sure, will turn to Account.*

AT length we agreed upon this Expedient; That when a Customer comes for one of these, and desires in Confidence to know the Author; he will tell him very privately, as a Friend, naming

* Pere d'
Orleans.

which ever of the Wits shall happen to be that Week in the Vogue; and if *Durfy*'s last Play should be in Course, I had as lieve he may be the Person as *Congreve*. This I mention, because I am wonderfully well acquainted with the present Relish of Courteous Readers; and have often observed, with singular Pleasure, that a *Fly* driven from a *Honey-pot*, will immediately, with very good Appetite alight, and finish his Meal on an *Excrement*.

I have one Word to say upon the Subject of *Profound Writers*, who are grown very numerous of late; And, I know very well, the judicious World is resolved to list me in that Number. I conceive therefore, as to the Business of being *Profound*, that it is with *Writers*, as with *Wells*; A Person with good Eyes may see to the Bottom of the deepest, provided any *Water* be there; and, that often, when there is nothing in the World at the Bottom, besides *Dryness* and *Dirt*, tho' it be but a Yard and half under Ground, it shall pass, however, for wondrous *Deep*, upon no wiser a Reason than because it is wondrous *Dark*.

I am now trying an Experiment very frequent among Modern Authors; which is, to *write upon Nothing*; When the Subject is utterly exhausted, to let the Pen still move on; by some called, the Ghost of Wit, delighting to walk after the Death of its Body. And to say the Truth, there seems to be no Part of Knowledge in fewer Hands, than That of Discerning *when to have Done*. By the Time that an Author has writ out a Book, he and his Readers are become old Acquaintance, and grow very loth to part: So that I have sometimes known it to be in Writing, as in Visiting, where the Ceremony of taking Leave, has employ'd more Time than the whole Conversation before. The Conclusion of a Treatise, resembles the Conclusion of Human Life, which hath sometimes been compared to the End of a Feast; where few are satisfied to depart, *ut plenus vitæ conviva*: For Men will sit down after the fullest Meal, tho' it be only to *doze*, or to *sleep* out the rest of the Day. But, in this latter, I differ extreamly from other Writers; and shall be too proud, if by all my Labors, I can have any ways contributed to the *Repose* of Mankind in * Times so turbulent

---

* *This was writ before the Peace of* Riswick.

and unquiet as these. Neither, do I think such an Employment so very alien from the Office of a *Wit*, as some would suppose. For among a very Polite Nation in **Greece*, there were the *same* Temples built and consecrated to *Sleep* and the *Muses*, between which two Deities, they believed the strictest Friendship was established.

* *Trezenii*
Pausan. l. 2.

I have one concluding Favour, to request of my Reader; that he will not expect to be equally diverted and informed by every Line, or every Page of this Discourse; but give some Allowance to the Author's Spleen, and short Fits or Intervals of Dullness, as well as his own; And lay it seriously to his Conscience, whether, if he were walking the Streets, in dirty Weather, or a rainy Day; he would allow it fair Dealing in Folks at their Ease from a Window, to Critick his Gate, and ridicule his Dress at such a Juncture.

In my Disposure of Employments of the Brain, I have thought fit to make *Invention* the *Master*, and to give *Method* and *Reason*, the Office of its *Lacquays*. The Cause of this Distribution was, from observing it my peculiar Case, to be often under a Temptation of being *Witty*, upon Occasions, where I could be neither *Wise* nor *Sound*, nor any thing to the Matter in hand. And, I am too much a Servant of the *Modern* Way, to neglect any such Opportunities, whatever Pains or Improprieties I may be at, to introduce them. For, I have observed, that from a laborious Collection of Seven Hundred Thirty Eight *Flowers*, and *shining Hints* of the best *Modern* Authors, digested with great Reading, into my Book of *Common-places*; I have not been able after five Years to draw, hook, or force into common Conversation, any more than a Dozen. Of which Dozen, the one Moiety failed of Success, by being dropt among unsuitable Company; and the other cost me so many Strains, and Traps, and *Ambages* to introduce, that I at length resolved to give it over. Now, this Disappointment, (to discover a Secret) I must own, gave me the first Hint of setting up for an *Author*; and, I have since found among some particular Friends, that it is become a very general Complaint, and has produced the same Effects upon many others. For, I have remarked many a *towardly Word*, to be wholly neglected or despised in *Discourse*, which hath passed very

smoothly, with some Consideration and Esteem, after its Preferment and Sanction in *Print*. But now, since by the Liberty and
Encouragement of the Press, I am grown absolute Master of
the Occasions and Opportunities, to expose the Talents I have
acquired; I already discover, that the *Issues* of my *Observanda*
begin to grow too large for the *Receipts*. Therefore, I shall here
pause awhile, till I find, by feeling the World's Pulse, and my
own, that it will be of absolute Necessity for us both, to resume
my Pen.

FINIS.

Before the Title of the Battle

A

Full and True Account

OF THE

BATTEL

Fought laſt *FRIDAY*,

Between the

Antient and the *Modern*

BOOKS

IN

St. *JAMES*'s

LIBRARY.

LONDON:

Printed in the Year, MDCCX.

THE
BOOKSELLER
TO THE
READER.

THE following Discourse, as it is unquestionably of the same Author, so it seems to have been written about the same time with the former, I mean, the Year 1697, when the famous Dispute was on Foot, about *Antient and Modern Learning*. The Controversy took its Rise from an Essay of Sir *William Temple*'s, upon that Subject; which was answer'd by *W. Wotton*, B.D. with an Appendix by Dr. *Bently*, endeavouring to destroy the Credit of *Æsop* and *Phalaris*, for Authors, whom Sir *William Temple* had in the Essay before-mentioned, highly commended. In that Appendix, the Doctor falls hard upon a new Edition of *Phalaris*, put out by the Honourable *Charles Boyle* (now *Earl* of *Orrery*) to which, Mr. *Boyle* replyed at large, with great Learning and Wit; and the Doctor, voluminously, rejoyned. In this Dispute, the Town highly resented to see a Person of Sir *William Temple*'s Character and Merits, roughly used by the two Reverend Gentlemen aforesaid, and without any manner of Provocation. At length, there appearing no End of the Quarrel, our Author tells us, that the BOOKS in St. *James*'s Library, looking upon themselves as Parties principally concerned, took up the Controversie, and came to a decisive Battel; But, the Manuscript, by the Injury of Fortune, or Weather, being in several Places imperfect, we cannot learn to which side the Victory fell.

I must warn the Reader, to beware of applying to Persons what is here meant, only of Books in the most literal Sense. So, when *Virgil* is mentioned, we are not to understand the Person of a famous Poet, call'd by that Name, but only certain Sheets of Paper, bound up in Leather, containing in Print, the Works of the said Poet, and so of the rest.

THE
PREFACE
OF THE
AUTHOR.

SATYR *is a sort of* Glass, *wherein Beholders do generally discover every body's Face but their Own; which is the chief Reason for that kind of Reception it meets in the World, and that so very few are offended with it. But if it should happen otherwise, the Danger is not great; and, I have learned from long Experience, never to apprehend Mischief from those Understandings, I have been able to provoke; For, Anger and Fury, though they add Strength to the Sinews of the Body, yet are found to relax those of the Mind, and to render all its Efforts feeble and impotent.*

THERE *is a* Brain *that will endure but one* Scumming: *Let the Owner gather it with Discretion, and manage his little Stock with Husbandry; but of all things, let him beware of bringing it under the Lash of his Betters; because, That will make it all bubble up into Impertinence, and he will find no new Supply: Wit, without knowledge, being a Sort of* Cream, *which gathers in a Night to the Top, and by a skilful Hand, may be soon* whipt *into* Froth; *but once scumm'd away, what appears underneath will be fit for nothing, but to be thrown to the Hogs.*

A Full and True
ACCOUNT
OF THE
BATTEL
Fought last FRIDAY, &c.

WHOEVER examines with due Circumspection into the * *Annual Records* of *Time*, will find it remarked, that *War is the Child of Pride*, and *Pride the Daughter of Riches*; The former of which Assertions may be soon granted; but one cannot so easily subscribe to the latter: For *Pride* is nearly related to Beggary and *Want*, either by Father or Mother, and sometimes by both; And, to speak naturally, it very seldom happens among Men to fall out, when all have enough: Invasions usually travelling from *North* to *South*, that is to say, from Poverty upon Plenty. The most antient and natural Grounds of Quarrels, are *Lust* and *Avarice*; which, tho' we may allow to be Brethren or collateral Branches of *Pride*, are certainly the Issues of *Want*. For, to speak in the Phrase of Writers upon the Politicks, we may observe in the Republick of *Dogs*, (which in its Original seems to be an Institution of the *Many*) that the whole State is ever in the profoundest Peace, after a full Meal; and, that Civil Broils arise among them, when it happens For one great *Bone* to be seized on by some *leading Dog*, who either divides it among the *Few*, and then it falls to an *Oligarchy*, or keeps it to Himself, and then it runs up to a *Tyranny*. The same Reasoning also, holds Place among them, in those Dissensions we behold upon a Turgescency in any of their Females. For, the Right of Possession lying in common (it being impossible to establish a Property in so delicate a Case)

Jealousies and Suspicions do so abound, that the whole Commonwealth of that Street, is reduced to a manifest *State of War*, of every *Citizen* against every *Citizen*; till some One of more Courage, Conduct, or Fortune than the rest, seizes and enjoys the Prize; Upon which, naturally arises Plenty of Heart-burning, and Envy, and Snarling against the *Happy Dog*. Again, if we look upon any of these Republicks engaged in a Forein War, either of Invasion or Defence, we shall find, the same Reasoning will serve, as to the Grounds and Occasions of each; and, that *Poverty*, or *Want*, in some Degree or other, (whether Real, or in Opinion, which makes no Alteration in the Case) has a great Share, as well as *Pride*, on the Part of the Aggressor.

Now, whoever will please to take this Scheme, and either reduce or adapt it to an Intellectual State, or Commonwealth of Learning, will soon discover the first Ground of Disagreement between the two great Parties at this Time in Arms; and may form just Conclusions upon the Merits of either Cause. But the Issue or Events of this War are not so easie to conjecture at: For, the present Quarrel is so enflamed by the warm Heads of either Faction, and the Pretensions *somewhere or other* so exorbitant, as not to admit the least Overtures of Accommodation: This Quarrel first began (as I have heard it affirmed by an old Dweller in the Neighbourhood) about a small Spot of Ground, *lying* and *being* upon one of the two Tops of the Hill *Parnassus*; the highest and largest of which, had it seems, been time out of Mind, in quiet Possession of certain Tenants, call'd the *Antients*; And the other was held by the *Moderns*. But, these disliking their present Station, sent certain Ambassadors to the *Antients*, complaining of a great Nuisance, how the Height of that Part of *Parnassus*, quite spoiled the Prospect of theirs, especially towards the *East*; and therefore, to avoid a War, offered them the Choice of this Alternative; either that the *Antients* would please to remove themselves and their Effects down to the lower Summity, which the *Moderns* would graciously surrender to them, and advance in their Place; or else, that the said *Antients* will give leave to the *Moderns* to come with Shovels and Mattocks, and level the said Hill, as low as they shall think it convenient. To which, the *Antients* made Answer: How little they expected such a Message as this, from a Colony, whom they had admitted out of their own Free Grace, to so near a Neighbourhood. That, as to their own Seat, they were *Aborigines* of it, and therefore, to talk with them of a Removal or Surrender, was a Language they did not understand. That, if the Height of the Hill, on their side, shortned the Prospect of the *Moderns*, it was a Disadvantage they could not help, but desired them to consider, whether that Injury (if it be any) were not largely recompenced by the *Shade* and *Shelter* it afforded them. That, as to levelling or digging down, it was either Folly or Ignorance to propose it, if they did, or did not know, how that side of the Hill was an entire Rock, which would break their Tools and Hearts; without any Damage to itself. That they would therefore advise the *Moderns*, rather to raise their own side of the Hill, than dream of pulling down that of the *Antients*, to the former of which, they would not only give Licence, but also largely contribute. All this was rejected by the *Moderns*, with much Indignation, who still insisted upon one of the two Expedients; And so this Difference broke out into a long and obstinate War, maintain'd on the one Part, by Resolution, and by the Courage of certain Leaders and Allies; but, on the other, by the greatness of their Number, upon all Defeats, affording continual Recruits. In this Quarrel, whole Rivulets of *Ink* have been exhausted, and the Virulence of both Parties enormously augmented. Now, it must here be understood, that *Ink* is the great missive Weapon, in all Battels of the *Learned*, which, convey'd thro' a sort of Engine, call'd a *Quill*, infinite Numbers of these are darted at the Enemy, by the Valiant on each side, with equal Skill and Violence, as if it were an Engagement of *Porcupines*. This malignant Liquor was compounded by the Engineer, who invented it, of two Ingredients, which are *Gall* and *Copperas*, by its Bitterness and Venom, to *Suit* in some Degree, as well as to *Foment* the Genius of the Combatants. And as the *Grecians*, after an Engagement, when they could not *agree* about the Victory, were wont to set up Trophies on both sides, the beaten Party being content to be at the same Expence, to keep it self in Countenance (A laudable and antient Custom, happily reviv'd of late, in the Art of War) so the *Learned*, after a sharp and bloody Dispute, do on both sides hang out their Trophies too, which-ever comes by the worst. These Trophies have largely inscribed on them the Merits of the Cause; a full impartial Account of such a Battel, and how the Victory fell clearly to the Party that set them up. They are known to the World under several Names; As, *Disputes*, *Arguments*, *Rejoynders*, *Brief Considerations*, *Answers*, *Replies*, *Remarks*, *Reflexions*, *Objections*, *Confutations*. For a very few Days they are fixed up in all Publick Places, either by themselves or their * Representatives, for Passengers to gaze at: From whence the chiefest and largest are removed to certain Magazines, they call, *Libraries*, there to remain in a Quarter purposely assign'd them, and from thenceforth, begin to be called, *Books of Controversie*.

* Their Title-Pages.

In these Books, is wonderfully instilled and preserved, the Spirit of each Warrier, while he is alive; and after his Death, his Soul transmigrates there, to inform them. This, at least, is the more common Opinion; But, I believe, it is with Libraries, as with other Cœmeteries, where some Philosophers affirm, that a certain Spirit, which they call *Brutum hominis*, hovers over the Monument, till the Body is corrupted, and turns to *Dust*, or to *Worms*, but then vanishes or dissolves: So, we may say, a restless Spirit haunts over every Book, till *Dust* or *Worms* have seized upon it; which to some, may happen in a few Days, but to others, later; And therefore, *Books* of Controversy, being of all others, haunted by the most disorderly Spirits, have always been confined in a separate Lodge from the rest; and for fear of mutual violence against each other, it was thought Prudent by our Ancestors, to bind them to the Peace with strong Iron Chains. Of which Invention, the original Occasion was this: When the Works of *Scotus* first came out, they were carried to a certain great Library, and had Lodgings appointed them; But this Author was no sooner settled, than he went to visit his Master *Aristotle*, and there both concerted together to seize *Plato* by main Force, and turn him out from his antient Station among the *Divines*, where he had peaceably dwelt near Eight Hundred Years. The Attempt succeeded, and the two Usurpers have reigned ever since in his stead: But to maintain Quiet for the future, it was decreed, that all *Polemicks* of the larger Size ,should be held fast with a Chain.

By this Expedient, the publick Peace of Libraries, might certainly have been preserved, if a new Species of controversial Books had not arose of late Years, instinct with a most malignant Spirit, from the War above-mentioned, between the *Learned*, about the higher Summity of *Parnassus*.

When these Books were first admitted into the Publick Libraries, I remember to have said upon Occasion, to several Persons concerned, how I was sure, they would create Broyls wherever they came, unless a World of Care were taken: And therefore, I advised, that the Champions of each side should be coupled together, or otherwise mixt, that like the blending of contrary Poysons, their Malignity might be employ'd among themselves. And it seems, I was neither an ill Prophet, nor an ill Counsellor; for it was nothing else but the Neglect of this Caution, which gave Occasion to the terrible Fight that happened on *Friday* last between the *Antient* and *Modern Books* in the *King's Library*. Now, because the Talk of this Battel is so fresh in every body's Mouth, and the Expectation of the Town so great to be informed in the Particulars; I, being possessed of all Qualifications requisite in an *Historian*, and retained by neither Party; have resolved to comply with the urgent *Importunity of my Friends*, by writing down a full impartial Account thereof.

The *Guardian* of the *Regal Library*, a Person of great Valor, but chiefly renowned for his * *Humanity*, had been a fierce Champion for the *Moderns*, and in an Engagement upon *Parnassus*, had vowed, with his own Hands, to knock down two of the *Antient* Chiefs, who guarded a small Pass on the superior Rock; but endeavouring to climb up, was cruelly obstructed by his own unhappy Weight, and tendency towards his Center; a Quality, to which, those of the *Modern* Party, are extreme subject; For, being light-headed, they have in Speculation, a wonderful Agility, and conceive nothing too high for them to mount; but in reducing to Practice, discover a mighty Pressure about their Posteriors and their Heels. Having thus failed in his Design, the

---

* *The Honourable Mr*. Boyle, *in the Preface to his Edition of* Phalaris, *says, he was refus'd a Manuscript by the Library-Keeper*, pro solita Humanitate suâ.

l

disappointed Champion bore a cruel Rancour to the *Antients*, which he resolved to gratifie, by shewing all Marks of his Favour to the *Books* of their Adversaries, and lodging them in the fairest Apartments; when at the same time, whatever *Book* had the boldness to own it self for an Advocate of the *Antients*, was buried alive in some obscure Corner, and threatned upon the least Displeasure, to be turned out of Doors. Besides, it so happened, that about this time, there was a strange Confusion of Place among all the *Books* in the Library; for which several Reasons were assigned. Some imputed it to a great heap of *learned Dust*, which a perverse Wind blew off from a Shelf of *Moderns* into the *Keeper*'s Eyes. Others affirmed, He had a Humour to pick the *Worms* out of the *Schoolmen*, and swallow them fresh and fasting; whereof some fell upon his *Spleen*, and some climbed up into his Head, to the great Perturbation of both. And lastly, others maintained, that by walking much in the dark about the Library, he had quite lost the Situation of it out of his Head; And therefore, in replacing his *Books*, he was apt to mistake, and clap *Des-Cartes* next to *Aristotle*; Poor *Plato* had got between *Hobbes* and the *Seven Wise Masters*, and *Virgil* was hemm'd in with *Dryden* on one side, and *Withers* on the other.

MEAN while, those *Books* that were Advocates for the *Moderns*, chose out one from among them, to make a Progress thro' the whole Library, examine the Number and Strength of their Party, and concert their Affairs. This Messenger performed all things very industriously, and brought back with him a List of their Forces, in all Fifty Thousand, consisting chiefly of *light Horse*, *heavy-armed Foot*, and *Mercenaries*; Whereof the *Foot* were in general but sorrily armed, and worse clad; Their *Horses* large, but extremely out of Case and Heart; However, some few by trading among the *Antients*, had furnisht themselves tolerably enough.

WHILE Things were in this Ferment; *Discord* grew extremely high, hot Words passed on both sides, and ill blood was plentifully bred. Here a solitary *Antient*, squeezed up among a whole Shelf of *Moderns*, offered fairly to dispute the Case, and to prove by manifest Reasons, that the Priority was due to them, from long Possession, and in regard of their Prudence, Antiquity, and above all, their great Merits towards the *Moderns*. But these denied the Premises, and seemed very much to wonder, how the *Antients* could pretend to insist upon their Antiquity, when it was so plain (if they went to that) that the *Moderns* were much the more * *Antient* of the two. As for any Obligations they owed to the *Antients*, they renounced them all. *'Tis true*, said they, *we are informed, some few of our Party have been so mean to borrow their Subsistence from You; But the rest, infinitely the greater Number (and especially, we* French *and* English) *were so far from stooping to so base an Example, that there never passed, till this very hour, six Words between us. For, our* Horses *are of our own breeding, our* Arms *of our own forging, and our* Cloaths *of our own cutting out and sowing.* Plato was by chance upon the next Shelf, and observing those that spoke to be in the ragged Plight, mentioned a while ago; their *Jades* lean and foundred, their *Weapons* of rotten Wood, their *Armour* rusty, and nothing but Raggs underneath; he laugh'd loud, and in his pleasant way, swore, *By* G——, *he believ'd them.*

* *According to the Modern Paradox.*

Now, the *Moderns* had not proceeded in their late Negotiation, with Secrecy enough to escape the Notice of the Enemy. For, those Advocates, who had begun the Quarrel, by setting first on Foot the Dispute of Precedency, talkt so loud of coming to a Battel, that *Temple* happened to over-hear them, and gave immediate Intelligence to the *Antients*; who thereupon drew up their scattered Troops together, resolving to act upon the defensive; Upon which, several of the *Moderns* fled over to their Party, and among the rest, *Temple* himself. This *Temple* having been educated and long conversed among the *Antients*, was, of all the *Moderns*, their greatest Favorite, and became their greatest Champion.

THINGS were at this Crisis, when a material Accident fell out. For, upon the highest Corner of a large Window, there dwelt a certain *Spider*, swollen up to the first Magnitude, by the Destruction of infinite Numbers of *Flies*, whose Spoils lay scattered before the Gates of his Palace, like human Bones before the Cave of some Giant. The Avenues to his Castle were guarded with Turn-pikes, and Palissadoes, all after the *Modern* way of Fortification. After you had passed several Courts, you came to the Center, wherein you might behold the *Constable* himself in his own Lodgings, which had Windows fronting to each Avenue, and Ports to sally out upon all Occasions of Prey or Defence. In this Mansion he had for some Time dwelt in Peace and Plenty, without Danger to his *Person* by *Swallows* from above, or to his *Palace* by *Brooms* from below: When it was the Pleasure of Fortune to conduct thither a wandring *Bee*, to whose Curiosity a broken Pane in the Glass had discovered it self; and in he went, where expatiating a while, he at last happened to alight upon one of the outward Walls of the *Spider's* Cittadel; which yielding to the unequal Weight, sunk down to the very Foundation. Thrice he endeavoured to force his Passage, and Thrice the Center shook. The *Spider* within, feeling the terrible Convulsion, supposed at first, that *Nature* was approaching to her final Dissolution; or else, that *Beelzebub* with all his Legions, was come to revenge the Death of many thousands of his Subjects, whom his Enemy had slain and devoured. However, he at length valiantly resolved to issue forth, and meet his Fate. Mean while, the *Bee* had acquitted himself of his Toils, and posted securely at some Distance, was employed in cleansing his Wings, and disengaging them from the ragged Remnants of the Cobweb. By this Time the *Spider* was adventured out, when beholding the Chasms, and Ruins, and Dilapidations of his Fortress, he was very near at his Wit's end, he stormed and swore like a Mad-man, and swelled till he was ready to burst. At length, casting his Eye upon the *Bee*, and wisely gathering Causes from Events, (for they knew each other by Sight) *A Plague split you,* said he, *for a giddy Son of a Whore; Is it you, with a Vengeance, that have made this Litter here? Could you not look before you, and be d——n'd? Do you think I have nothing else to do (in the Devil's Name) but to Mend and Repair after your Arse?* Good Words, Friend, said the *Bee*, (having now pruned himself, and being disposed to drole) *I'll give you my Hand and Word to come near your Kennel no more; I was never in such a confounded Pickle since I was born.* Sirrah, replied the *Spider*, *if it were not for breaking an old Custom in our Family, never to stir abroad against an Enemy, I should come and teach you better Manners.* I pray, have Patience, said the *Bee*, *or you will spend your Substance, and for ought I see, you may stand in need of it all, towards the Repair of your House. Rogue, Rogue,* replied the *Spider, yet, methinks, you should have more Respect to a Person, whom all the World allows to be so much your Betters. By my Troth,* said the *Bee, the Comparison will amount to a very good Jest, and you will do me a Favour, to let me know the Reasons, that all the World is pleased to use in so hopeful a Dispute.* At this, the *Spider* having swelled himself into the Size and Posture of a Disputant, began his Argument in the true Spirit of Controversy, with a Resolution to be heartily scurrilous and angry, to urge *on* his own Reasons, without the least Regard to the Answers or Objections of his Opposite; and fully predetermined in his Mind against all Conviction.

NOT to disparage my self, said he, *by the Comparison with such a Rascal; What art thou but a Vagabond without House or Home, without Stock or Inheritance? Born to no Possession of your own, but a Pair of Wings, and a Drone-Pipe. Your Livelihood is an universal Plunder upon Nature; a Freebooter over Fields and Gardens; and for the sake of Stealing, will rob a Nettle as readily as a Violet. Whereas I am a domestick Animal, furnisht with a Native Stock within my self. This large Castle (to shew my Improvements in the Mathematicks) is all built with my own Hands, and the Materials extracted altogether out of my own Person.*

I am glad, answered the *Bee, to hear you grant at least, that I am come honestly by my Wings and my Voice, for then, it seems, I am obliged to Heaven alone for my Flights and my Musick; and Providence would never have bestowed me two such Gifts, without designing them for the noblest Ends. I visit, indeed, all the Flowers and Blossoms of the Field and the Garden, but whatever I collect from thence, enriches my self, without the least Injury to their Beauty, their Smell, or their Taste. Now, for you and your Skill in Architecture, and other Mathematicks, I have little to say: In that Building of yours, there might, for ought I know, have been Labor and Method enough, but by woful Experience for us both, 'tis too plain, the Materials are nought, and I hope, you will henceforth take Warning, and consider Duration and matter, as well as method and Art. You, boast, indeed, of being obliged to no other Creature, but of drawing, and spinning out all from your self; That is to say, if we may judge of the Liquor in the Vessel by what issues out, You possess a good plentiful Store of Dirt and Poison in your Breast; And, tho' I would by no means, lessen or disparage your genuine Stock of*

*either, yet, I doubt you are somewhat obliged for an Encrease of both, to
a little foreign Assistance. Your inherent Portion of Dirt, does not fail
of Acquisitions, by Sweepings exhaled from below: and one Insect fur-
nishes you with a share of Poison to destroy another. So that in short,
the Question comes all to this; Whether is the nobler Being of the two,
That which by a lazy Contemplation of four Inches round; by an over-
weening Pride, which feeding and engendering on it self, turns all into
Excrement and Venom; producing nothing at last, but Fly-bane and a
Cobweb: Or That, which, by an universal Range, with long Search,
much Study, true Judgment, and Distinction of Things, brings home
Honey and Wax.*

THIS Dispute was managed with such Eagerness, Clamor,
and Warmth, that the two Parties of *Books* in Arms below, stood
Silent a while, waiting in Suspense what would be the Issue;
which was not long undetermined: For the *Bee* grown impatient
at so much loss of Time, fled strait away to a bed of Roses,
without looking for a Reply; and left the *Spider* like an Orator,
collected in himself, and just prepared to burst out.

IT happened upon this Emergency, that *Æsop* broke silence
first. He had been of late most barbarously treated by a strange
Effect of the *Regent's Humanity*, who had tore off his Title-page,
sorely defaced one half of his Leaves, and chained him fast
among a Shelf of *Moderns*. Where soon discovering how high
the Quarrel was like to proceed, He tried all his Arts, and turned
himself to a thousand Forms: At length in the borrowed Shape
of an *Ass*, the *Regent* mistook Him for a *Modern*; by which means,
he had Time and Opportunity to escape to the *Antients*, just
when the *Spider* and the *Bee* were entring into their Contest; to
which He gave His Attention with a world of Pleasure; and
when it was ended, swore in the loudest Key, that in all his Life,
he had never known two Cases so parallel and adapt to each
other, as That in the Window, and this upon the Shelves. The
Disputants, said he, *have admirably managed the Dispute between
them, have taken in the full Strength of all that is to be said on both
sides, and exhausted the Substance of every Argument pro and con. It
is but to adjust the Reasonings of both to the present Quarrel, then to
compare and apply the Labors and Fruits of each, as the Bee has
learnedly deduced them; and we shall find the Conclusions fall plain and*

close upon the Moderns *and* Us. *For, pray Gentlemen, was ever any thing so* Modern *as the* Spider *in his Air, his Turns, and his Paradoxes? He argues in the Behalf of* You *his Brethren, and Himself, with many Boastings of his native Stock, and great Genius; that he Spins and Spits wholly from himself, and scorns to own any Obligation or Assistance from without. Then he displays to you his great Skill in Architecture, and Improvement in the Mathematicks. To all this, the* Bee, *as an Advocate, retained by us the* Antients, *thinks fit to Answer; That if one may judge of the great Genius or Inventions of the* Moderns, *by what they have produced, you will hardly have Countenance to bear you out in boasting of either. Erect your Schemes with as much Method and Skill as you please; yet, if the materials be nothing but Dirt, spun out of your own Entrails (the Guts of* Modern *Brains) the Edifice will conclude at last in a* Cobweb: *The Duration of which, like that of other* Spiders *Webs, may be imputed to their being forgotten, or neglected, or hid in a Corner. For any Thing else of Genuine, that the* Moderns *may pretend to, I cannot recollect; unless it be a large Vein of Wrangling and Satyr, much of a Nature and Substance with the* Spider's *Poison; which, however they pretend to spit wholly out of themselves, is improved by the same Arts, by feeding upon the* Insects *and* Vermin *of the Age. As for* Us, *the* Antients, *We are content with the* Bee, *to pretend to Nothing of our own, beyond our* Wings *and our* Voice: *that is to say, our* Flights *and our* Language; *For the rest, whatever we have got, has been by infinite Labor, and search, and ranging thro' every Corner of Nature: The Difference is, that instead of* Dirt *and* Poison, *we have rather chose to fill our Hives with* Honey *and* Wax, *thus furnishing Mankind with the two Noblest of Things, which are* Sweetness *and* Light.

'Tis wonderful to conceive the Tumult arisen among the *Books,* upon the Close of this long Descant of *Æsop;* Both Parties took the Hint, and heightened their Animosities so on a sudden, that they resolved it should come to a Battel. Immediately, the two main Bodies withdrew under their several Ensigns, to the farther Parts of the Library, and there entred into Cabals, and Consults upon the present Emergency. The *Moderns* were in very warm Debates upon the Choice of their *Leaders,* and nothing less than the Fear impending from their Enemies, could have kept them from Mutinies upon this Occasion. The Difference was greatest among the *Horse,* where every private *Trooper* pretended to the chief Command, from *Tasso* and *Milton,* to *Dryden* and *Withers.* The *Light-Horse* were Commanded by *Cowly,* and *Despreaux.* There, came the *Bowmen* under their valiant Leaders, *Des-Cartes, Gassendi,* and *Hobbes,* whose Strength was such, that they could shoot their Arrows beyond the *Atmosphere,* never to fall down again, but turn like that of *Evander,* into *Meteors,* or like the *Canon-ball* into *Stars. Paracelsus* brought a *Squadron* of *Stink-Pot-Flingers* from the snowy Mountains of *Rhœtia.* There, came a vast Body of *Dragoons,* of different Nations, under the leading of *Harvey,* their great *Aga:* Part armed with *Scythes,* the Weapons of Death; Part with *Launces* and long *Knives,* all steept in *Poison*; Part shot *Bullets* of a most malignant Nature, and used *white Powder* which infallibly killed without *Report.* There, came several Bodies of *heavy-armed Foot,* all *Mercenaries,* under the Ensigns of *Guiccardine, Davila, Polydore Virgil, Buchanan, Mariana, Cambden,* and others. The *Engineers* were commanded by *Regiomontanus* and *Wilkins.* The rest were a confused Multitude, led by *Scotus, Aquinas,* and *Bellarmine*; of mighty Bulk and Stature, but without either Arms, Courage, or Discipline. In the last Place, came infinite Swarms of * *Calones,* a disorderly Rout led by *Lestrange*; Rogues and Raggamuffins, that follow the Camp for nothing but the Plunder; All without *Coats* to cover them.

THE Army of the *Antients* was much fewer in Number; *Homer* led the *Horse,* and *Pindar* the *Light-Horse; Euclid* was chief *Engineer: Plato* and *Aristotle* commanded the *Bowmen, Herodotus* and *Livy* the *Foot, Hippocrates* the *Dragoons.* The *Allies,* led by *Vossius* and *Temple,* brought up the Rear.

ALL things violently tending to a decisive Battel; *Fame,* who much frequented, and had a large Apartment formerly assigned her in the *Regal Library,* fled up strait to *Jupiter,* to whom she delivered a faithful account of all that passed between the two Parties below. (For, among the Gods, she always tells Truth.) *Jove* in great concern, convokes a Council in the *Milky-Way.* The Senate assembled, he declares the Occasion of convening

---

* *These are Pamphlets, which are not bound or cover'd.*

them; a bloody Battel just impendent between two mighty Armies of *Antient* and *Modern* Creatures, call'd *Books*, wherein the Celestial Interest was but too deeply concerned. *Momus*, the Patron of the *Moderns*, made an Excellent Speech in their Favor, which was answered by *Pallas* the Protectress of the *Antients*. The Assembly was divided in their affections; when *Jupiter* commanded the Book of Fate to be laid before Him. Immediately were brought by *Mercury*, three large Volumes in Folio, containing Memoirs of all Things past, present, and to come. The Clasps were of Silver, double Gilt; the Covers, of Celestial Turky-leather, and the Paper such as here on Earth might almost pass for Vellum. *Jupiter* having silently read the Decree, would communicate the Import to none, but presently shut up the Book.

WITHOUT the Doors of this Assembly, there attended a vast Number of light, nimble Gods, menial Servants to *Jupiter*: These are his ministring Instruments in all Affairs below. They travel in a Caravan, more or less together, and are fastened to each other like a Link of Gally-slaves, by a light Chain, which passes from them to *Jupiter*'s great Toe: And yet in receiving or delivering a Message, they may never approach above the lowest Step of his Throne, where he and they whisper to each other thro' a long hollow Trunk. These Deities are call'd by mortal Men, *Accidents*, or *Events*; but the Gods call them, *Second Causes*. *Jupiter* having delivered his Message to a certain Number of these Divinities, they flew immediately down to the Pinnacle of the Regal Library, and consulting a few Minutes, entered unseen, and disposed the Parties according to their Orders.

MEAN while, *Momus* fearing the worst, and calling to mind an antient Prophecy, which bore no very good Face to his Children the *Moderns*; bent his Flight to the Region of a malignant Deity, call'd *Criticism*. She dwelt on the Top of a snowy Mountain in *Nova Zembla*; there *Momus* found her extended in her Den, upon the Spoils of numberless Volumes half devoured. At her right Hand sat *Ignorance*, her Father and Husband, blind with Age; at her left, *Pride* her Mother, dressing her up in the Scraps of Paper herself had torn. There, was *Opinion* her Sister, light of Foot, hoodwinkt, and headstrong, yet giddy and perpetually turning. About her play'd her Children, *Noise* and *Impudence*, *Dullness* and *Vanity*, *Positiveness*, *Pedantry*, and *Ill-Manners*. The Goddess herself had Claws like a Cat: Her Head, and Ears, and Voice, resembled those of an *Ass*; Her Teeth fallen out before; Her Eyes turned inward, as if she lookt only upon herself: Her Diet was the overflowing of her own *Gall*: Her *Spleen* was so large, as to stand prominent like a Dug of the first Rate, nor wanted Excrescencies in form of Teats, at which a Crew of ugly Monsters were greedily sucking; and, what is wonderful to conceive, the bulk of Spleen encreased faster than the Sucking could diminish it. *Goddess*, said *Momus*, *can you sit idly here, while our devout Worshippers, the* Moderns, *are this Minute entring into a cruel Battel, and, perhaps, now lying under the Swords of their Enemies; Who then hereafter, will ever sacrifice, or build Altars to our Divinities? Haste therefore to the* British Isle, *and, if possible, prevent their Destruction, while I make Factions among the Gods, and gain them over to our Party.*

MOMUS having thus delivered himself, staid not for an answer, but left the Goddess to her own Resentment; Up she rose in a Rage, and as it is the Form upon such Occasions, began a Soliloquy. *'Tis I* (said she) *who give Wisdom to Infants and Idiots; By Me, Children grow wiser than their Parents. By Me,* Beaux *become Politicians; and* School-boys, *Judges of Philosophy. By Me, Sophisters debate, and conclude upon the Depths of Knowledge; and Coffeehouse Wits instinct by Me, can correct an Author's Style, and display his minutest Errors, without understanding a Syllable of his Matter or his Language. By Me, Striplings spend their Judgment, as they do their Estate, before it comes into their Hands. 'Tis I, who have deposed Wit and Knowledge from their Empire over* Poetry, *and advanced my self in their stead. And shall a few* upstart Antients *dare to oppose me?— But, come, my aged Parents, and you, my Children dear, and thou my beauteous Sister; let us ascend my Chariot, and haste to assist our devout* Moderns, *who are now sacrificing to us a* Hecatomb, *as I perceive by that grateful Smell, which from thence reaches my Nostrils.*

The Goddess and her Train having mounted the Chariot, which was drawn by *tame Geese*, flew over infinite Regions, shedding her Influence in due Places, till at length, she arrived at her beloved Island of *Britain*; but in hovering over its *Metropolis*, what Blessings did she not let fall upon her Seminaries of

Gresham and *Covent-Garden*? And now she reach'd the fatal Plain of St. *James's* Library, at what time the two Armies were upon the Point to engage; where entring with all her Caravan, unseen, and landing upon a Case of Shelves, now desart, but once inhabited by a Colony of *Virtuoso's*, she staid a while to observe the Posture of both Armies.

BUT here, the tender Cares of a Mother began to fill her Thoughts, and move in her Breast. For, at the Head of a Troop of *Modern Bow-men*, she cast her Eyes upon her Son *Wotton*; to whom the Fates had assigned a very short Thread. *Wotton*, a young Hero, whom an unknown Father of mortal Race, begot by stollen Embraces with this Goddess. He was the Darling of his Mother, above all her Children, and she resolved to go and comfort Him. But first, according to the good old Custom of Deities, she cast about to change her Shape; for fear the Divinity of her Countenance might dazzle his Mortal Sight, and overcharge the rest of his Senses. She therefore gathered up her Person into an *Octavo* Compass: Her Body grew white and arid, and split in pieces with Driness; the thick turned into Pastboard, and the thin into Paper, upon which, her Parents and Children, artfully strowed a Black Juice, or Decoction of Gall and Soot, in Form of Letters; her Head, and Voice, and Spleen, kept their primitive Form, and that which before, was a Cover of Skin, did still continue so. In which Guise, she march'd on towards the *Moderns*, undistinguishable in Shape and Dress from the *Divine Bentley*, *Wotton's* dearest Friend. *Brave Wotton*, said the Goddess, *Why do our Troops stand idle here, to spend their present Vigour and Opportunity of the Day? Away, let us haste to the Generals, and advise to give the Onset immediately.* Having spoke thus, she took the ugliest of her Monsters, full glutted from her Spleen, and flung it invisibly into his Mouth; which flying strait up into his Head, squeez'd out his Eye-Balls, gave him a distorted Look, and half over-turned his Brain. Then she privately ordered two of her beloved Children, *Dulness* and *Ill-Manners*, closely to attend his Person in all Encounters. Having thus accoutred him, she vanished in a Mist, and the *Hero* perceived it was the Goddess, his Mother.

THE destined Hour of Fate, being now arrived, the Fight

began; whereof, before I dare adventure to make a particular Description, I must, after the Example of other Authors, petition for a hundred Tongues, and Mouths, and Hands, and Pens; which would all be too little to perform so immense a Work. Say, Goddess, that presidest over History; who it was that first advanced in the Field of Battel. *Paracelsus*, at the Head of his *Dragoons*, observing *Galen* in the adverse Wing, darted his Javelin with a mighty Force, which the brave *Antient* received upon his Shield, the Point breaking in the second fold. *   *   *

Hic pauca desunt.   *   *   *   *   *   *   *   *

They bore the wounded *Aga*, on their Shields to his Chariot *
*   *   *   *   *   *   *   *

Desunt nonnulla.   *   *   *   *   *   *   *   *

*   *   *   *   *   *   *   *   *   *

Then *Aristotle* observing *Bacon* advance with a furious Mien, drew his Bow to the Head, and let fly his Arrow, which mist the valiant *Modern*, and went hizzing over his Head; but *Des-Cartes* it hit; The Steel Point quickly found a *Defect* in his *Head-piece*; it pierced the Leather and the Past-board, and went in at his Right Eye. The Torture of the Pain, whirled the valiant *Bow-man* round, till Death, like a Star of superior Influence, drew him into his own *Vortex*.   *   *   *   *   *   *

Ingens hiatus hic in MS.   *   *   *   *   *   *   *   *

when *Homer* appeared at the Head of the Cavalry, mounted on a furious Horse, with Difficulty managed by the Rider himself, but which no other Mortal durst approach; He rode among the Enemies Ranks, and bore down all before him. Say, Goddess, whom he slew first, and whom he slew last. First, *Gondibert* advanced against Him, clad in heavy Armour, and mounted on a staid sober Gelding, not so famed for his Speed as his Docility in kneeling, whenever his Rider would mount or alight. He had made a Vow to *Pallas*, that he would never leave * *Vid. Homer.* the Field, till he had spoiled * *Homer* of his Armour; Madman, who had never once *seen* the Wearer, nor understood his Strength. Him *Homer* overthrew, Horse and Man to the Ground, there to be trampled and choak'd in the Dirt. Then, with a long Spear, he slew *Denham*, a stout *Modern*, who from his * Father's side, derived his Lineage from *Apollo*, but his Mother was of Mortal Race. He fell, and bit the Earth. The Celestial Part *Apollo* took, and made it a Star, but the Terrestrial lay wallowing upon the Ground. Then *Homer* slew *Wesley* with a kick of his Horse's heel; He took *Perrault* by mighty Force out of his Saddle, then hurl'd him at *Fontenelle*, with the same Blow dashing out both their Brains.

ON the left Wing of the Horse, *Virgil* appeared in shining Armor, compleatly fitted to his Body; He was mounted on a dapple grey Steed, the slowness of whose Pace, was an Effect of the highest Mettle and Vigour. He cast his Eye on the adverse Wing, with a desire to find an Object worthy of his valour, when behold, upon a sorrel Gelding of a monstrous Size, appear'd a Foe, issuing from among the thickest of the Enemy's Squadrons; But his Speed was less than his Noise; for his Horse, old and lean, spent the Dregs of his Strength in a high Trot, which tho' it made slow advances, yet caused a loud Clashing of his Armor, terrible to hear. The two Cavaliers had now approached within the Throw of a Lance, when the Stranger desired a Parley, and lifting up the Vizard of his Helmet, a Face hardly appeared from within, which after a pause, was known for that of the renowned *Dryden*. The brave *Antient* suddenly started, as one possess'd with Surprize and Disappointment together: For, the Helmet was nine times too large for the Head, which appeared Situate far in the hinder Part, even like the Lady in a Lobster, or like a Mouse under a Canopy of State, or like a shrivled Beau from within the Pent-house of a modern Perewig: And the voice was suited to the Visage, sounding weak and remote. *Dryden* in a long Harangue soothed up the good *Antient*, called him *Father*, and by a large deduction of Genealogies, made it plainly appear, that they were nearly related. Then he humbly proposed an Ex-

---

* *Sir* John Denham's *Poems are very Unequal, extremely Good, and very Indifferent, so that his Detractors said, he was not the real Author of* Coopers-Hill.

change of Armor, as a lasting Mark of Hospitality between
them. *Virgil* consented (for the Goddess *Diffidence* came unseen,

Vid. Homer. and cast a Mist before his Eyes) tho' his was of
Gold, and cost a hundred Beeves, the others but
of rusty Iron. However, this glittering Armor became the
Modern yet worse than his Own. Then, they agreed to exchange
Horses; but when it came to the Trial, *Dryden* was afraid, and
utterly unable to mount.   *   *   *   *   *   *

Alter hiatus *   *   *   *   *   *   *   *
in MS.   *   *   *   *   *   *   *   *

*   *   *   * *Lucan* appeared upon a fiery Horse, of
admirable Shape, but head-strong, bearing the Rider where he
list, over the Field; he made a mighty Slaughter among the
Enemy's Horse; which Destruction to stop, *Blackmore*, a famous
Modern (but one of the *Mercenaries*) strenuously opposed himself;
and darted a Javelin, with a strong Hand, which falling short of
its Mark, struck deep in the Earth. Then *Lucan* threw a Lance;
but *Æsculapius* came unseen, and turn'd ·off the Point. *Brave*
Modern, *said* Lucan, *I perceive some God protects you, for never did
my Arm so deceive me before; But, what Mortal can contend with a
God? Therefore, let us Fight no longer, but present Gifts to each other.*
Lucan then bestowed the *Modern a Pair of Spurs*, and *Blackmore*
gave *Lucan* a Bridle.

             *   *   *   *   *   *   *
Pauca desunt. *   *   *   *   *   *   *   *

Creech; But, the Goddess *Dulness* took a Cloud, formed into the
Shape of *Horace*, armed and mounted, and placed it in a flying
Posture before Him. Glad was the Cavalier, to begin a Combat
with a flying Foe, and pursued the Image, threatning loud; till
at last it led him to the peaceful Bower of his Father *Ogleby*, by
whom he was disarmed, and assigned to his Repose.

THEN *Pindar* slew——, and ——, and *Oldham*, and —— and
Afra the *Amazon* light of foot; Never advancing in a direct Line,
but wheeling with incredible Agility and Force, he made a terrible Slaughter among the Enemies *Light-Horse*. Him, when
Cowley observed, his generous Heart burnt within him, and he
advanced against the fierce *Antient*, imitating his Address, and
Pace, and Career, as well as the Vigour of his Horse, and his own

Skill would allow. When the two Cavaliers had approach'd within the Length of three Javelins; first *Cowley* threw a Lance, which miss'd *Pindar*, and passing into the Enemy's Ranks, fell ineffectual to the Ground. Then *Pindar* darted a Javelin, so large and weighty, that scarce a dozen *Cavaliers*, as *Cavaliers* are in our degenerate Days, could raise it from the Ground: yet he threw it with Ease, and it went by an unerring Hand, singing through the Air; Nor could the *Modern* have avoided present Death, if he had not luckily opposed the Shield that had been given Him by *Venus*. And now both Hero's drew their Swords, but the *Modern* was so aghast and disordered, that he knew not where he was; his Shield dropt from his Hands; thrice he fled, and thrice he could not escape; at last he turned, and lifting up his Hands, in the Posture of a Suppliant, *God-like* Pindar, said he, *spare my Life, and possess my Horse with these Arms; besides the Ransom which my Friends will give, when they hear I am alive, and your Prisoner.* Dog, said Pindar, *Let your Ransom stay with your Friends; But your Carcass shall be left for the* Fowls of the Air, *and the* Beasts of the Field. With that, he raised his Sword, and with a mighty Stroak, cleft the wretched *Modern* in twain, the Sword pursuing the Blow; and one half lay panting on the Ground, to be trod in pieces by the Horses Feet, the other half was born by the frighted Steed thro' the Field. This * *Venus* took, and wash'd it seven times in *Ambrosia*, then struck it thrice with a Sprig of *Amarant*; upon which, the Leather grew round and soft, the Leaves turned into Feathers, and being gilded before, continued gilded still; so it became a *Dove*, and She harness'd it to her Chariot.

* * * * * * * * * *
* * * * * * * *Hiatus valdè*
* * * * * * * *deflendus in MS.*
* * * * * * * * * *

DAY being far spent, and the numerous Forces of the *Moderns* half inclining to a Retreat, there issued forth from a Squadron of their *heavy armed Foot*, a Captain, whose Name was *Bentley*; in Person, the

The Episode of Bentley *and* Wotton.

---

* *I do not approve the Author's Judgment in this, for I think* Cowley's *Pindaricks are much preferable to his* Mistress.

most deformed of all the *Moderns*; Tall, but without Shape or Comeliness; Large, but without Strength or Proportion. His Armour was patch'd up of a thousand incoherent Pieces; and the Sound of it, as he march'd, was loud and dry, like that made by the Fall of a Sheet of Lead, which an *Etesian* Wind blows suddenly down from the Roof of some Steeple. His Helmet was of old rusty Iron, but the Vizard was Brass, which tainted by his Breath, corrupted into Copperas, nor wanted Gall from the same Fountain; so, that whenever provoked by Anger or Labour, an atramentous Quality, of most malignant Nature, was seen to distil from his Lips. In his * right Hand he grasp'd a Flail, and (that he might never be unprovided of an *offensive* Weapon) a Vessel full of *Ordure* in his Left: Thus, compleatly arm'd, he advanc'd with a slow and heavy Pace, where the *Modern* Chiefs were holding a Consult upon the Sum of Things; who, as he came onwards, laugh'd to behold his crooked Leg, and hump Shoulder, which his Boot and Armour vainly endeavouring to hide were forced to comply with, and expose. The Generals made use of him for his Talent of Railing; which kept within Government, proved frequently of great Service to their Cause, but at other times did more Mischief than Good; For at the least Touch of Offence, and often without any at all, he would, like a wounded Elephant, convert it against his Leaders. Such, at this Juncture, was the Disposition of *Bentley*, grieved to see the Enemy prevail, and dissatisfied with every Body's Conduct but his own. He humbly gave the *Modern* Generals to understand, that he conceived, with great Submission, they were all a Pack of *Rogues*, and *Fools*, and *Sons of Whores*, and *d——mn'd Cowards*, and *confounded Loggerheads*, and *illiterate Whelps*, and *nonsensical Scoundrels*; That if Himself had been constituted General, those *presumptuous Dogs*, the *Antients*, would long before this, have been beaten out of the Field. *You*, said he, *sit here idle, but, when I, or any other valiant* Modern, *kill an Enemy, you are sure to seize the Spoil. But, I will not march one Foot against the Foe, till you all swear*

Vid. Homer. de Thersite.

---

*The Person here spoken of, is famous for letting fly at every Body without Distinction, and using mean and foul Scurrilities.

to me, that, whomever I take or kill, his Arms I shall quietly possess.
Bentley having spoke thus, *Scaliger* bestowing him a sower Look;
Miscreant Prater, said he, *Eloquent only in thine own Eyes, Thou*
railest without Wit, or Truth, or Discretion. The Malignity of thy
Temper perverteth Nature; Thy Learning *makes thee more* Barbarous, *thy Study of* Humanity, *more* Inhuman; *Thy* Converse *amongst*
Poets more groveling, miry, *and* dull. *All Arts of* civilizing *others,*
render thee rude *and* untractable; Courts *have taught thee* ill Manners,
and polite Conversation *has finish'd thee a* Pedant. *Besides, a greater*
Coward burtheneth not the Army. But never despond, I pass my Word,
whatever Spoil thou takest, shall certainly be thy own; though, I hope,
that vile Carcass will first become a prey to Kites and Worms.

BENTLEY durst not reply; but half choaked with Spleen
and Rage, withdrew, in full Resolution of performing some
great Achievment. With him, for his Aid and Companion, he
took his beloved *Wotton*; resolving by Policy or Surprize, to
attempt some neglected Quarter of the *Antients* Army. They
began their March over Carcasses of their slaughtered Friends;
then to the Right of their own Forces: then wheeled Northward,
till they came to *Aldrovandus*'s Tomb, which they pass'd on the
side of the declining Sun. And now they arrived with Fear towards the Enemy's Out-guards; looking about, if haply, they
might spy the Quarters of the Wounded, or some straggling
Sleepers, unarm'd and remote from the rest. As when two
Mungrel-Curs, whom *native Greediness*, and *domestick Want*, provoke, and join in Partnership, though fearful, nightly to invade
the Folds of some rich Grazier; They, with Tails depress'd, and
lolling Tongues, creep soft and slow; mean while, the conscious
Moon, now in her *Zenith*, on their guilty Heads, darts perpendicular Rays; Nor dare they bark, though much provok'd at her
refulgent Visage, whether seen in Puddle by Reflexion, or in
Sphear direct; but one surveys the Region round, while t'other
scouts the Plain, if haply, to discover at distance from the Flock,
some *Carcass* half devoured, the Refuse of gorged Wolves, or
ominous Ravens. So march'd this lovely, loving Pair of Friends,
nor with less Fear and Circumspection; when, at distance, they
might perceive two shining Suits of Armor, hanging upon an
Oak, and the Owners not far off in a profound Sleep. The two

m

Friends drew Lots, and the pursuing of this Adventure, fell to *Bentley*; On he went, and in his Van *Confusion* and *Amaze*; while *Horror* and *Affright* brought up the Rear. As he came near; Behold two Hero's of the *Antients* Army, *Phalaris* and *Æsop*, lay fast asleep: *Bentley* would fain have dispatch'd them both, and stealing close, aimed his Flail at *Phalaris*'s Breast. But, then, the Goddess *Affright* interposing, caught the *Modern* in her icy Arms, and dragg'd him from the Danger she foresaw; For both the dormant Hero's happened to turn at the same Instant, tho' soundly Sleeping, and busy in a Dream. * For *Phalaris* was just that Minute dreaming, how a most vile *Poetaster* had lampoon'd him, and how he had got him roaring in his *Bull*. And *Æsop* dream'd, that as he and the *Antient Chiefs* were lying on the Ground, a *Wild Ass* broke loose, ran about trampling and kicking, and dunging in their Faces. *Bentley* leaving the two Hero's asleep, seized on both their Armors, and withdrew in quest of his Darling *Wotton*.

HE, in the mean time, had wandred long in search of some Enterprize, till at length, he arrived at a small *Rivulet*, that issued from a Fountain hard by, call'd in the Language of mortal Men, *Helicon*. Here he stopt, and, parch'd with thirst, resolved to allay it in this limpid Stream. Thrice, with profane Hands, he essay'd to raise the Water to his Lips, and thrice it slipt all thro' his Fingers. Then he stoop'd prone on his Breast, but e'er his Mouth had kiss'd the liquid Crystal, *Apollo* came, and, in the Channel, held his *Shield* betwixt the *Modern* and the Fountain, so that he drew up nothing but *Mud*. For, altho' no Fountain on Earth can compare with the Clearness of *Helicon*, yet there lies at Bottom, a thick sediment of *Slime* and *Mud*; For, so *Apollo* begg'd of *Jupiter*, as a Punishment to those who durst attempt to taste it with unhallowed Lips, and for a Lesson to all, not to *draw too deep*, or *far from the Spring*.

AT the Fountain Head, *Wotton* discerned two Hero's; The one he could not distinguish, but the other was soon known for *Temple*, General of the *Allies* to the *Antients*. His Back was

---

* *This is according to* Homer, *who tells the Dreams of those who were kill'd in their Sleep.*

turned, and he was employ'd in Drinking large Draughts in his Helmet, from the Fountain, where he had withdrawn himself to rest from the Toils of the War. *Wotton*, observing him, with quaking Knees, and trembling Hands, spoke thus to Himself: *Oh, that I could kill this Destroyer of our Army, what Renown should I purchase among the Chiefs! But to issue out against Him, Man for Man, Shield against Shield, and Launce*   Vid. Homer. *against Launce; what* Modern *of us dare? For, he fights like a God, and* Pallas *or* Apollo *are ever at his Elbow. But, Oh,* Mother! *if what Fame reports, be true, that I am the Son of so great a Goddess, grant me to Hit* Temple *with this Launce, that the Stroak may send Him to Hell, and that I may return in Safety and Triumph, laden with his Spoils.* The first Part of his Prayer, the Gods granted, at the Intercession of His *Mother* and of *Momus*; but the rest, by a perverse Wind sent from *Fate*, was scattered in the Air. Then *Wotton* grasp'd his Launce, and brandishing it thrice over his head, darted it with all his Might, the *Goddess*, his *Mother*, at the same time, adding Strength to his Arm. Away the Launce went hizzing, and reach'd even to the Belt of the averted *Antient*, upon which, lightly grazing, it fell to the Ground. *Temple* neither felt the Weapon touch him, nor heard it fall; And *Wotton*, might have escaped to his Army, with the Honor of having remitted his Launce against so great a Leader, unrevenged; But, *Apollo* enraged, that a Javelin, flung by the Assistance of so foul a *Goddess*, should pollute his Fountain, put on the shape of ———, and softly came to young *Boyle*, who then accompanied *Temple*: He pointed, first to the Launce, then to the distant *Modern* that flung it, and commanded the young Hero to take immediate Revenge. *Boyle*, clad in a suit of Armor which had been *given him by all the Gods*, immediately advanced against the trembling Foe, who now fled before him. As a young Lion, in the *Libyan Plains*, or *Araby Desart*, sent by his aged Sire to hunt for Prey, or Health, or Exercise; He scours along, wishing to meet some Tiger from the Mountains, or a furious Boar; If Chance, a *Wild Ass*, with Brayings importune, affronts his Ear, the generous Beast, though loathing to distain his Claws with Blood so vile, yet much provok'd at the offensive Noise; which *Echo*, foolish Nymph, like her *ill-judging Sex*, repeats much louder, and with

more Delight than *Philomela*'s Song: He vindicates the Honor of
the Forest, and hunts the noisy, long-ear'd Animal. So *Wotton*
fled, so *Boyle* pursued. But *Wotton* heavy-arm'd, and slow of foot,
began to slack his Course; when his Lover *Bentley* appeared,
returning laden with the Spoils of the two sleeping *Antients*.
Boyle observed him well, and soon discovering the Helmet and
Shield of *Phalaris*, his Friend, both which he had lately with his
own Hands, new polish'd and gilded; Rage sparkled in His
Eyes, and leaving his Pursuit after *Wotton*, he furiously rush'd
on against this new Approacher. Fain would he be revenged on
both; but both now fled different Ways: * And as   *Vid. Homer.*
a Woman in a little House, that gets a painful
Livelihood by Spinning; if chance her *Geese* be scattered o'er the
Common, she courses round the Plain from side to side, com-
pelling here and there, the Straglers to the Flock; They cackle
loud, and flutter o'er the Champain. So *Boyle* pursued, so fled
this Pair of Friends: finding at length, their Flight was vain, they
bravely joyn'd, and drew themselves in *Phalanx*. First, *Bentley*
threw a Spear with all his Force, hoping to pierce the Enemy's
Breast; But *Pallas* came unseen, and in the Air took off the
Point, and clap'd on one of *Lead*, which after a dead Bang against
the Enemy's Shield, fell blunted to the Ground. Then *Boyle* observing well his Time, took a Launce of wondrous Length and
sharpness; and as this Pair of Friends compacted stood close
Side to Side, he wheel'd him to the right, and with unusual
Force, darted the Weapon. *Bentley* saw his Fate approach, and
flanking down his Arms, close to his Ribs, hoping to save his
Body; in went the Point, passing through Arm and Side, nor
stopt, or spent its Force, till it had also pierc'd the valiant *Wotton*, who going to sustain his dying Friend, shared his Fate. As,
when a skilful Cook has truss'd a Brace of *Woodcocks*, He, with
Iron Skewer, pierces the tender Sides of both, their Legs and
Wings close pinion'd to their Ribs; So was this pair of Friends
transfix'd, till down they fell, joyn'd in their Lives, joyn'd in

---

* *This is also, after the manner of* Homer; *the Woman's getting a
painful Livelihood by Spinning, has nothing to do with the Similitude, nor
would be excusable without such an Authority.*

their Deaths; so closely joyn'd, that *Charon* would mistake them both for one, and waft them over *Styx* for half his Fare. Farewel, beloved, loving Pair; Few Equals have you left behind: And happy and immortal shall you be, if all my Wit and Eloquence can make you.

AND, now   *   *   *   *   *   *   *
*   *   *   *   *   *   *   *   *
*   *   *   *   *   *
*   *   *   *   *Desunt cætera.*

FINIS.

A
DISCOURSE
Concerning the

Mechanical Operation

OF THE
SPIRIT
IN A
LETTER
To a FRIEND.

A
FRAGMENT.

LONDON:
Printed in the Year, MDCCX.

THE

BOOKSELLER's
Advertisement.

THE *following Discourse came into my Hands perfect and entire.
But there being several Things in it, which the present Age
would not very well bear, I kept it by me some Years, resolving
it should never see the Light. At length, by the Advice and Assistance
of a judicious Friend, I retrench'd those Parts that might give most
Offence, and have now ventured to publish the Remainder; Concerning
the Author, I am wholly ignorant; neither can I conjecture, whether it be
the same with That of the two foregoing Pieces, the Original having been
sent me at a different Time, and in a different Hand. The Learned
Reader will better determine; to whose Judgment I entirely submit it.*

A DISCOURSE

Concerning the

Mechanical Operation of the

SPIRIT, &c.

For T.H. *Esquire, at his Chambers in the Academy of the* Beaux Esprits *in* New-Holland.

S I R,

IT is now a good while since I have had in my Head something, not only very material, but absolutely necessary to my Health, that the World should be informed in. For, to tell you a Secret, I am able to *contain* it no longer. However, I have been perplexed for some time, to resolve what would be the most proper Form to send it abroad in. To which End, I have three Days been coursing thro' *Westminster-Hall*, and St. *Paul*'s *Church-yard*, and *Fleet-street*, to peruse *Titles*; and, I do not find any which holds so general a Vogue, as that of *A Letter to a Friend*: Nothing is more common than to meet with long Epistles address'd to Persons and Places, where, at first thinking, one would be apt to imagine it not altogether so necessary or Convenient; Such as, *a Neighbour at next Door, a mortal Enemy, a perfect Stranger*, or *a*

This Discourse is not altogether equal to the two Former, the best Parts of it being omitted; whether the Bookseller's Account be true, that he durst not print the rest, I know not, nor indeed is it easie to determine whether he may be rely'd on, in any thing he says of this, or the former Treatises, only as to the Time they were writ in, which, however, appears more from the Discourses themselves than his Relation.

Person of Quality in the Clouds; and these upon Subjects, in appearance, the least proper for Conveyance by the Post; as, *long Schemes in Philosophy; dark and wonderful Mysteries of State; Laborious Dissertations in Criticism and Philosophy*, *Advice to Parliaments*, and the like.

Now, Sir, to proceed after the Method in present Wear. (For, let me say what I will to the contrary, I am afraid you will publish this *Letter*, as soon as ever it comes to your Hands;) I desire you will be my Witness to the World, how careless and sudden a Scribble it has been; That it was but Yesterday, when You and I began accidentally to fall into Discourse on this Matter: That I was not very well, when we parted; That the Post is in such haste, I have had no manner of Time to digest it into Order, or correct the Style; And if any other Modern Excuses, for Haste and Negligence, shall occur to you in Reading, I beg you to insert them, faithfully promising they shall be thankfully acknowledged.

PRAY, Sir, in your next Letter to the *Iroquois Virtuosi*, do me the Favour to present my humble Service to that illustrious Body, and assure them, I shall send an Account of those *Phænomena*, as soon as we can determine them at *Gresham*.

I have not had a Line from the *Literati* of *Tobinambou*, these three last Ordinaries.

AND now, Sir, having dispatch'd what I had to say of Forms, or of Business, let me intreat, you will suffer me to proceed upon my Subject; and to pardon me, if I make no farther Use of the Epistolary Stile, till I come to conclude.

SECTION I.

T IS recorded of *Mahomet*, that upon a Visit he was going to pay in *Paradise*, he had an Offer of several Vehicles to conduct him upwards; as fiery Chariots, wing'd Horses, and celestial Sedans; but he refused them all, and would be born to Heaven upon nothing but his *Ass*. Now, this Inclination of *Mahomet*, as singular as it seems, hath been since taken up by a great Number of devout *Christians*; and doubtless, with very good Reason. For, since That *Arabian* is known to have borrowed a Moiety of his Religious System from the *Christian* Faith; it is but just he should pay Reprisals to such as would Challenge them; wherein the good People of *England*, to do them all Right, have not been backward. For, tho' there is not any other Nation in the World, so plentifully provided with Carriages for that Journey, either as to Safety or Ease; yet there are abundance of us, who will not be satisfied with any other Machine, beside this of *Mahomet*.

For my own part, I must confess to bear a very singular Respect to this Animal, by whom I take human Nature to be most admirably held forth in all its Qualities as well as Operations: And therefore, whatever in my small Reading, occurs, concerning this our Fellow-Creature, I do never fail to set it down, by way of Common-place; and when I have occasion to write upon Human Reason, Politicks, Eloquence, or Knowledge; I lay my *Memorandums* before me, and insert them with a wonderful Facility of Application. However, among all the Qualifications, ascribed to this distinguish'd Brute, by Antient or Modern Authors; I cannot remember this Talent, of bearing his Rider to Heaven, has been recorded for a Part of his Character, except in the two Examples mentioned already; Therefore, I conceive the Methods of this Art, to be a Point of useful Knowledge in very few Hands, and which the Learned World would gladly be better informed in. This is what I have undertaken to perform in the following Discourse. For, towards the Operation already mentioned, many peculiar Properties are required, both in the *Rider* and the *Ass*; which I shall endeavour to set in as clear a Light as I can.

But, because I am resolved, by all means, to avoid giving Offence to any Party whatever; I will leave off discoursing so closely to the *Letter* as I have hitherto done, and go on for the future by way of Allegory, tho' in such a manner, that the judicious Reader, may without much straining, make his Applications as often as he shall think fit. Therefore, if you please from hence forward, instead of the Term, *Ass*, we shall make use of *Gifted*, or *enlightned Teacher*; And the Word *Rider*, we will exchange for that of *Fanatick Auditory*, or any other Denomination of the like Import. Having settled this weighty Point; the great Subject of Enquiry before us, is to examine, by what Methods this *Teacher* arrives at his *Gifts* or *Spirit*, or *Light*; and by what Intercourse between him and his Assembly, it is cultivated and supported.

IN all my Writings, I have had constant Regard to this great End, not to suit and apply them to particular Occasions and Circumstances of Time, of Place, or of Person; but to calculate them for universal Nature, and Mankind in general. And of such Catholick use, I esteem this present Disquisition: For I do not remember any other Temper of Body, or Quality of Mind, wherein all Nations and Ages of the World have so unanimously agreed, as That of a *Fanatick* Strain, or Tincture of *Enthusiasm*; which improved by certain Persons or Societies of Men, and by them practised upon the rest, has been able to produce Revolutions of the greatest Figure in History; as will soon appear to those who know any thing of *Arabia*, *Persia*, *India*, or *China*, of *Morocco* and *Peru*: Farther, it has possessed as great a Power in the Kingdom of Knowledge, where it is hard to assign one Art or Science, which has not annexed to it some *Fanatick* Branch: Such are the *Philosopher's Stone;* * *The Grand Elixir; The Planetary Worlds; The Squaring of the Circle; The Summum bonum*; Utopian *Commonwealths*; with some others of less or subordinate

* Some Writers hold them for the same, others not.

Note; which all serve for nothing else, but to employ or amuse this Grain of *Enthusiasm*, dealt into every Composition.

BUT, if this Plant has found a Root in the Fields of *Empire*, and of *Knowledge*, it has fixt deeper, and spread yet farther upon *Holy Ground*. Wherein, though it hath pass'd under the general Name of *Enthusiasm*, and perhaps arisen from the same Original, yet hath it produced certain Branches of a very different Nature, however often mistaken for each other. The Word in its universal Acceptation, may be defined, *A lifting up of the Soul or its Faculties above Matter*. This Description will hold good in general; but I am only to understand it, as applied to *Religion*; wherein there are three general Ways of ejaculating the Soul, or transporting it beyond the Sphere of Matter. The first, is the immediate Act of God, and is called, *Prophecy* or *Inspiration*. The second, is the immediate Act of the Devil, and is termed *Posses-sion*. The third, is the Product of natural Causes, the effect of strong Imagination, Spleen, violent Anger, Fear, Grief, Pain, and the like. These three have been abundantly treated on by Authors, and therefore shall not employ my Enquiry. But, the fourth Method of *Religious Enthusiasm*, or launching out the Soul, as it is purely an Effect of Artifice and *Mechanick Operation*, has been sparingly handled, or not at all, by any Writer; because tho' it is an Art of great Antiquity, yet having been confined to few Persons, it long wanted those Advancements and Refine-ments, which it afterwards met with, since it has grown so Epidemick, and fallen into so many cultivating Hands.

It is therefore upon this *Mechanical Operation of the Spirit*, that I mean to treat, as it is at present performed by our *British Workmen*. I shall deliver to the Reader the Result of many judi-cious Observations upon the Matter; tracing, as near as I can, the whole Course and Method of this *Trade*, producing parallel Instances, and relating certain Discoveries that have luckily fal-len in my way.

I have said, that there is one Branch of *Religious Enthusiasm*, which is purely an Effect of Nature; whereas, the Part I mean to handle, is wholly an Effect of Art, which, however, is inclined to work upon certain Natures and Constitutions, more than others. Besides, there is many an Operation, which in its Original, was purely an Artifice, but through a long Succession of Ages, hath grown to be natural. *Hippocrates*, tells us, that among our Ances-tors, the *Scythians*, there was a Nation call'd, * Longheads, which at first began by a Custom   * *Macrocephali.* among Midwives and Nurses, of molding, and squeezing, and bracing up the Heads of Infants; by which means, Nature shut out at one Passage, was forc'd to seek another, and finding room above, shot upwards, in the Form of a Sugar-Loaf; and being diverted that way, for some Generations, at last found it out of her self, needing no Assistance from the Nurse's Hand. This was the Original of the *Scythian Long-heads*, and thus did Custom, from being a second Nature proceed to be a first. To all which, there is something very analogous among Us of this Nation, who are the undoubted Posterity of that refined People. For, in the Age of our Fathers, there arose a Generation of Men in this Island, call'd *Round-heads*, whose Race is now spread over three Kingdoms, yet in its Beginning, was meerly an Operation of Art, produced by a pair of Cizars, a Squeeze of the Face, and a black Cap. These Heads, thus formed into a perfect Sphere in all Assemblies, were most exposed to the view of the Female Sort, which did influence their Conceptions so effectually, that Nature, at last, took the Hint, and did it of her self; so that a *Round-head* has been ever since as familiar a Sight among Us, as a *Long-head* among the *Scythians*.

UPON these Examples, and others easy to produce, I desire the curious Reader to distinguish, First between an Effect grown from *Art* into *Nature*, and one that is natural from its Beginning; Secondly, between an Effect wholly natural, and one which has only a natural Foundation, but where the Superstructure is entirely Artificial. For, the first and the last of these, I understand to come within the Districts of my Subject. And having obtained these allowances, they will serve to remove any objections that may be raised hereafter against what I shall advance.

THE Practitioners of this famous Art, proceed in general upon the following Fundamental; That, *the Corruption of the Senses is the Generation of the Spirit*: Because the *Senses* in Men are so many Avenues to the Fort of *Reason*, which in this Operation is wholly block'd up. All Endeavours must be therefore used, either to divert, bind up, stupify, fluster, and amuse the *Senses*, or else to justle them out of their Stations; and while they are either absent, or otherwise employ'd or engaged in a Civil War against each other, the *Spirit* enters and performs its Part.

Now, the usual Methods of managing the Senses upon such Conjunctures, are what I shall be very particular in delivering, as far as it is lawful for me to do; but having had the Honour to be Initiated into the Mysteries of every Society, I desire to be excused from divulging any Rites, wherein the *Profane* must have no Part.

BUT here, before I can proceed farther, a very dangerous Objection must, if possible, be removed: For, it is positively denied by certain Criticks, that the *Spirit* can by any means be introduced into an Assembly of Modern Saints, the Disparity

being so great in many material Circumstances, between the
Primitive Way of Inspiration, and that which is practised in the
present Age. This they pretend to prove from the second Chapter of the *Acts*, where comparing both, it appears; First, that *the
Apostles were gathered together with one accord in one place*; by which
is meant, an universal Agreement in Opinion, and Form of
Worship; a Harmony (say they) so far from being found between any two Conventicles among Us, that it is in vain to expect
it between any two Heads in the same. Secondly, the *Spirit* instructed the Apostles in the Gift of speaking several Languages;
a Knowledge so remote from our Dealers in this Art, that they
neither understand Propriety of Words, or Phrases in their own.
Lastly, (say these Objectors) The Modern Artists do utterly
exclude all Approaches of the *Spirit*, and bar up its antient Way
of entring, by covering themselves so close, and so industriously
a top. For, they will needs have it as a Point clearly gained, that
the *Cloven Tongues* never sat upon the Apostles Heads, while
their Hats were on.

Now, the Force of these Objections, seems to consist in the
different Acceptation of the Word, *Spirit*: which if it be understood for a supernatural Assistance, approaching from without,
the Objectors have Reason, and their Assertions may be allowed;
But the *Spirit* we treat of here, proceeding entirely from within,
the Argument of these Adversaries is wholly eluded. And upon
the same Account, our Modern Artificers, find it an Expedient
of absolute Necessity, to cover their Heads as close as they can,
in order to prevent Perspiration, than which nothing is observed
to be a greater Spender of Mechanick Light, as we may, perhaps,
farther shew in convenient Place.

To proceed therefore upon the *Phænomenon* of *Spiritual Mechanism*, It is here to be noted, that in forming and working up the
Spirit, the Assembly has a considerable Share, as well as the
Preacher; The Method of this *Arcanum*, is as follows. They
violently strain their Eye balls inward, half closing the Lids;
Then, as they sit, they are in a perpetual Motion of *See-saw*,
making long Hums at proper Periods, and continuing the
Sound at equal Height, chusing their Time in those Intermis-
sions, while the Preacher is at Ebb. Neither is this Practice, in

n

any part of it, so singular or improbable, as not to be traced in distant Regions, from Reading and Observation. For, first, the * *Jauguis*, or enlightened Saints of *India*, see all their Visions, by help of an acquired straining and pressure of the Eyes. Secondly, the Art of *See-saw* on a Beam, and swinging by Session upon a Cord, in order to raise artificial Extasies, hath been derived to Us, from our † *Scythian* Ancestors, where it is practised at this Day, among the Women. Lastly, the whole Proceeding, as I have here related it, is performed by the Natives of *Ireland*, with a considerable Improvement; And it is granted, that this noble Nation, hath of all others, admitted fewer Corruptions, and degenerated least from the Purity of the Old *Tartars*. Now it is usual for a Knot of *Irish*, Men and Women, to abstract themselves from Matter, bind up all their Senses, grow visionary and spiritual, by Influence of a short Pipe of Tobacco, handed round the Company; each preserving the Smoak in his Mouth, till it comes again to his Turn to take in fresh: At the same Time, there is a Consort of a continued gentle Hum, repeated and renewed by Instinct, as Occasion requires, and they move their Bodies up and down, to a Degree, that sometimes their Heads and Points lie parallel to the Horizon. Mean while, you may observe their Eyes turn'd up in the Posture of one, who endeavours to keep himself awake; by which, and many other Symptoms among them, it manifestly appears, that the Reasoning Faculties are all suspended and superseded, that Imagination hath usurped the Seat, scattering a thousand Deliriums over the Brain. Returning from this Digression, I shall describe the Methods, by which the *Spirit* approaches. The Eyes being disposed according to Art, at first, you can see nothing, but after a short pause, a small glimmering Light begins to appear, and dance before you. Then, by frequently moving your Body up and down, you perceive the Vapors to ascend very fast, till you are perfectly dosed and flustred like one who drinks too much in a Morning. Mean while, the Preacher is also at work; He begins a loud Hum, which pierces you quite thro'; This is immediately returned by the Audience, and you find your self prompted to imitate them, by a meer spontaneous Impulse, without knowing what you do.

Marginal notes:
* *Bernier, Mem. de Mogol.*
† *Guagnini Hist. Sarmat.*

The *Interstitia* are duly filled up by the Preacher, to prevent too long a Pause, under which the *Spirit* would soon faint and grow languid.

THIS is all I am allowed to discover about the Progress of the *Spirit*, with relation to that part, which is born by the *Assembly*; But in the Methods of the Preacher, to which I now proceed, I shall be more large and particular.

SECTION II.

YOU will read it very gravely remarked in the Books of those illustrious and right eloquent Pen-men, the Modern Travellers; that the fundamental Difference in Point of Religion, between the wild *Indians* and Us, lies in this; that We worship *God*, and they worship the *Devil*. But, there are certain Criticks, who will by no means admit of this Distinction; rather believing, that all Nations whatsoever, adore the *true God*, because, they seem to intend their Devotions to some invisible Power, of greatest *Goodness* and *Ability* to help them, which perhaps will take in the brightest Attributes ascribed to the Divinity. Others, again, inform us, that those Idolaters adore two *Principles*; the *Principle* of *Good*, and That of *Evil*: Which indeed, I am apt to look upon as the most Universal Notion, that Mankind, by the meer Light of Nature, ever entertained of Things Invisible. How this Idea hath been managed by the *Indians* and Us, and with what Advantage to the Understandings of either, may well deserve to be examined. To me, the difference appears little more than this, That They are put oftener upon their Knees by their *Fears*, and We by our *Desires*; That the former set them a *Praying*, and Us a *Cursing*. What I applaud them for, is their Discretion, in limiting their Devotions and their Deities to their several Districts, nor ever suffering the Liturgy of the *white* God, to cross or interfere with that of the *Black*. Not so with Us, who pretending by the Lines and Measures of our Reason, to extend the Dominion of one invisible Power, and contract that of the other, have discovered a gross Ignorance in the Natures of Good and Evil, and most horribly confounded the Frontiers of both.

After Men have lifted up the Throne of their Divinity to the *Cælum Empyræum*, adorned him with all such Qualities and Accomplishments, as themselves seem most to value and possess: After they have sunk their *Principle* of *Evil* to the lowest Center, bound him with Chains, loaded him with Curses, furnish'd him with viler Dispositions than any *Rake-hell* of the Town, accoutred him with Tail, and Horns, and huge Claws, and Sawcer Eyes; I laugh aloud, to see these Reasoners, at the same time, engaged in wise Dispute, about certain Walks and Purlieus, whether they are in the Verge of God or the Devil, seriously debating, whether such and such Influences come into Mens Minds, from above or below, or whether certain Passions and Affections are guided by the Evil Spirit or the Good.

> *Dum fas atque nefas exiguo fine libidinum*
> *Discernunt avidi——*

Thus do Men establish a Fellowship of *Christ* with *Belial*, and such is the Analogy they make between *cloven Tongues*, and *cloven Feet*. Of the like Nature is the Disquisition before us: It hath continued these hundred Years an even Debate, whether the Deportment and the Cant of our *English* Enthusiastick Preachers, were *Possession*, or *Inspiration*, and a World of Argument has been drained on either side, perhaps, to little Purpose. For, I think, it is in *Life* as in *Tragedy*, where, it is held, a Conviction of great Defect, both in Order and Invention, to interpose the Assistance of preternatural Power, without an absolute and last Necessity. However, it is a Sketch of Human Vanity, for every Individual, to imagine the whole Universe is interess'd in his meanest Concern. If he hath got cleanly over a Kennel, some Angel, unseen, descended on purpose to help him by the Hand; if he hath knockt his Head against a Post, it was the Devil, for his Sins, let loose from Hell, on purpose to buffet him. Who, that sees a little paultry Mortal, droning, and dreaming, and drivelling to a Multitude, can think it agreeable to common good Sense, that either Heaven or Hell should be put to the Trouble of Influence or Inspection upon what he is about? Therefore, I am resolved immediately, to weed this Error out of Mankind, by making it clear, that this Mystery, of venting spiritual Gifts is nothing but a *Trade*, acquired by as much Instruction, and mastered by equal Practice and Application as others are. This will best appear, by describing and deducing the whole Process of the Operation, as variously as it hath fallen under my Knowledge or Experience.

* * * * * * * * * *
* * * * * * * * * *
* * * * * * * *Here the whole Scheme*
* * * * * * * *of spiritual Mechanism*
* * * * * * * *was deduced and ex-*
* * * * * * * *plained, with an Appear-*
* * * * * * * *ance of great reading and*
* * * * * * * *observation; but it was*
* * * * * * * *thought neither safe nor*
* * * * * * * *Convenient to Print it.*
* * * * * * * * * *

HERE it may not be amiss, to add a few Words upon the laudable Practice of wearing *quilted Caps*; which is not a Matter of meer Custom, Humor, or Fashion, as some would pretend, but an Institution of great Sagacity and Use; these, when moistned with Sweat, stop all Perspiration, and by reverberating the Heat, prevent the Spirit from evaporating any way, but at the Mouth; even as a skilful Housewife, that covers her Still with a wet Clout, for the same Reason, and finds the same Effect. For, it is the Opinion of Choice *Virtuosi*, that the Brain is only a Crowd of little Animals, but with Teeth and Claws extremely sharp, and therefore, cling together in the Contexture we behold, like the Picture of *Hobbes*'s *Leviathan*, or like Bees in perpendicular swarm upon a Tree, or like a Carrion corrupted into Vermin, still preserving the Shape and Figure of the Mother Animal. That all Invention is formed by the Morsure of two or more of these Animals, upon certain capillary Nerves, which proceed from thence, whereof three Branches spread into the Tongue, and two into the right Hand. They hold also, that these Animals are of a Constitution extremely cold; that their Food is the Air we attract, their Excrement Phlegm; and that what we vulgarly call Rheums, and Colds, and Distillations, is nothing else but an Epidemical Looseness, to which that little Commonwealth is very subject, from the Climate it lyes under. Farther, that nothing less than a violent Heat, can disentangle these Creatures from their hamated Station of Life, or give them Vigor and Humor, to imprint the Marks of their little Teeth. That if the Morsure be Hexagonal, it produces Poetry; the Circular gives Eloquence; If the Bite hath been Conical, the Person, whose Nerve is so affected, shall be disposed to write upon the Politicks; and so of the rest.

I shall now Discourse briefly, by what kind of Practices the Voice is best governed, towards the Composition and Improvement of the *Spirit*; for, without a competent Skill in tuning and toning each Word, and Syllable, and Letter, to their due Cadence, the whole Operation is incompleat, misses entirely of its effect on the Hearers, and puts the Workman himself to continual Pains for new Supplies, without Success. For, it is to be understood, that in the Language of the Spirit, *Cant* and *Droning* supply the Place of *Sense* and *Reason*, in the Language of Men: Because, in Spiritual Harangues, the Disposition of the Words according to the Art of Grammar, hath not the least Use, but the Skill and Influence wholly lye in the Choice and Cadence of the Syllables; Even as a discreet *Composer*, who in setting a Song, changes the Words and Order so often, that he is forced to make it *Nonsense*, before he can make it *Musick*. For this Reason, it hath been held by some, that the Art of Canting is ever in greatest Perfection, when managed by *Ignorance*: Which is thought to be enigmatically meant by *Plutarch*, when he tells us, that the best Musical Instruments were made from the Bones of an *Ass*. And the profounder Criticks upon that Passage, are of Opinion, the Word in its genuine Signification, means no other than a *Jaw-bone*: tho' some rather think it to have been the *Os sacrum*; but in so nice a Case, I shall not take upon me to decide: The Curious are at Liberty, to *pick* from it whatever they please.

THE first Ingredient, towards the Art of Canting, is a competent Share of *Inward Light*: that is to say, a large Memory, plentifully fraught with Theological Polysyllables, and mysterious Texts from holy Writ, applied and digested by those Methods, and Mechanical Operations already related: The Bearers of this *Light*, resembling *Lanthorns*, compact of Leaves from old *Geneva* Bibles; Which Invention, Sir *Humphry Edwyn*, during his Mayoralty, of happy Memory, highly approved and advanced; affirming, the Scripture to be now fulfilled, where it says, *Thy Word is a Lanthorn to my Feet, and a Light to my Paths.*

Now, the Art of *Canting* consists in skilfully adapting the Voice, to whatever Words the Spirit delivers, that each may strike the Ears of the Audience, with its most significant Cadence. The Force, or Energy of this Eloquence, is not to be found, as among antient Orators, in the Disposition of Words to a Sentence, or the turning of long Periods; but agreeable to the Modern Refinements in Musick, is taken up wholly in dwelling, and dilating upon Syllables and Letters. Thus it is frequent for a single *Vowel* to draw Sighs from a Multitude; and for a whole Assembly of Saints to sob to the Musick of one solitary *Liquid.* But these are Trifles; when even Sounds inarticulate are observed to produce as forcible Effects. A Master Work-man shall *blow his Nose so powerfully*, as to pierce the Hearts of his People, who are disposed to receive the *Excrements* of his Brain with the same Reverence, as the *Issue* of it. Hawking, Spitting, and Belching, the Defects of other Mens Rhetorick, are the Flowers, and Figures, and Ornaments of his. For, the *Spirit* being the same in all, it is of no Import through what Vehicle it is convey'd.

It is a Point of too much Difficulty, to draw the Principles of this famous Art within the Compass of certain adequate Rules. However, perhaps, I may one day, oblige the World with my Critical Essay upon the Art of *Canting, Philosophically, Physically, and Musically considered.*

But, among all Improvements of the *Spirit*, wherein the Voice hath born a Part, there is none to be compared with That of *conveying the Sound thro' the Nose*, which under the Denomination of **Snuffling*, hath passed with so great Applause in the World. The Originals of this Institution are very dark; but having been initiated into the Mystery of it, and Leave being given me to publish it to the World, I shall deliver as direct a Relation as I can.

This Art, like many other famous Inventions, owed its Birth, or at least, Improvement and Perfection, to an Effect of Chance,

---

* *The* Snuffling *of Men, who have lost their Noses by lewd Courses, is said to have given Rise to that Tone, which our Dissenters did too much Affect.* W. Wotton.

but was established upon solid Reasons, and hath flourished in this Island ever since, with great Lustre. All agree, that it first appeared upon the Decay and Discouragement of *Bag-pipes*, which having long suffered under the Mortal Hatred of the *Brethren*, tottered for a Time, and at last fell with *Monarchy*. The Story is thus related.

As yet, *Snuffling* was not; when the following Adventure happened to a *Banbury Saint*. Upon a certain Day, while he was far engaged among the Tabernacles of the *Wicked*, he felt the Outward Man put into odd Commotions, and strangely prick'd forward by the Inward: An Effect very usual among the Modern Inspired. For, some think, that the *Spirit* is apt to feed on the *Flesh*, like hungry Wines upon raw Beef. Others rather believe, there is a perpetual Game at *Leap-Frog* between both; and, sometimes, the *Flesh* is uppermost, and sometimes the *Spirit*; adding, that the former, while it is in the State of a *Rider*, wears huge *Rippon* Spurs, and when it comes to the Turn of being *Bearer*, is wonderfully headstrong, and hard-mouth'd. However it came about, the *Saint* felt his *Vessel* full *extended* in every Part (a very natural Effect of strong *Inspiration*;) and the Place and Time falling out so unluckily, that he could not have the Convenience of Evacuating upwards, by Repetition, Prayer, or Lecture; he was forced to open an inferior Vent. In short, he wrestled with the Flesh so long, that he at length subdued it, coming off with honourable Wounds, all *before*. The Surgeon had now cured the Parts, primarily affected; but the Disease driven from its Post, flew up into his Head; And, as a skilful General, valiantly attack'd in his Trenches, and beaten from the Field, by flying Marches withdraws to the Capital City, breaking down the Bridges to prevent Pursuit; So the Disease repell'd from its first Station, fled before the *Rod* of *Hermes*, to the upper Region, there fortifying it self; but, finding the Foe making Attacks at the *Nose*, broke down the *Bridge*, and retir'd to the *Head*-Quarters. Now, the Naturalists observe, that there is in human Noses, an *Idiosyncrasy*, by Virtue of which, the more the Passage is obstructed, the more our Speech delights to go through, as the Musick of a Flagelate is made by the *Stops*. By this Method, the Twang of the Nose, becomes perfectly to resemble the *Snuffle* of a Bag-pipe, and is found to be equally attractive of *British* Ears; whereof the Saint had sudden Experience, by practising his new Faculty with wonderful Success in the Operation of the *Spirit*: For, in a short Time, no Doctrine pass'd for Sound and Orthodox, unless it were delivered thro' the Nose. Strait, every Pastor copy'd after this Original; and those, who could not otherwise arrive to a Perfection, spirited by a noble Zeal, made use of the same Experiment to acquire it. So that, I think, it may be truly affirmed, the *Saints* owe their Empire to the *Snuffling* of one *Animal*, as *Darius* did his, to the *Neighing* of another; and both Stratagems were performed by the same Art; for we read, how the * *Persian Beast* acquired his Faculty, by *covering a Mare* the Day   * *Herodot.* Before.

I should now have done, if I were not convinced, that whatever I have yet advanced upon this Subject, is liable to great Exception. For, allowing all I have said to be true, it may still be justly objected, that there is in the Commonwealth of *artificial Enthusiasm*, some real Foundation for Art to work upon in the Temper and Complexion of Individuals, which other Mortals seem to want. Observe, but the Gesture, the Motion, and the Countenance, of some choice Professors, tho' in their most familiar Actions, you will find them of a different Race from the rest of human Creatures. Remark your commonest Pretender to a Light *within*, how dark, and dirty, and gloomy he is *without*; As Lanthorns, which the more Light they bear in their Bodies, cast out so much the more Soot, and Smoak, and fuliginous Matter to adhere to the Sides. Listen, but to their ordinary Talk, and look on the Mouth that delivers it; you will imagine you are hearing some antient Oracle, and your Understanding will be *equally* informed. Upon these, and the like Reasons, certain Objectors pretend to put it beyond all Doubt, that there must be a sort of preternatural *Spirit*, possessing the Heads of the Modern Saints; And some will have it to be the *Heat* of Zeal, working upon the *Dregs* of Ignorance, as other *Spirits* are produced from *Lees*, by the Force of Fire. Some again think, that when our earthly Tabernacles are disordered and desolate, shaken and out of Repair; the *Spirit* delights to dwell within them, as Houses are said to be haunted, when they are forsaken and gone to Decay.

To set this Matter in as fair a Light as possible; I shall here, very briefly, deduce the History of *Fanaticism*, from the most early Ages to the present. And if we are able to fix upon any one material or fundamental Point, wherein the chief Professors have universally agreed, I think we may reasonably lay hold on That, and assign it for the great Seed or Principle of the *Spirit*.

THE most early Traces we meet with, of *Fanaticks*, in antient Story, are among the *Ægyptians*, who instituted those Rites, known in *Greece* by the Names of *Orgya*, *Panegyres*, and *Dionysia*, whether introduced there by *Orpheus* or *Melampus*, we shall not

Diod. Sic. L. 1. Plut. de Iside & Osyride. dispute at present, nor in all likelihood, at any time for the future. These Feasts were celebrated to the Honor of *Osyris*, whom the *Grecians* called *Dionysius*, and is the same with *Bacchus*: Which has betray'd some superficial Readers to imagine, that the whole Business was nothing more than a Set of roaring, scouring Companions, overcharg'd with Wine; but this is a scandalous Mistake foisted on the World, by a sort of Modern Authors, who have too *literal* an Understanding; and, because Antiquity is to be traced *backwards*, do therefore, like *Jews*, begin their Books at the wrong End, as if Learning were a sort of *Conjuring*. These are the Men, who pretend to understand a Book, by scouting thro' the *Index*, as if a Traveller should go about to describe a *Palace*, when he had seen nothing but the *Privy*; or like certain Fortune-tellers in *Northern America*, who have a Way of reading a Man's Destiny, by peeping in his *Breech*. For, at the Time of instituting these

* Herod. L. 2. Mysteries, * there was not one Vine in all *Egypt*, the Natives drinking nothing but *Ale*; which Liquor seems to have been far more antient than Wine, and has the Honor of owing its Invention and Progress, not only to the

† Diod. Sic. L. 1. & 3. † *Egyptian Osyris*, but to the *Grecian Bacchus*, who in their famous Expedition, carried the Receipt of it along with them, and gave it to the Nations they visited or subdued. Besides, *Bacchus* himself, was very seldom, or never

* Id. L. 4. Drunk: For, it is recorded of him, that he was the first * Inventor of the *Mitre*, which he wore con-

tinually on his Head (as the whole Company of *Bacchanals* did)
to prevent Vapors and the Head-ach, after hard Drinking. And
for this Reason (say some) the *Scarlet Whore*, when she makes the
Kings of the Earth drunk with her Cup of Abomination, is always sober her self, tho' she never balks the Glass in her Turn,
being, it seems, kept upon her Legs by the Virtue of her *Triple
Mitre*. Now, these Feasts were instituted in imitation of the
famous Expedition *Osyris* made thro' the World, and of the
Company that attended him, whereof the *Bac-*   *See the Particu-*
chanalian Ceremonies were so many Types and   *lars in* Diod. Sic.
Symbols. From which Account, it is manifest,   L. 1. *&* 3.
that the Fanatick Rites of these *Bacchanals*, cannot be imputed to
Intoxications by Wine, but must needs have had a deeper Foun-
dation. What this was, we may gather large Hints from certain
Circumstances in the Course of their Mysteries. For, in the first
Place, there was in their Processions, an entire *Mixture and Con-
fusion of Sexes*; they affected to ramble about Hills and Desarts:
Their Garlands were of *Ivy* and *Vine*, Emblems of Cleaving and
Clinging; or of *Fir*, the Parent of *Turpentine*. It is added, that
they imitated *Satyrs*, were attended by *Goats*, and rode upon
Asses, all Companions of great Skill and Practice in Affairs of
Gallantry. They bore for their Ensigns, certain curious Figures,
perch'd upon long Poles, made into the Shape and Size of the
Virga genitalis, with its *Appurtenances*, which were so many
Shadows and Emblems of the whole Mystery, as well as Trophies set up by the Female Conquerors. Lastly, in a certain
Town of *Attica*, the whole Solemnity * strip't   * *Dionysia*
of all its Types, was performed in *puris naturali-*   *Brauronia.*
bus, the Votaries, not flying in Coveys, but sorted into Couples.
The same may be farther conjectured from the Death of *Orpheus*,
one of the Institutors of these Mysteries, who was torn in Pieces
by Women, because he refused to † *communicate*   † *Vid. Pho-*
his *Orgyes* to them; which others explained, by   *tium in excer-*
telling us, he had *castrated* himself upon Grief,   *ptis è Conone.*
for the Loss of his Wife.

OMITTING many others of less Note, the next *Fanaticks* we
meet with, of any Eminence, were the numerous Sects of *Hereticks* appearing in the five first Centuries of the *Christian Æra*,

from *Simon Magus* and his Followers, to those of *Eutyches*. I have collected their Systems from infinite Reading, and comparing them with those of their Successors in the several Ages since, I find there are certain Bounds set even to the Irregularities of Human Thought, and those a great deal narrower than is commonly apprehended. For, as they all frequently interfere, even in their wildest Ravings; So there is one fundamental Point, wherein they are sure to meet, as Lines in a Center, and that is the *Community of Women*: Great were their Sollicitudes in this Matter, and they never fail'd of certain Articles in their Schemes of Worship, on purpose to establish it.

THE last *Fanaticks* of Note, were those which started up in *Germany*, a little after the *Reformation* of *Luther*; Springing, as *Mushrooms* do at the *End of a Harvest*; Such were *John* of *Leyden*, *David George*, *Adam Neuster*, and many others; whose Visions and Revelations, always terminated in *leading about half a dozen Sisters, apiece*, and making That Practice a fundamental Part of their System. For, Human Life is a continual Navigation, and, if we expect our *Vessels* to pass with Safety, thro' the Waves and Tempests of this fluctuating World, it is necessary to make a good Provision of the *Flesh*, as Sea-men lay in store of *Beef* for a long Voyage.

Now from this brief Survey of some Principal Sects, among the *Fanaticks*, in all Ages (having omitted the *Mahometans* and others, who might also help to confirm the Argument I am about) to which I might add several among our selves, such as the *Family of Love*, *Sweet Singers of Israel*, and the like: And from reflecting upon that fundamental Point in their Doctrines, about *Women*, wherein they have so unanimously agreed; I am apt to imagine, that the Seed or Principle, which has ever put Men upon *Visions* in Things *Invisible*, is of a Corporeal Nature: For the profounder Chymists inform us, that the Strongest *Spirits* may be extracted from *Human Flesh*. Besides, the Spinal Marrow, being nothing else but a Continuation of the Brain, must needs create a very free Communication between the Superior Faculties and those below: And thus the *Thorn in the Flesh* serves for a *Spur* to the *Spirit*. I think, it is agreed among Physicians, that nothing affects the Head so much, as a tentiginous Humor, re pelled and elated to the upper Region, found by daily practice, to run frequently up into Madness. A very eminent Member of the Faculty, assured me, that when the *Quakers* first appeared, he seldom was without some Female Patients among them, for the *furor*———. Persons of a visionary Devotion, either Men or Women, are in their Complexion, of all others, the most amorous: For, *Zeal* is frequently kindled from the same Spark with other Fires, and from inflaming Brotherly Love, will proceed to raise That of a Gallant. If we inspect into the usual Process of modern Courtship, we shall find it to consist in a devout Turn of the Eyes, called *Ogling*; an artificial Form of Canting and Whining by rote, every Interval, for want of other Matter, made up with a Shrug, or a Hum, a Sigh or a Groan; The Style compact of insignificant Words, Incoherences and Repetition. These, I take, to be the most accomplish'd Rules of Address to a Mistress; and where are these performed with more Dexterity, than by the *Saints*? Nay, to bring this Argument yet closer, I have been informed by certain Sanguine Brethren of the first Class, that in the Height and *Orgasmus* of their Spiritual exercise it has been frequent with them * * * * * ; immediately after which, they found the *Spirit* to relax and flag of a sudden with the Nerves, and they were forced to hasten to a Conclusion. This may be farther Strengthened, by observing, with Wonder, how unaccountably all Females are attracted by Visionary or Enthusiastick Preachers, tho' never so contemptible in their *outward Men*; which is usually supposed to be done upon Considerations, purely Spiritual, without any carnal Regards at all. But I have Reason to think, the *Sex* hath certain Characteristicks, by which they form a truer Judgment of Human Abilities and Performings, than we our selves can possibly do of each other. Let That be as it will, thus much is certain, that however Spiritual Intrigues begin, they generally conclude like all others; they may branch upwards toward Heaven, but the Root is in the Earth. Too intense a Contemplation is not the Business of Flesh and Blood; it must by the necessary Course of Things, in a little Time, let go its Hold, and fall into *Matter*. Lovers, for the sake of Celestial Converse, are but another sort of *Platonicks*, who pretend to see Stars and Heaven in Ladies Eyes, and to look or think no lower; but the same *Pit* is provided for both; and they seem a perfect Moral to the Story of that Philosopher, who, while his Thoughts and Eyes were fixed upon the *Constellations*, found himself seduced by his *lower Parts* into a *Ditch*.

I had somewhat more to say upon this Part of the Subject; but the Post is just going, which forces me in great Haste to conclude,

S I R,

Yours, &c.

*Pray, burn this
   Letter as soon
   as it comes to
   your Hands.*

F I N I S.

A Discourse *of the* Contests *and* Dissentions *in* Athens *&* Rome

A

DISCOURSE

OF THE

Contests and *Dissensions*

BETWEEN THE

NOBLES and the COMMONS

I N

ATHENS and *ROME*,

WITH THE

Consequences they had upon both those

STATES.

————Si tibi vera videtur
Dede manus; & si falsa est accingere contra.   Lucret.

LONDON:

Printed for *John Nutt* near *Stationers-Hall.*   1701.

o

A

DISCOURSE

OF THE

Contests and *Dissentions*

BETWEEN THE

NOBLES and the COMMONS in *Athens*
and *Rome* ; with the Consequences they had
upon both those STATES.

—— *Si tibi vera videtur,*
Dede manus ; & si falsa est, accingere contra.
LUCRET.

Written in the Year 1701.

CHAP. I.

IT is agreed, that in all Government there is an absolute unlimited Power, which naturally and originally seems to be
placed in the whole Body, wherever the executive Part of it
lies. This holds in the Body natural: For wherever we place the
Beginning of Motion, whether from the Head, or the Heart, or
the animal Spirits in general, the Body moves, and acts by a
Consent of all its Parts. This unlimited Power placed funda-
mentally in the Body of a People, is what the best Legislators of
all Ages have endeavoured, in their several Schemes, or Institutions of Government, to deposite in such Hands as would preserve the People from Rapine, and Oppression within, as well

as Violence from without. Most of them seem to agree in this; that it was a Trust too great to be committed to any one Man, or Assembly; and therefore they left the Right still in the whole Body; but the Administration, or executive Part, in the Hands of *One*, the *Few*, or the *Many*: Into which three Powers, all independent Bodies of Men seem naturally to divide. For by all I have read of those innumerable and petty Common-wealths in *Italy*, *Greece*, and *Sicily*, as well as the great ones of *Carthage* and *Rome*; it seems to me, that a free People met together, whether by *Compact* or *Family Government*, as soon as they fall into any Acts of Civil Society, do, of themselves, divide into three Powers. The first is, that of some one eminent Spirit, who having signalized his Valour, and Fortune in Defence of his Country, or by the Practice of popular Arts at home, becomes to have great Influence on the People, to grow their Leader in warlike Expeditions, and to preside, after a sort, in their Civil Assemblies: And this is grounded upon the Principles of Nature and common Reason, which in all Difficulties and Dangers, where Prudence or Courage is required, do rather incite us to fly for Counsel or Assistance to a single Person than a Multitude. The second natural Division of Power, is of such Men who have acquired large Possessions, and consequently Dependances, or descend from Ancestors, who have left them great Inheritances, together with an Hereditary Authority: These easily uniting in Thoughts and Opinions, and acting in Concert, begin to enter upon Measures for securing their Properties; which are best upheld by preparing against Invasions from Abroad, and maintaining Peace at Home. This commences a great Council, or Senate of Nobles for the weighty Affairs of the Nation. The last Division is of the Mass, or Body of the People; whose Part of Power is great, and undisputable, whenever they can unite either collectively, or by Deputation to exert it. Now the three Forms of Government, so generally known in the Schools, differ only by the Civil Administration being placed in the Hands of One, or sometimes Two, (as in *Sparta*) who were called *Kings*; or in a Senate, who were called the *Nobles*; or in the People Collective or Representative, who may be called the *Commons*: Each of these had frequently the executive Power in *Greece*, and sometimes in *Rome*: But the

Power in the last Resort, was always meant by Legislators to be held in Ballance among all Three. And it will be an eternal Rule in Politicks, among every free People, that there is a Ballance of Power to be carefully held by every State within it self, as well as among several States with each other.

THE true Meaning of a Ballance of Power, either without, or within a State, is best conceived by considering what the Nature of a Ballance is. It supposes three Things. First, the Part which is held, together with the Hand that holds it; and then the two Scales, with whatever is weighed therein. Now consider several States in a Neighbourhood: In order to preserve Peace between these States, it is necessary they should be formed into a Ballance, whereof one, or more are to be Directors, who are to divide the rest into equal Scales, and upon Occasions remove from one into the other, or else fall with their own Weight into the lightest: So in a State within it self, the Ballance must be held by a third Hand, who is to deal the remaining Power with the utmost Exactness into each Scale. Now it is not necessary, that the Power should be equally divided between these three; for the Ballance may be held by the Weakest, who by his Address and Conduct, removing from either Scale, and adding of his own, may keep the Scales duly poised. Such was that of the two Kings of *Sparta*; the Consular Power in *Rome*; that of the Kings of *Media* before the Reign of *Cyrus*, as represented by *Xenophon*; and that of the several limited States in the *Gothick* Institutions.

WHEN the Ballance is broke, whether by the Negligence, Folly, or Weakness of the Hand that held it, or by mighty Weights fallen into either Scale; the Power will never continue long in equal Division between the two remaining Parties, but (until the Ballance is fixed anew) will run entirely into one. This gives the truest Account of what is understood in the most ancient and approved *Greek* Authors, by the Word *Tyranny*; which is not meant for the seizing of the uncontrouled, or absolute Power into the Hands of a single Person; (as many superficial Men have grosly mistaken) but for the breaking of the Ballance by whatever Hand, and leaving the Power wholly in one scale. For *Tyranny* and *Usurpation* in a State, are by no Means confined to any Number, as might easily appear from Examples enough; and, because the Point is material, I shall cite a few to prove it.

Dionys. THE *Romans* having sent to *Athens*, and the *Greek*
Hal. l. 10. Cities of *Italy*, for the Copies of the best Laws, chose ten Legislators to put them into Form; and during the Exercise of their Office, suspended the Consular Power, leaving the Administration of Affairs in their Hands. These very Men, although chosen for such a Work, as the digesting a Body of Laws for the Government of a free State, did immediately usurp arbitrary Power, ran into all the Forms of it, had their Guards and Spies, after the Practice of the Tyrants of those Ages; affected kingly State, destroyed the Nobles, and oppressed the People; one of them proceeding so far as to endeavour to force a Lady of great Virtue; the very Crime which gave Occasion to the Expulsion of the Regal Power but sixty Years before, as this Attempt did to that of the *Decemviri*.

THE *Ephori* in *Sparta* were, at first, only certain Persons deputed by the Kings to judge in Civil Matters, while *They* were employed in the Wars. These Men, at several Times, usurped the absolute Authority, and were as cruel Tyrants as any in their Age.

Thucid. SOON after the unfortunate Expedition into *Sicily*,
lib. 8. the *Athenians* chose four Hundred Men for Administration of Affairs, who became a Body of Tyrants, and were called in the Language of those Ages, an *Oligarchy*, or Tyranny of the *Few*; under which hateful Denomination, they were soon after deposed in great Rage by the People.

Xenoph. WHEN *Athens* was subdued by *Lysander*, he ap-
de Rebus pointed Thirty Men for the Administration of that
Græc. l. 2. City, who immediately fell into the rankest Tyranny: But this was not all: For conceiving their Power, not founded on a *Basis* large enough, they admitted three Thousand into a Share of the Government; and thus fortified, became the cruelest Tyranny upon Record. They murdered, in cold Blood, great Numbers of the best Men, without any Provocation; from the meer Lust of Cruelty, like *Nero*, or *Caligula*. This was such a

Number of Tyrants together, as amounted to near a third Part
of the whole City. For *Xenophon* tells us, that the City
contained about ten Thousand Houses, and allowing *Memorab.*
one Man to every House, who could have any Share *lib. 3.*
in the Government, (the rest consisting of Women, Children,
and Servants) and making other obvious Abatements; these
Tyrants, if they had been careful to adhere together, might have
been a Majority even of the People collective.

IN the Time of the second *Punick* War, the Bal-
lance of Power in *Carthage* was got on the Side of the *Polyb. Frag.*
People, and this to a Degree, that some Authors *lib. 6.*
reckon the Government to have been then among them a *Dominatio Plebis*, or *Tyranny of the Commons*; which, it seems, they
were at all Times apt to fall into, and was at last among the
Causes that ruined their State: And the frequent Murders of their
Generals, which *Diodorus* tells us was grown to an
established Custom among them, may be another *lib. 20.*
Instance, that Tyranny is not confined to Numbers.

I SHALL mention but one Example more, among a great
Number that might be produced; it is related by the Author last
cited. The Orators of the People at *Argos*, (whether
you will stile them in modern Phrase, *Great Speakers* *lib. 15.*
in the House, or only in general, Representatives of the People
Collective) stirred up the COMMONS against the NOBLES; of
whom 1600 were murdered at once; and, at last, the Orators
themselves, because they left off their Accusations; or to speak
intelligibly, because they *withdrew their Impeachments*; having, it
seems, raised a Spirit they were not able to lay. And this last
Circumstance, as Cases have lately stood, may perhaps be worth
noting.

FROM what hath been already advanced, several Conclusions
may be drawn.

FIRST, That a mixt Government partaking of the known
Forms received in the Schools, is, by no Means, of *Gothick* Invention, but hath Place in Nature and Reason; seems very well
to agree with the Sentiments of most Legislators, and to have
been followed in most States, whether they have appeared under
the Name of Monarchies, Aristocracies, or Democracies. For,

not to mention the several Republicks of this Composition in *Gaul* and *Germany*, described by *Cæsar* and *Tacitus*; *Polybius* tells

Frag. lib. 6. us, the best Government is that which consists of three Forms, *Regno*, *Optimatium*, & *Populi Imperio*: Which may be fairly translated, the *Kings*, *Lords*, and *Commons*. Such was that of *Sparta*, in its primitive Institution by *Lycurgus*; who observing the Corruptions, and Depravations to which every of these was subject, compounded his Scheme out of all; so that it was made up of *Reges*, *Seniores*, & *Populus*. Such also was the State of *Rome*, under its Consuls: And the Author tells us, that the *Romans* fell upon this Model purely by Chance, (which I take to have been Nature and common Reason) but the *Spartans* by Thought, and Design. And such at *Carthage* was the *Summa Reipublicæ*, or Power in the last Resort; for they had

Id. ib. their Kings called *Suffetes*, and a Senate which had the Power of *Nobles*, and the *People* had a Share established too.

SECONDLY, It will follow, That those Reasoners, who employ so much of their Zeal, their Wit, and their Leisure for upholding the Ballance of Power in *Christendom*, at the same Time that by their Practices they are endeavouring to destroy it at home; are not such mighty Patriots, or so much in the true Interest of their Country, as they would affect to be thought; but seem to be employed like a Man, who pulls down with his right Hand what he has been building with his left.

THIRDLY, This makes appear the Error of those, who think it an uncontroulable Maxim, that Power is always safer lodged in many Hands than in one. For, if these many Hands be made up, only from one of the three Divisions before-mentioned; it is plain from those Examples already produced, and easy to be paralleled in other Ages and Countries, that they are as capable of enslaving the Nation, and of acting all Manner of *Tyranny* and *Oppression*, as it is possible for a single Person to be; although we should suppose their Number to be not only of four or five Hundred, but above three Thousand.

AGAIN, It is manifest from what hath been said, that in order to preserve the Ballance in a mixed State, the Limits of Power deposited with each Party ought to be ascertained, and generally known. The Defect of this is the Cause that introduces those Strugglings in a State about *Prerogative* and *Liberty*, about Encroachments of the *Few*, upon the Rights of the *Many*, and of the *Many* upon the Privileges of the *Few*; which ever did, and ever will conclude in a Tyranny; First, either of the *Few*, or the *Many*, but at last infallibly of a single Person. For, which ever of the three Divisions in a State is upon the Scramble for more Power than its own, (as one or other of them generally is) unless due Care be taken by the other two; upon every new Question that arises, they will be sure to decide in favour of themselves, talk much of *inherent Right*; they will nourish up a dormant Power, and reserve Privileges in *petto*, to exert upon Occasions, to serve Expedients, and to urge upon Necessities. They will make large Demands, and scanty Concessions, ever coming off considerable Gainers: Thus at length the Ballance is broke, and Tyranny let in; from which Door of the three it matters not.

To pretend to a *declarative* Right upon any Occasion whatsoever, is little less than to make use of the whole Power; That is, to declare an Opinion to be Law, which hath always been contested, or perhaps never started before such an Incident brought it on the Stage. Not to consent to the enacting of such a Law, which has no View besides the general Good, unless another Law shall at the same Time pass with no other View, but that of advancing the Power of one Party alone; what is this, but to claim a positive Voice as well as a negative? To pretend that great Changes and Alienations of Property have created new and great Dependences, and consequently new Additions of Power, as some Reasoners have done, is a most dangerous Tenet: If Dominion must follow Property, let it follow in the same Pace: For Changes in Property through the Bulk of a Nation make slow Marches, and its due Power always attends it. To conclude, that whatever Attempt is begun by an Assembly, ought to be pursued to the End, without regard to the greatest Incidents that may happen to alter the Case; to count it mean, and below the *Dignity of a House*, to quit a Prosecution; to resolve upon a Conclusion, before it is possible to be apprised of the Premisses: To act thus, I say, is to affect not only absolute Power, but Infallibility too. Yet such unaccountable Proceedings as these have popular Assemblies engaged in, for want of fixing the due Limits of *Power* and *Privilege*.

GREAT Changes may, indeed, be made in a Government, yet the Form continue, and the Ballance be held; but large Intervals of Time must pass between every such Innovation, enough to melt down, and make it of a Piece with the Constitution. Such we are told were the Proceedings of *Solon*, when he modelled anew the *Athenian* Commonwealth. And what Convulsions in our own, as well as other States, have been bred by a Neglect of this Rule, is fresh and notorious enough: It is too soon, in all Conscience, to repeat this Error again.

HAVING shewn that there is a natural Ballance of Power in all free States, and how it hath been divided sometimes by the People themselves, as in *Rome*; at others by the Institutions of the Legislators, as in the several States of *Greece* and *Sicily*: The next thing is to examine what Methods have been taken to break or overthrow this Ballance; which every one of the three Parties hath continually endeavoured, as Opportunities have served; as might appear from the Stories of most Ages and Countries. For, absolute Power in a particular State, is of the same Nature with universal Monarchy in several States adjoining to each other. So endless and exorbitant are the Desires of Men, whether considered in their Persons or their States, that they will grasp at all, and can form no Scheme of perfect Happiness with less. Ever since Men have been united into Governments, the Hopes and Endeavours after universal Monarchy have been bandied among them, from the Reign of *Ninus*, to this of the *most Christian King*: In which Pursuits, Commonwealths have had their Share, as well as Monarchs: So the *Athenians*, the *Spartans*, the *Thebans*, and the *Achaians*, did several Times aim at the universal Monarchy of *Greece*: So the Commonwealths of *Carthage* and *Rome*, affected the universal Monarchy of the then known World. In like Manner hath absolute Power been pursued by the several Parties of each particular State; wherein single Persons have met with most Success, although the Endeavours of the *Few* and the *Many* have been frequent enough: Yet, being neither so uniform in their Designs, nor so direct in their Views, they neither could manage nor maintain the Power they had got; but were ever deceived by the Popularity, and Ambition of some single Person. So that it will be always a wrong Step in Policy, for the *Nobles*, or *Commons* to carry their Endeavours after Power so far, as to overthrow the Ballance: And it would be enough to damp their Warmth in such Pursuits, if they could once reflect, that in such a Course they will be sure to run upon the very Rock that they meant to avoid; which I suppose they would have us think, is the Tyranny of a single Person.

MANY Examples might be produced of the Endeavours from each of these three Rivals after absolute Power: But I shall suit my Discourse to the Time I am writing it; and relate only such Dissentions in *Greece* and *Rome*, between the *Nobles* and *Commons*, with the Consequences of them, wherein the latter were the Aggressors.

I SHALL begin with *Greece*, where my Observations shall be confined to *Athens*; although several Instances might be brought from other States thereof.

CHAP. II.

Of the Dissentions *in* Athens, *between the* Few *and the* Many.

THESEUS is the first, who is recorded with any Appearance of Truth to have brought the *Grecians* from a barbarous Manner of Life, among scattered Villages, into Cities; and to have established the *popular State* in *Athens*, assigning to himself the Guardianship of the Laws, and chief Command in War. He was forced, after some Time, to leave the *Athenians* to their own Measures, upon Account of their seditious Temper, which ever continued with them till the final Dissolution of their Government by the *Romans*. It seems, the Country about *Attica* was the most barren of any in *Greece*; through which Means, it happened that the Natives were never expelled by the Fury of Invaders, (who thought it not worth a Conquest) but continued always *Aborigines*; and therefore retained, through all Revolutions, a Tincture of that turbulent Spirit wherewith their Government began. This Institution of *Theseus* appears to have been rather a Sort of mixed Monarchy than a popular State; and for ought we know, might continue so during the Series of Kings till the Death of *Codrus*. From this last Prince, *Solon* was said to be descended; who finding the People engaged in two violent Factions, of the P o o r and the R i c h, and in great Confusion thereupon; refusing the Monarchy which was offered him, chose rather to cast the Government after another Model, wherein he made due Provision for settling the Ballance of Power, chusing a Senate of 400, and disposing the Magistracies, and Offices according to Mens Estates; leaving to the Multitude their Votes in Electing, and the Power of judging certain Processes by Appeal. This Council of 400 was chosen, 100 out of each Tribe; and seems to have been a Body Representative of the People; although the People Collective reserved a Share of Power to themselves. It is a Point of History perplexed enough; but thus much is certain, that the Ballance of Power was provided for; else *Pysistratus*, (called by Authors the Tyrant of *Athens*) could never have governed so peaceably as he did, without changing any of *Solon*'s Laws. These several Powers, together with that of the *Archon*, or *Herodot. lib.* 1. chief Magistrate, made up the Form of Government in *Athens*, at what Time it began to appear upon the Scene of Action and Story.

The first great Man bred up under this Institution was *Miltiades*, who lived about Ninety Years after *Solon*; and is reckoned to have been the first great Captain not only of *Athens*, but of all *Greece*. From the Time of *Miltiades* to that of *Phocion*, who is looked upon as the last famous General of *Athens*, are about 130 Years: After which they were subdued and insulted by *Alexander*'s Captains, and continued under several Revolutions, a small truckling State of no Name, or Reputation, untill they fell with the rest of *Greece* under the Power of the *Romans*.

DURING this Period from *Miltiades* to *Phocion*, I shall trace the Conduct of the *Athenians*, with relation to their Dissentions between the PEOPLE and some of their GENERALS; who, at that Time, by their Power and Credit in the Army, in a warlike Commonwealth, and often supported by each other, were, with the Magistrates and other Civil Officers, a Sort of Counterpoise to the Power of the People, who since the Death of *Solon*, had already made great Encroachments. What these Dissentions were, how founded, and what the Consequences of them, I shall briefly and impartially relate.

I MUST here premise, that the *Nobles* in *Athens* were not at this Time a Corporate Assembly, that I can gather; therefore the Resentments of the Commons were usually turned against particular Persons, and by way of Articles of Impeachment. Whereas the Commons in *Rome*, and some other States, (as will appear in proper Place) although they followed this Method upon Occasion, yet generally pursued the Enlargement of their Power, by more set Quarrels of one entire Assembly against another. However, the Custom of particular Impeachments being not limited to former Ages, any more than that of general Struggles, and Dissentions betwixt fixed Assemblies of Nobles and Commons; and the Ruin of *Greece* having been owing to the former, as that of *Rome* was to the latter; I shall treat on both expresly; that those States, who are concerned in either (if at least there be any such now in the World) may, by observing the Means and Issues of former Dissentions, learn whether the Causes are alike in theirs; and if they find them to be so, may consider whether they ought not justly to apprehend the same Effects.

To speak of every particular Person, impeached by the Commons of *Athens*, within the Compass designed, would introduce the History of almost every great Man they had among them. I shall therefore take Notice only of six, who living in that Period of Time when *Athens* was at the Height of its Glory, (as indeed it could not be otherwise, while such Hands were at the Helm) although *impeached for high Crimes and Misdemeanors*, such as *Bribery, arbitrary Proceedings, misapplying, or imbezling publick Funds, ill Conduct at Sea*, and the like; were honoured and lamented by their Country, as the Preservers of it, and have had the Veneration of all Ages since justly paid to their Memories.

MILTIADES was one of the *Athenian* Generals against the *Persian* Power; and the famous Victory at *Marathon* was chiefly owing to his Valour and Conduct. Being sent some time after to reduce the Island *Paros*, he mistook a great Fire at Distance for the *Fleet*, and being no ways a Match for the Enemy, set sail to *Athens*. At his Arrival he was *impeached* by the Commons for Treachery, although not able to appear by reason of his Wounds; fined 30000 Crowns, and died in Prison. Although the Consequences of this Proceeding upon the Affairs of *Athens*, were no more than the untimely Loss of so great and good a Man, yet I could not forbear relating it.

THEIR next great Man was *Aristides*: Besides the mighty Service he had done his Country in the Wars; he was a Person of the strictest Justice, and best acquainted with the Laws, as well as Forms of their Government; so that he was in a Manner *Chancellor* of *Athens*. This Man, upon a slight and false Accusation of *favouring arbitrary Power*, was banished by *Ostracism*; which rendered into modern *English*, would signify, that they voted *he should be removed from their Presence and Councils for ever*. But, they had soon the Wit to recal him; and to that Action owed the Preservation of their State by his future Services. For, it must be still confessed in Behalf of the *Athenian* People, that they never conceived themselves perfectly infallible, nor arrived to the Heights of *modern Assemblies*, to make *Obstinacy* confirm what *sudden Heat* and *Temerity* began. They thought it not *below the Dignity* of an Assembly to endeavour at correcting an ill Step; at least to repent, although it often fell out too late.

THEMISTOCLES was at first a *Commoner* himself. It was he who raised the *Athenians* to their *Greatness at Sea*, which he thought to be the true and constant Interest of that Commonwealth; and the famous Naval Victory over the *Persians* at *Salamis*, was owing to his Conduct. It seems, the People observed somewhat of Haughtiness in his Temper and Behaviour, and therefore banished him for five Years; but finding some slight Matter of Accusation against him, they sent to seize his Person, and he hardly escaped to the *Persian* Court; from whence, if the Love of his Country had not surmounted its base Ingratitude to him, he had many Invitations to return at the Head of the *Persian* Fleet, and take a terrible Revenge; but he rather chose a voluntary Death.

The People of *Athens* impeached *Pericles* for *misapplying the publick Revenues to his own private Use*. He had been a Person of great Deservings from the Republick, was an *admirable Speaker*, and very popular; *his Accounts were confused; and he wanted Time to adjust them*; therefore, meerly to divert that Difficulty, and the Consequences of it, he was forced to engage his Country in the *Peloponnesian* War, the longest that ever was known in *Greece*; and which ended in the utter Ruin of *Athens*.

The same People having resolved to subdue *Sicily*, sent a mighty Fleet under the Command of *Nicias*, *Lamachus*, and *Alcibiades*; the two former, Persons of Age and Experience; the last, a young Man of noble Birth, excellent Education, and a plentiful Fortune. A little before the Fleet set sail, it seems, one Night, the Stone Images of *Mercury*, placed in several Parts of the City, were all pared in the Face: This Action the *Athenians* interpreted for a Design of destroying the popular State; and *Alcibiades*, having been formerly noted for the like Frolicks and Excursions, was immediately accused of this. He, whether conscious of his Innocence, or assured of the Secrecy, offered to come to his Tryal before he went to his Command: This the *Athenians* refused: But as soon as he was got to *Sicily*, they sent for him back, designing to take the Advantage, and prosecute him in the Absence of his Friends, and of the Army, where he was very powerful. It seems, he understood the Resentments of a popular Assembly too well to trust them; and therefore, instead of returning, escaped to *Sparta*; where his Desire of Revenge prevailing over his Love to his Country, he became its greatest Enemy. Mean while, the *Athenians* before *Sicily*, by the Death of one Commander, and the Superstition, Weakness, and perfect ill Conduct of the other, were utterly destroyed; the whole Fleet taken, a miserable Slaughter made of the Army, whereof hardly one ever returned. Some Time after this, *Alcibiades* was recalled upon his own Conditions, by the Necessities of the People, and made chief Commander at Sea and Land; but his Lieutenant engaging against his positive Orders, and being beaten by *Lysander*; *Alcibiades* was again disgraced and banished. However, the *Athenians* having lost all Strength and Heart since their Misfortune at *Sicily*, and now deprived of the only Person that was able to recover their Losses, repent of their Rashness, and endeavour, in vain, for his Restoration; the *Persian* Lieutenant, to whose Protection he fled, making him a Sacrifice to the Resentments of *Lysander*, the General of the *Lacedemonians*; who now reduceth all the Dominions of the *Athenians*, takes the City, razes their Walls, ruins their Works, and changes the Form of their Government; which, although again restored for some Time by *Thrasybulus*, (as their Walls were rebuilt by *Conon*) yet here we must date the Fall of the *Athenian* Greatness; the Dominion and chief Power in *Greece*, from that Period, to the Time of *Alexander* the Great, which was about fifty Years, being divided between the *Spartans* and *Thebans*: Although *Philip*, *Alexander*'s Father, (*the most Christian King* of that Age) had, indeed, some Time before, begun to break in upon the Republicks of *Greece*, by Conquest or *Bribery*; particularly *dealing large Money among some popular Orators*; by which he brought many of them (as the Term of Art was then) to *Philippize*.

In the Time of *Alexander* and his Captains, the *Athenians* were offered an Opportunity of recovering their Liberty, and being restored to their former State; but the wise Turn they thought to give the Matter, was by an Impeachment and Sacrifice of the Author, to hinder the Success. For, after the Destruction of *Thebes* by *Alexander*, this Prince designing the Conquest of *Athens*, was prevented by *Phocion*, the *Athenian* General, then Ambassador from that State; who, by his great Wisdom and Skill at Negociation, diverted *Alexander* from his Design, and restored the *Athenians* to his Favour. The very same Success he had with *Antipater* after *Alexander*'s Death; at which Time, the Government was new regulated by *Solon*'s Laws: But *Polyperchon*, in Hatred to *Phocion*, having, by Order of the young King, (whose Governor he was) restored those whom *Phocion* had banished; the Plot succeeded, *Phocion* was accused by *popular Orators*, and put to Death.

Thus was the most powerful Commonwealth of all *Greece*, after great Degeneracies from the Institution of *Solon*, utterly destroyed by that rash, jealous and inconstant Humour of the People, which was never satisfied to see a General either *victorious*, or *unfortunate*: Such ill Judges, as well as Rewarders, have *popular Assemblies* been, of those who best deserved from them.

Now the Circumstance, which makes these Examples of more Importance, is, that this very Power of the People in *Athens*, claimed so confidently for an *inherent Right*, and insisted on as the *undoubted Privilege of an* Athenian *born*, was the rankest Encroachment imaginable, and the grossest Degeneracy from the Form that *Solon* left them. In short, their Government was grown into a *Dominatio Plebis*, or *Tyranny of the People*; who, by Degrees, had broke and overthrown the Ballance which that Legislator had very well fixed and provided for. This appears not only from what hath been already said of that Law-giver,   *lib.* 28. but more manifestly from a Passage in *Diodorus*; who tells us, *That* Antipater, *one of* Alexander's *Captains, abrogated the popular Government,* (in Athens) *and restored the Power of Suffrages and Magistracy, to such, only, as were worth two Thousand Drachmas; by which Means,* (says he) *that Republick came to be again administered by the Laws of* Solon. By this Quotation, it is manifest, that

P

this great Author looked upon *Solon*'s Institution, and a popular Government to be two different Things. And as for this Restoration by *Antipater*, it had neither Consequence nor Continuance worth observing.

I MIGHT easily produce many more Examples, but these are sufficient: And it may be worth the Reader's Time to reflect, a little, on the Merits of the Cause, as well as of the Men who had been thus dealt with by their Country. I shall direct him no further, than by repeating, that *Aristides* was the most renowned by the People themselves for his exact *Justice, and Knowledge in the Law*. That *Themistocles* was a most fortunate Admiral, and had got *a mighty Victory over the great King of* Persia's *Fleet*. That *Pericles* was *an able Minister of State, an excellent Orator, and a Man of Letters*: And lastly, that *Phocion*, besides the Success of his Arms, was also renowned for his *Negotiations abroad; having, in an Embassy, brought the greatest Monarch of the World, at that Time, to the Terms of an honourable Peace, by which his Country was preserved*.

I SHALL conclude my Remarks upon *Athens*, with the Character given us of that People by *Polybius. About this Time,* (says he) *the* Athenians *were governed by two Men, quite sunk in their Affairs; had little or no Commerce with the rest of* Greece; *and were become great Reverencers of crowned Heads*.

FOR, from the Time of *Alexander*'s Captains, till *Greece* was subdued by the *Romans*, (to the latter Part of which, this Description of *Polybius* falls in) *Athens* never produced one famous Man, either for Councils or Arms, or hardly for Learning. And, indeed, it was a dark insipid Period through all *Greece*: For, except

Polyb. the *Achaian* League under *Aratus* and *Philopæmen*; and the Endeavours of *Agis* and *Cleomenes*, to restore the State of *Sparta*, so frequently harassed with Tyrannies, occasioned by the popular Practices of the *Ephori*; there was very little worth recording. All which Consequences may, perhaps, be justly imputed to this Degeneracy of *Athens*.

CHAP. III.

Of the Dissentions between the Patricians *and* Plebeians *in* Rome; *with the Consequences they had upon that State.*

HAVING, in the foregoing Chapter, confined my self to the Proceedings of the COMMONS, only by the Method of *Impeachments* against particular Persons, with the fatal Effects they had upon the State of *Athens*; I shall now treat of the *Dissentions* at *Rome*, between the People and the Collective Body of the *Patricians* or *Nobles*. It is a large Subject; but I shall draw it into as narrow a Compass as I can.

AS *Greece*, from the most antient Accounts we have of it, was divided into several Kingdoms, so was most Part of *Italy* into several petty Commonwealths. And, as those Kings in *Greece* are said to have been deposed by their people, upon the Score of their arbitrary Proceed- *Dionys. Halica.* ings; so, on the contrary, the Commonwealths of *Italy* were all swallowed up, and concluded in the Tyranny of the *Roman* Emperors. However, the Differences between those *Grecian* Monarchies, and *Italian* Republicks, were not very great: For, by the Accounts *Homer* gives us of those *Grecian* Princes, who came to the Siege of *Troy*, as well as by several Passages in the *Odysses*; it is manifest, that the Power of these Princes, in their several States, was much of a Size with that of the Kings in *Sparta*, the Archon at *Athens*, the Suffetes at *Carthage*, and the Consuls in *Rome*: So that a limited and divided Power, seems to have been the most antient and inherent Principle of both those People, in Matters of Government. And such did that of *Rome* continue from the Time of *Romulus*, although with some Interruptions, to *Julius Cæsar*; when it ended in the Tyranny of a single Person. During which Period, (not many Years longer than from the *Norman* Conquest to our Age) the Commons were growing, by Degrees, into Power and Property, gaining Ground upon the *Patricians*, as it were Inch by Inch, till at last they quite overturned the Ballance; leaving all Doors open to the Practices of popular and ambitious Men, who destroyed the wisest Republick, and enslaved the noblest People that ever entered upon the Stage of the World. By what Steps and Degrees this was brought to pass, shall be the Subject of my present Enquiry.

WHILE *Rome* was governed by Kings, the Monarchy was altogether elective. *Romulus* himself, when he had built the City, was declared King by the universal Consent of the People, and by Augury, which was then understood for *Divine Appointment*. Among other Divisions he made of the People, one was into *Patricians* and *Plebeians*: The former were like the Barons of *England*, some time after the Conquest; and the latter are also described to be almost exactly what our Commons were then: For, they were Dependants upon the *Patricians*, whom they chose for their Patrons and Protectors, to answer for their Appearance, and defend them in any Process: They also supplied their Patrons with Money, in Exchange for their Protection. This Custom of *Patronage*, it seems, was very ancient, and long practised among the *Greeks*.

OUT of these *Patricians*, *Romulus* chose an Hundred to be a *Senate*, or *Grand Council*, for Advice and Assistance to him in the Administration. The Senate, therefore, originally consisted all of Nobles, and were, of themselves, a *standing Council*; the *People* being only convoked upon such Occasions, as by this Institution of *Romulus*, fell into their Cognizance: These were to constitute Magistrates, to give their Votes for making Laws, and to advise upon entering on a War. But, the two former of these popular Privileges, were to be confirmed by Authority of the Senate; and the last was only permitted at the King's Pleasure. This was the utmost Extent of Power pretended by the *Commons* in the Time of *Romulus*; all the rest being divided between the King and the Senate; the whole agreeing very nearly with the Constitution of *England*, for some Centuries after the Conquest.

AFTER a Year's *Interregnum* from the Death of *Romulus*, the Senate, of their own Authority, chose a Successor, and a Stranger, meerly upon the Fame of his Virtue, without asking the Consent of the Commons; which Custom they likewise observed in the two following Kings. But, in the Election of

Tarquinius Priscus, the fifth King, we first hear mentioned, that it was done, *Populi impetratâ veniâ*; which, indeed, was but very reasonable for a free People to expect; although I cannot remember, in my little Reading, by what Incidents they were brought to advance so great a Step. However it were, this Prince, in Gratitude to the People, by whose Consent he was chosen, elected a Hundred Senators out of the Commons; whose Number, with former Additions, was now amounted to three Hundred.

THE People, having once discovered their own Strength, did soon take Occasion to exert it, and that by very great Degrees. For, at this King's Death, (who was murdered by the Sons of a former) being at a Loss for a Successor, *Servius Tullius*, a Stranger, and of mean Extraction, was chosen Protector of the Kingdom, by the *People*, without the Consent of the Senate; at which the Nobles being displeased, he wholly applied himself to gratify the Commons; and was by them declared and confirmed no longer Protector, but King.

TH IS Prince first introduced the Custom of giving Freedom to Servants, so as to become Citizens of equal Privileges with the rest; which very much contributed to encrease the Power of the *People*.

THUS, in a very few Years, the Commons proceeded so far as to wrest even the Power of chusing a King, entirely out of the Hands of the Nobles: Which was so great a Leap, and caused such a Convulsion and Struggle in the State, that the Constitution could not bear it; but Civil Dissentions arose, which immediately were followed by the Tyranny of a single Person, as this was by the utter Subversion of the Regal Government, and by a Settlement upon a new Foundation. For, the Nobles, spighted at this Indignity done them by the Commons, firmly united in a Body, deposed this Prince by plain Force, and chose *Tarquin the Proud*; who, running into all the Forms and Methods of Tyranny; after a cruel Reign, was expelled by an universal Concurrence of Nobles and People, whom the Miseries of his Reign had reconciled.

WHEN the Consular Government began, the Ballance of Power between the Nobles and Plebeians was fixed a-new. The two first Consuls were nominated by the Nobles, and confirmed by the Commons; and a Law was enacted, That no Person should bear any Magistracy in *Rome*, *injussu Populi*; that is, without *Consent of the Commons*.

IN such turbulent Times as these, many of the poorer Citizens had contracted numerous Debts, either to the richer Sort among themselves, or to Senators and other Nobles: And the Case of Debtors in *Rome*, for the first four * Centuries, was, after the set Time for Payment, no Choice, but either to pay, or be the Creditor's Slave. In this Juncture, the Commons leave the City in Mutiny and Discontent; and will not return, but upon Condition to be acquitted of all their Debts; and moreover, that certain Magistrates be chosen yearly, whose Business it shall be to defend the Commons from Injuries. These are called, *Tribunes of the People*; their Persons are held sacred and inviolable, and the People bind themselves, by Oath, never to abrogate the Office. By these Tribunes, in Process of Time, the People were grosly imposed on, to serve the Turns and Occasions of revengeful or ambitious Men; and to commit such Exorbitances, as could not end, but in the Dissolution of the Government.

* *Ab Urbe conditâ.*

THESE Tribunes, a Year or two after their Institution, kindled great Dissentions between the Nobles and the Commons; on the Account of *Coriolanus*, a Nobleman, whom the latter had *impeached*; and the Consequences of whose Impeachment (if I had not confined my self to *Grecian* Examples for that Part of my Subject) had like to have been so fatal to their State. And, from this Time, the Tribunes begun a Custom of accusing, to the People, whatever Noble they pleased; several of whom were banished, or put to Death, in every Age.

AT this Time, the *Romans* were very much engaged in Wars with their neighbouring States; but upon the least Intervals of Peace, the Quarrels between the Nobles and the Plebeians would revive; and one of the most frequent Subjects of their Differences, was the *conquered Lands*, which the Commons would fain have divided among the Publick; but the Senate could not be brought to give their Consent. For several of the wisest among the Nobles, began to apprehend the growing Power of the

People; and therefore, knowing what an Accession thereof would accrue to them, by such an Addition of Property, used all Means to prevent it: For this, the *Appian* Family was most noted; and, thereupon most hated by the Commons. One of them, having made a Speech against this Division of Lands, was impeached by the People of high Treason, and a Day appointed for his Tryal; but, he disdaining to make his Defence, chose rather the usual *Roman* Remedy of killing himself: After whose Death, the Commons prevailed, and the Lands were divided among them.

THIS Point was no sooner gained, but new Dissentions began: For the Plebeians would fain have a Law enacted, to lay all Mens Rights and Privileges upon the same Level; and to enlarge the Power of every Magistrate, within his own Jurisdiction, as much as that of the Consuls. The Tribunes also obtained to have their Number doubled, which before was five; and the Author tells us, that their Insolence and Power encreased with their Number; and the Seditions were also doubled with it. *Dionys. Halica.*

BY the Beginning of the fourth Century, from the Building of *Rome*, the Tribunes proceeded so far, in the Name of the Commons, as to accuse and fine the Consuls themselves, who represented the kingly Power. And the Senate observing, how, in all Contentions, they were forced to yield to the Tribunes and People, thought it their wisest Course to give way also to Time: Therefore a Decree was made to send Ambassadors to *Athens*, and the other *Grecian* Commonwealths, planted in that Part of *Italy* called *Græcia Major*, to make a Collection of the best Laws; out of which, and some of their own, a new complete Body of Law was formed, afterwards known by the Name of the *Laws of the Twelve Tables*.

TO digest these Laws into Order, ten Men were chosen, and the Administration of all Affairs left in their Hands: What Use they made of it, hath been already shewn. It was certainly a great Revolution, produced entirely by the many unjust Encroachments of the People; and might have wholly changed the Fate of *Rome*, if the Folly and Vice of those who were chiefly concerned, could have suffered it to take Root.

A FEW Years after, the Commons made farther Advances on the Power of the Nobles; demanding, among the rest, that the Consulship, which hitherto had only been disposed to the former, should now lie in common to the Pretensions of any *Roman* whatsoever. This, although it failed at present, yet afterwards obtained, and was a mighty Step to the Ruin of the Commonwealth.

WHAT I have hitherto said of *Rome*, hath been chiefly collected out of that exact and diligent Writer *Dionysius Halicarnasseus*; whose History (through the Injury of Time) reacheth no farther than to the Beginning of the fourth Century, after the Building of *Rome*. The rest I shall supply from other Authors; although I do not think it necessary to deduce this Matter any further, so very particularly as I have hitherto done.

To point at what Time the Ballance of Power was most equally held between the *Lords* and *Commons* in *Rome*, would, perhaps, admit a Controversy. *Polybius* tells us, that in the second *Punick* War, the *Carthaginians* were declining, because the Ballance was got too much on the Side of the People; whereas the *Romans* were in their greatest Vigour, by the Power remaining in the Senate; yet this was between two and three Hundred Years after the Period *Dionysius* ends with; in which Time, the Commons had made several further Acquisitions. This, however, must be granted, that (untill about the Middle of the fourth Century) when the Senate appeared resolute at any Time upon exerting their Authority, and adhered closely together, they did often carry their Point. Besides, it is observed by the best Authors, that in all the Quarrels and Tumults at *Rome*; from the Expulsion of the Kings; although the People frequently proceeded to rude contumelious Language, and sometimes so far as to pull and hale one another about the *Forum*; yet no Blood was ever drawn in any popular Commotions, until the Time of the *Gracchi*: However, I am of Opinion, that the Ballance had begun many Years before to lean to the popular Side. But this Default was corrected, partly by the Principle just mentioned, of never drawing Blood in a Tumult; partly by the warlike Genius of the People, which, in those Ages,

Fragm. lib. 6.

Dionysius Hal. Plutarch, &c.

was almost perpetually employed; and partly by their great Commanders, who, by the Credit they had in their Armies, fell into the Scales as a farther Counterpoise to the growing Power of the People. Besides, *Polybius*, who lived in the Time of *Scipio Africanus* the Younger, had the same Apprehensions of the continual Encroachments made by the Commons; and being a Person of as great Abilities, and as much Sagacity as any of his Age; from observing the Corruptions which, he saith, had already entered into the *Roman* Constitution, did very nearly foretel what would be the Issue of them. His Words are very remarkable, and with little Addition may be rendered to this Purpose. *That those Abuses and Corruptions,* *lib. 5.* *which in Time destroy a Government, are sown along with the very Seeds of it, and both grow up together: And that, as Rust eats away Iron, and Worms devour Wood; and both are a Sort of Plagues, born and bred along with the Substance they destroy; so with every Form and Scheme of Government that Man can invent, some Vice, or Corruption creeps in with the very Institution, which grows up along with, and at last destroys it.* The same Author, in another Place, ventures so far as to guess at the particular Fate which *Fragm.* would attend the *Roman* Government. He saith, its *lib. 6.* Ruin would arise from the popular Tumults, which would introduce a *Dominatio Plebis*, or Tyranny of the People: Wherein, it is certain, he had Reason; and therefore, might have adventured to pursue his Conjectures so far, as to the Consequences of a popular Tyranny; which, as perpetual Experience teacheth, never fails to be followed by the arbitrary Government of a single Person.

About the Middle of the fourth Century, from the Building of *Rome*, it was declared lawful for *Nobles* and *Plebeians* to intermarry; which Custom, among many other States, hath proved the most effectual Means to ruin the former, and raise the latter.

And now, the greatest Employments in the State were, one after another, by Laws forceably enacted by the *Commons*, made free to the People; the *Consulship* it self, the Office of *Censor*, that of the *Questors*, or *Commissioners of the Treasury*, the Office of *Prætor*, or *Chief Justice*, the *Priesthood*, and even that of *Dictator*: The Senate, after long Opposition, yielding, meerly for present

Quiet, to the continual urging Clamours of the *Commons*, and of the *Tribunes* their Advocates. A Law was likewise enacted, that the *Plebiscita*, or, *a Vote of the House of Commons*, should be of universal Obligation: Nay, in Time, the Method of enacting Laws was wholly inverted: For, whereas the Senate used, of old, to confirm the *Plebiscita*; the People did at last, as they pleased, confirm, or disannul the *Senatusconsulta*.

Dionys. lib. 2.

APPIUS CLAUDIUS brought in a Custom of admitting to the Senate, the Sons of Freed Men, or of such who had once been Slaves; by which, and succeeding Alterations of the like Nature, that great Council degenerated into a most corrupt and factious Body of Men divided against it self; and its Authority became despised.

THE Century and half following, to the End of the third *Punick* War, by the Destruction of *Carthage*, was a very busy Period at *Rome*: The Intervals between every War being so short, that the *Tribunes* and *People* had hardly leisure, or Breath to engage in domestick Dissentions: However, the little Time they could spare, was generally employed the same way. So *Terentius Leo*, a *Tribune*, is recorded to have basely prostituted the Privileges of a *Roman* Citizen, in perfect Spight to the *Nobles*. So the great *African Scipio*, and his Brother, after all their mighty Services, were impeached by an ungrateful *Commons*.

HOWEVER, the warlike Genius of the People, and continual Employment they had for it, served to divert this Humour from running into a Head, till the Age of the *Gracchi*.

THESE Persons entering the Scene, in the Time of a full Peace, fell violently upon advancing the Power of the People, by reducing into Practice all those Encroachments, which they had been so many Years gaining. There were, at that Time, certain *Conquered Lands* to be divided; beside a *great private Estate left by a King*. These, the Tribunes, by Procurement of the elder *Gracchus*, declared by their legislative Authority, were not to be disposed of by the *Nobles*; but by the *Commons* only. The younger Brother pursued the same Design; and besides, obtained a Law, that all *Italians* should vote at Elections, as well as the Citizens of *Rome*: In short, the whole Endeavours of them both,

perpetually turned upon retrenching the *Nobles* Authority in all
Things, but especially in the Matter of *Judicature*. And, although
they both lost their Lives in those Pursuits, yet they traced out
such Ways, as were afterwards followed by *Marius*, *Sylla*, *Pompey*, and *Cæsar*, to the Ruin of the *Roman* Freedom and Greatness.

FOR, in the Time of *Marius*; *Saturninus*, a Tribune, procured
a Law, that the Senate should be bound, by Oath, to agree to
whatever the People would enact: And *Marius* himself, while
he was in that Office of Tribune, is recorded to have, with great
Industry, used all Endeavours for depressing the *Nobles*, and
raising the People; particularly, for cramping the former in their
Power of Judicature; which was *their most antient inherent Right*.

SYLLA, by the same Measures, became absolute Tyrant of
Rome: He added three Hundred Commons to the Senate, which
perplexed the Power of the whole Order, and rendered it ineffectual; then, flinging off the Mask, he abolished the Office of
Tribune, as being only a Scaffold to Tyranny: whereof he had
no further Use.

As to *Pompey* and *Cæsar*; *Plutarch* tells us, that their Union for
pulling down the *Nobles*, (by their Credit with the People) was
the Cause of the Civil War, which ended in the Tyranny of the
latter; both of them, in their Consulships, having used all Endeavours and Occasions for sinking the Authority of the *Patricians*, and giving Way to all Encroachments of the People,
wherein they expected best to find their own Account.

FROM this Deduction of popular Encroachments in *Rome*,
the Reader will easily judge how much the Ballance was fallen
upon that Side. Indeed, by this Time the very Foundation was
removed, and it was a moral Impossibility, that the Republick
could subsist any longer. For, the Commons having usurped
the Offices of the State, and trampled on the Senate, there was
no Government left, but a *Dominatio Plebis*: Let us, therefore,
examine how they proceeded in this Conjuncture.

I THINK it is an universal Truth, that the People are much
more dextrous at pulling down, and setting up, than at preserving what is fixed: And they are not fonder of seizing more than
their own, than they are of delivering it up again to the *worst
Bidder*, with their own into the Bargain. For, although in their

corrupt Notions of Divine Worship, they are apt to multiply their Gods; yet their earthly Devotion is seldom paid to above one Idol at a Time, of their own Creation; whose *Oar* they pull with less Murmuring, and much more Skill, than when they *share the Lading*, or even *hold the Helm*.

THE several Provinces of the *Roman* Empire, were now governed by the great Men of their State; those upon the Frontiers with powerful Armies, either for Conquest, or Defence. These Governors, upon any Designs of Revenge, or Ambition, were sure to meet with a divided Power at home; and therefore bent all their Thoughts, and Applications, to close in with the People; who were now, by many Degrees, the stronger Party. Two of the greatest Spirits that *Rome* ever produced, happened to live at the same Time, and to be engaged in the same Pursuit; and this at a Juncture the most dangerous for such a Contest. These were *Pompey* and *Cæsar*; two Stars of such a Magnitude, that their *Conjunction* was as likely to be fatal, as their *Opposition*.

THE *Tribunes* and People, having now subdued all Competitors, began the last Game of a prevalent Populace, which is that of chusing themselves a *Master*; while the Nobles foresaw, and used all Endeavours left them, to prevent it. The People, at first, made *Pompey* their Admiral, with full Power over all the *Mediterranean*; soon after, Captain-General of all the *Roman* Forces, and Governor of *Asia*. *Pompey*, on the other Side, restored the Office of *Tribune*, which *Sylla* had put down; and, in his Consulship, procured a Law for *examining into the Miscarriages of Men in Office, or Command, for Twenty Years past*. Many other Examples of *Pompey*'s Popularity, are left us on Record; who was a perfect Favourite of the People, and designed to be more; but his Pretensions grew stale, for want of a timely Opportunity to introduce them upon the Stage. For *Cæsar*, with his Legions in *Gaul*, was a perpetual Check upon his Designs; and in the Arts of pleasing the People, did soon after get many Lengths beyond him. He tells us himself, that the Senate, by a bold Effort, having made some severe Decrees against his Proceedings, and against the Tribunes; these all left the City, and went over to his Party, and consequently along with them the Affections and Interests of the People; which is further manifest, from the Accounts he gives us of the Citizens, in several Towns, mutinying against their Commanders, and delivering both to his Devotion. Besides, *Cæsar*'s publick and avowed Pretensions for beginning the Civil War, were to restore the Tribunes and the People, oppressed (as he pretended) by the *Nobles*.

THIS forced *Pompey*, against his Inclinations, upon the Necessity of changing Sides, for fear of being forsaken by both; and of closing in with the Senate and chief Magistrates, by whom he was chosen General against *Cæsar*.

THUS, at length, the *Senate* (at least the primitive Part of them, the *Nobles*) under *Pompey*, and the *Commons* under *Cæsar*, came to a final Decision of the long Quarrels between them. For, I think, the Ambition of private Men, did, by no Means, begin, or occasion this War; although Civil Dissentions never fail of introducing, and spiriting the Ambition of private Men; who thus become, indeed, the great Instruments for deciding of such Quarrels, and at last are sure to seize on the Prize. But no Man, who sees a Flock of Vultures hovering over two Armies ready to engage, can justly charge the Blood drawn in the Battle to them, although the Carcasses fall to their Share. For, while the Ballance of Power is equally held, the Ambition of private Men, whether Orators or great Commanders, gives neither Danger nor Fear, nor can possibly enslave their Country; but, That once broken, the divided Parties are forced to unite each to its Head; under whose Conduct, or Fortune, one Side is, at first, victorious, and, at last, both are Slaves. And, to put it past Dispute, that this entire Subversion of the *Roman* Liberty and Constitution, was altogether owing to those Measures which had broke the Ballance between the *Patricians* and *Plebeians*; whereof the Ambition of particular Men, was but an Effect and Consequence; we need only consider, that when the uncorrupted Part of the Senate, had, by the Death of *Cæsar*, made one great Effort to restore their former State and Liberty, the Success did not answer their Hopes; but that whole Assembly was so sunk in its Authority, that those Patriots were forced to fly, and give way to the Madness of the People; who, by their own Dispositions, stirred up with the Harangues of their Orators, were now wholly bent upon single and despotick Slavery. Else, how could such a Profligate as *Antony*, or a Boy of Eighteen, like *Octavius*, ever dare to dream of giving the Law to such an Empire and People? Wherein the latter succeeded, and entailed the vilest Tyranny that Heaven, in its Anger, ever inflicted on a corrupt and poisoned People: And this, with so little Appearance, at *Cæsar*'s Death, that when *Cicero* wrote to *Brutus*, how he had prevailed by his Credit with *Octavius*, to promise him (*Brutus*) Pardon and Security for his Person; that Great *Roman* received the Notice with the utmost Indignity, and returned *Cicero* an Answer (yet upon Record) full of the highest Resentment and Contempt for such an Offer, and from such a Hand.

HERE ended all Shew, or Shadow, of Liberty in *Rome*: Here was the Repository of all the wise Contentions and Struggles for Power, between the Nobles and Commons, lapped up safely in the Bosom of a *Nero* and a *Caligula*, a *Tiberius*, and a *Domitian*.

LET us now see from this Deduction of particular Impeachments, and general Dissentions in *Greece* and *Rome*, what Conclusions may naturally be formed for Instruction of any other State, that may haply, upon many Points, labour under the like Circumstances.

CHAP. IV.

UPON the Subject of *Impeachments* we may observe, that the Custom of accusing the *Nobles* to the *People*, either by themselves, or their Orators, (now stiled, *An Impeachment in the Name of the Commons*) hath been very antient, both in *Greece* and *Rome*, as well as *Carthage* ; and therefore may seem to be the inherent Right of a free People; nay, perhaps it is really so: But then, it is to be considered, *First*, that this Custom was peculiar to Republicks; or such States where the Administration lay principally in the Hands of the Commons; and ever raged more, or less, according to their Encroachments upon absolute Power; having been always looked upon, by the wisest Men, and best Authors of those Times, as an Effect of Licentiousness, and not of Liberty; a Distinction which no Multitude, either *represented* or *collective*, hath been, at any Time, very nice in observing. However, perhaps this Custom, in a popular State, of impeaching particular Men, may seem to be nothing else but the People's chusing, upon Occasion, to exercise their own Jurisdiction in Person; as if a King of *England* should sit as Chief Justice in his Court of *King's-Bench*; which, they say, in former Times he sometimes did. But, in *Sparta*, which was called a kingly Government, although the People were perfectly free; yet, because the Administration was in the two Kings, and the *Ephori*, (with the Assistance of the Senate) we read of no Impeachments by the People; nor was the Process against great Men, either upon Account of Ambition, or ill Conduct, although it reached sometimes to Kings themselves, ever formed that way, as I can recollect; but only passed through those Hands where the Administration lay. So likewise, during the Regal Government in *Rome*, although it was instituted a mixt Monarchy, and the People made great Advances in Power; yet I do not remember to have read of one Impeachment from the Commons against a Patrician, until the Consular State began, and the People had made great Encroachments upon the Administration.

ANOTHER Thing to be considered is; that allowing this Right of Impeachment to be as inherent as they please; yet, if the Commons have been perpetually mistaken in the Merits of the Causes and the Persons, as well as in the Consequences of such Impeachments upon the Peace of the State; we cannot conclude less, than that the Commons in *Greece* and *Rome*, (whatever they may be in other States) were, by no Means, qualified either as Prosecutors, or Judges, in such Matters; and therefore, that it would have been prudent, to reserve these Privileges dormant, never to be produced but upon very great and urging Occasions, where the State is in apparent Danger, the universal Body of the People in Clamours against the Administration, and no other Remedy in View. But for a few popular Orators, or Tribunes, upon the Score of *personal Piques*; or *to employ the Pride they conceive in seeing themselves at the Head of a Party*; or *as a Method for Advancement*; or *moved by certain powerful Arguments, that could make* Demosthenes *Philippize*: For such Men, I say, when the State would, of it self, gladly be quiet, and hath besides Affairs of the last Importance, upon the Anvil; to *impeach* Miltiades *after a great Naval Victory, for not pursuing the* Persian *Fleet: To impeach* Aristides, *the Person most versed among them in the Knowledge and Practice of their Laws, for a blind Suspicion of his acting in an arbitrary Way, (that is, as they expounded it, not in Concert with the People:)* To impeach Pericles, *after all his Services, for a few inconsiderable Accounts; or to impeach* Phocion, *who had been guilty of no other Crime, but negotiating a Treaty for the Peace and Security of his Country*: What could the Continuance of such Proceedings end in, but the utter Discouragement of all virtuous Actions and Persons, and consequently in the Ruin of a State? Therefore, the Historians of those Ages, seldom fail to set this Matter in all its Lights; leaving us the highest and most honourable *Ideas* of those Persons, who suffered by the Persecution of the People, together with the fatal Consequences they had; and how the Persecutors seldom failed to repent when it was too late.

THESE Impeachments perpetually falling upon many of the best Men, both in *Greece* and *Rome*, are a Cloud of Witnesses, and Examples enough to discourage Men of Virtue and Abilities from engaging in the Service of the Publick; and help, on t'other

Side, to introduce the Ambitious, the Covetous, the Superficial, and the Ill-designing; who are as apt to be bold and forward, and medling, as the former are to be cautious and modest, and reserved. This was so well known in *Greece*, that an Eagerness after Employments in the State, was looked upon by wise Men, as the worst Title a Man could set up; and made *Plato* say, *That if all Men were as good as they ought; the Quarrel in a Commonwealth would be, not as it is now, who* should *be Ministers of State, but who should* not *be so*. And *Socrates* is introduced by *Xenophon* severely chiding a Friend of his for not *lib.* 3. *Memorab.* entering into the publick Service, when he was every way qualified for it. Such a Backwardness there was at that Time among good Men to engage with an usurping People, and a Set of *pragmatical ambitious Orators*. And *Diodorus* tells us, that when the *Petalism* was erected at *Syracuse*, in *lib.* 11. Imitation of the *Ostracism* at *Athens*, it was so notoriously levelled against all who had either Birth or Merit to recommend them, that whoever possessed either, withdrew for Fear, and would have no Concern in publick Affairs. So that the People themselves were forced to abrogate it for fear of bringing all things into Confusion.

THERE is one Thing more to be observed, wherein all the Popular Impeachments in *Greece* and *Rome* seem to have agreed; and that was, a Notion they had of being concerned in *Point of Honour* to condemn whatever Person they Impeached, however frivolous the Articles were upon which they began; or however weak the Surmises, whereon they were to proceed in their Proofs. For, to conceive, that the Body of the People could be mistaken, was an Indignity not to be imagined, till the Consequences had convinced them when it was past Remedy. And I look upon this as a Fate to which all Popular Accusations are subject; although I should think that the Saying, *Vox Populi, Vox Dei*, ought to be understood of the Universal Bent and Current of a People; not the *bare Majority* of a few Representatives; which is often procured by *little Arts*, and great Industry and Application; wherein those, who engage in the Pursuits of Malice and Revenge, are much more sedulous than such as would prevent them.

q

FROM what hath been deduced of the *Dissentions* in *Rome*, between the two Bodies of Patricians and Plebeians, several Reflections may be made.

First, That when the Ballance of Power is duly fixed in a State, nothing is more dangerous and unwise than to give way to the *first Steps* of Popular Encroachments; which is usually done either in hopes of procuring Ease and Quiet from some vexatious Clamour; or else *made Merchandize, and merely bought and sold*. This is breaking into a Constitution to serve a present Expedient, or supply a present Exigency: The Remedy of an Empirick, to stifle the present Pain, but with certain Prospect of sudden and terrible Returns. When a Child grows easy and content by being humoured, and when a Lover becomes satisfied by small Compliances, without further Pursuits; then expect to find popular Assemblies content with small Concessions. If there could one single Example be brought from the whole Compass of History, of any one popular Assembly, who after beginning to contend for Power, ever sat down quietly with a certain Share: Or if one Instance could be produced of a popular Assembly, that ever knew, or proposed, or declared what Share of Power was their due; then might there be some Hopes that it were a Matter to be adjusted by Reasonings, by Conferences, or Debates: But since all that is manifestly otherwise, I see no other Course to be taken in a settled State, than a steady constant Resolution in those to whom the rest of the Ballance is entrusted, never to give Way so far to popular Clamours, as to make the least Breach in the Constitution; through which a Million of Abuses and Encroachments will certainly in Time force their Way.

AGAIN, From this Deduction, it will not be difficult to gather and assign certain Marks of popular Encroachments; by observing of which, those who hold the Ballance in a State, may judge of the Degrees, and by early Remedies and Application, put a Stop to the fatal Consequences that would otherwise ensue. What those Marks are, hath been at large deduced, and need not be here repeated.

ANOTHER Consequence is this, That (with all Respect for popular Assemblies be it spoke) it is hard to recollect one Folly,

Infirmity or Vice, to which a single Man is subjected, and from which a Body of Commons either collective or represented can be wholly exempt. For, besides that they are composed of Men with all their Infirmities about them; they have also the ill Fortune to be generally led and influenced by the very worst among themselves; I mean, *Popular Orators, Tribunes,* or, as they are now stiled, *Great Speakers, Leading Men,* and the like. From whence it comes to pass, that in their Results we have sometimes found the same Spirit of Cruelty and Revenge, of Malice and Pride; the same Blindness and Obstinacy, and Unsteadiness; the same ungovernable Rage and Anger; the same Injustice, Sophistry and Fraud, that ever lodged in the Breast of any Individual.

AGAIN, In all Free States the Evil to be avoided is *Tyranny,* that is to say, the *Summa Imperii,* or unlimitted Power solely in the Hands of the *One,* the *Few,* or the *Many.* Now, we have shewn, that although most Revolutions of Government in *Greece* and *Rome* began with the Tyranny of the People, yet they generally concluded in that of a single Person. So that an úsurping Populace is its own *Dupe*; a meer Underworker, and a Purchaser in Trust for some single Tyrant; whose State and Power they advance to their own Ruin, with as blind an Instinct, as those Worms that die with weaving magnificent Habits for Beings of a superior Nature to their own.

CHAP. V.

SOME Reflections upon the late publick Proceedings among us, and that Variety of Factions, in which we are still so intricately engaged, gave Occasion to this Discourse. I am not conscious that I have forced one Example, or put it into any other Light than it appeared to me, long before I had Thoughts of producing it.

I CANNOT conclude without adding some particular Remarks upon the present Posture of Affairs, and Dispositions in this Kingdom.

THE Fate of Empire is grown a common Place: That all Forms of Government having been instituted by Men, must be mortal like their Authors, and have their Periods of Duration limited, as well as those of private Persons; this is a Truth of vulgar Knowledge and Observation. But there are few who turn their Thoughts to examine how these Diseases in a State are bred, that hasten its End; which would, however, be a very useful Enquiry. For, although we cannot prolong the Period of a Commonwealth beyond the Decree of Heaven, or the Date of its Nature, any more than human Life, beyond the Strength of the Seminal Virtue; yet we may manage a sickly Constitution, and preserve a strong one; we may watch and prevent Accidents; we may turn off a great Blow from without, and purge away an ill Humour that is lurking within: And by these and other such Methods, render a State long-lived, although not immortal. Yet some Physicians have thought, that if it were practicable to keep the several Humours of the Body in an exact equal Ballance of each with its Opposite, it might be immortal; and so perhaps would a political Body, if the Ballance of Power could be always held exactly even. But I doubt, this is as almost impossible in the Practice as the other.

IT hath an Appearance of Fatality, and that the Period of a State approacheth, when a Concurrence of many Circumstances, both within and without, unite towards its Ruin; while the whole

Body of the People are either stupidly negligent, or else giving in with all their Might, to those very Practices that are working their Destruction. To see whole Bodies of Men breaking a Constitution by the very same Errors that so many have been broke before: To observe opposite Parties, who can agree in nothing else, yet firmly united in such Measures as must certainly ruin their Country: In short, to be encompassed with the greatest Dangers from without; to be torn by many virulent Factions within; then to be secure and senseless under all this, and to make it the very least of our Concern: These and some others that might be named, appear to me to be the most likely Symptoms in a State of a *Sickness unto Death*.

> *Quod procul à nobis flectat Fortuna gubernans.*
> *Et ratio potius, quam res persuadeat ipsa,*   Lucr.

THERE are some Conjunctures wherein the Death or Dissolution of Government is more lamentable in its Consequences than it would be in others. And, I think, a State can never arrive to its Period in a more deplorable *Crisis*, than at a Time when some *Prince in the Neighbourhood*, of vast Power and Ambition, lies hovering like a Vulture to devour, or at least dismember its dying Carcase; by which Means, it becomes only a Province or Acquisition to some mighty Monarchy, without Hopes of a Resurrection.

I KNOW very well, there is a Set of sanguine Tempers, who deride and ridicule in the Number of Fopperies all such Apprehensions as these. They have it ready in their Mouths, that the People of *England* are of a Genius and Temper, never to admit Slavery among them; and they are furnished with a great many Common-Places upon that Subject. But it seems to me, that such Discoursers do reason upon short Views, and a very moderate Compass of Thought. For, I think it a great Error to count upon the Genius of a Nation as a standing Argument in all Ages; since there is hardly a Spot of Ground in *Europe*, where the Inhabitants have not frequently and entirely changed their Temper and Genius. Neither can I see any Reason, why the Genius of a Nation should be more fixed in the Point of Government, than in their Morals, their Learning, their Religion, their common Humour and Conversation, their Diet and their Complexion; which do all notoriously vary, almost in every Age; and may every one of them have great Effects upon Men's Notions of Government.

SINCE the *Norman* Conquest, the Ballance of Power in *England* hath often varied, and sometimes been wholly overturned: The Part which the Commons had in it, *that most disputed Point in its Original, Progress, and Extent*, was by their own Confessions, but a very inconsiderable Share. Generally speaking, they have been gaining ever since, although with frequent Interruptions, and slow Progress. The abolishing of *Villanage*, together with the Custom introduced (or permitted) among the Nobles of selling their Lands in the Reign of *Henry* the Seventh, was a mighty Addition to the Power of the Commons; yet I think a much greater happened in the Time of his Successor, at the Dissolution of the Abbeys: For this turned the *Clergy* wholly out of the Scale, who had so long filled it; and placed the *Commons* in their Stead; who in a few Years became possessed of vast Quantities of those and other Lands, by Grant or Purchase. About the Middle of Queen *Elizabeth*'s Reign, I take the Power between the Nobles and the Commons, to have been in more equal Ballance than it was ever before or since. But then, or soon after, arose a Faction in *England*; which, under the Name of *Puritan*, began to grow popular, by molding up their new Schemes of Religion with *Republican* Principles in Government; who gaining upon the *Prerogative*, as well as the *Nobles*, under several Denominations, for the Space of about Sixty Years, did at last overthrow the Constitution; and, according to the usual Course of such Revolutions, did introduce a Tyranny, first of the People, and then of a single Person.

IN a short Time after, the old Government was revived. But the Progress of Affairs, for almost Thirty Years, under the Reigns of two weak Princes, is a Subject of a very different Nature; when the Ballance was in Danger to be overturned by the Hands that held it; which was, at last, very seasonably prevented by the late Revolution. However, as it is the Talent of Human Nature to run from one Extream to another; so, in a very few Years, we have made mighty Leaps from Prerogative Heights into the Depths of Popularity; and, I doubt, to the very last Degree that our Constitution will bear. It were to be wished, that the most august Assembly of the Commons, would please to form a *Pandect* of their own Power and Privileges, to be confirmed by the entire legislative Authority; and that in as solemn a Manner (if they please) as the *Magna Charta*. But to fix one Foot of their Compass wherever they think fit, and extend the other to such terrible Lengths, without describing any Circumference at all; is to leave us, and themselves, in a very uncertain State, and in a Sort of *Rotation*, that the Author of the *Oceana* never dreamt of. I believe the most hardy Tribune will not venture to affirm, at present, that any just Fears of Encroachment are given us from the Regal Power, or the *Few*; And, is it then impossible to err on the other Side? How far must we proceed, or where shall we stop? *The Raging of the Sea*, and *the Madness of the People*, are put together in Holy Writ; and it is God, alone, who can say to either, *Hitherto shalt thou pass, and no farther*.

THE Ballance of Power, in a limited State, is of such absolute Necessity, that *Cromwell* himself, before he had perfectly confirmed his Tyranny; having some Occasions for the Appearance of a Parliament, was forced to create and erect an entire new House of Lords, (such as it was) for a Counterpoise to the Commons. And, indeed, considering the Vileness of the Clay, I have sometimes wondered, that no Tribune of that Age, durst ever venture to ask the *Potter*, *What dost thou make?* But it was then about the last Act of a popular Usurpation; and *Fate*, or *Cromwell*, had already prepared them for that of a single Person.

I HAVE been often amazed at the rude, passionate, and mistaken Results, which have, at certain Times, fallen from great Assemblies, both antient and modern; and of other Countries as well as our own. This gave me the Opinion I mentioned a while ago; that publick Conventions are liable to all the Infirmities, Follies, and Vices of private Men. To which, if there be any Exception, it must be of such Assemblies, who act by *universal Concert, upon publick Principles, and for publick Ends*; such as proceed upon Debates without *unbecoming Warmths*, or *Influence from particular Leaders and Inflamers*; such whose Members, instead *of canvassing to procure Majorities for their private Opinions, are ready to comply with general sober Results, although contrary to their own Sentiments*. Whatever Assemblies act by these, and other Methods of the like Nature, must be allowed to be exempt from several Imperfections, to which particular Men are subjected. But I think, the Source of most Mistakes and Miscarriages, in Matters debated by publick Assemblies, ariseth from the Influence of private Persons upon great Numbers; stiled in common Phrase, *leading Men and Parties*. And therefore, when we sometimes meet a *few Words* put together, which is called the *Vote*, or *Resolution* of an Assembly, and which we cannot possibly reconcile to *Prudence*, or *publick Good*; it is most charitable to conjecture, that such a Vote hath been conceived, and born, and bred in a private Brain; afterwards raised and supported by an obsequious Party; and then, with usual Methods confirmed by an *artificial* Majority. For, let us suppose five Hundred Men, mixed, in Point of Sense and Honesty, as usually Assemblies are; and let us suppose these Men proposing, debating, resolving, voting, according to the meer natural Motions of their own little, or much Reason and Understanding; I do allow, that Abundance of indigested and abortive, many pernicious and foolish Overtures would arise, and float a few Minutes; but then they would die, and disappear. Because, this must be said in Behalf of human Kind; that common Sense, and plain Reason, while Men are disengaged from acquired Opinions, will ever have some general Influence upon their Minds; Whereas, the Species of Folly and Vice are infinite, and so different in every Individual, that they could never procure a Majority, if other Corruptions did not enter to pervert Mens Understandings, and misguide their Wills.

To describe how Parties are bred in an Assembly, would be a Work too difficult at present, and perhaps not altogether safe. *Periculosæ plenum opus aleæ*. Whether those who are Leaders, usually arrive at that Station, more by a Sort of Instinct, or secret Composition of their Nature, or Influence of the Stars, than by the Possession of any great Abilities; may be a Point of much Dispute: But when the Leader is once fixed, there will never fail to be Followers. And Man is so apt to *imitate*, so much of the Nature of *Sheep*, (*Imitatores, servum Pecus*) that whoever is so bold to give the first *great Leap over the Heads of those about him*, (although he be the worst of the Flock) shall be quickly followed by the rest. Besides; when Parties are once formed, the Stragglers look so ridiculous, and become so insignificant, that they have no other way, but to run into the Herd, which, at least, will hide and protect them; and where to be much considered, requires only to be very violent.

But there is one Circumstance, with relation to Parties, which I take to be, of all others, most pernicious in a State; and I would be glad any Partizan would help me to a tolerable Reason, that because *Clodius* and *Curio* happen to agree with me in a few singular Notions, I must therefore blindly follow them in all: Or, to state it at best, that because *Bibulus*, the *Party-man*, is persuaded that *Clodius* and *Curio*, do really propose the Good of their Country, as their chief End; therefore *Bibulus* shall be wholly guided and governed by them, in the Means and Measures towards it. Is it enough for *Bibulus*, and the rest of the Herd to say, without further examining, *I am of the Side with* Clodius, *or I vote with* Curio? Are these proper Methods to form and make up what they think fit to call the *united Wisdom of the Nation?* Is it not possible, that, upon some Occasions, *Clodius* may be bold and insolent, born away by his Passion, malicious and revengeful; that *Curio* may be corrupt, and expose to Sale his Tongue, or his Pen. I conceive it far below the Dignity, both of human Nature, and human Reason, to be engaged in any Party, the most plausible soever, upon such servile Conditions.

This Influence of *One* upon *Many*, which seems to be as great in a People *represented*, as it was of old in the Commons *collective*, together with the Consequences it has had upon the Legislature; hath given me frequent Occasion to reflect upon what *Diodorus* tells us of one *Charondas*, a Lawgiver to the *Sybarites*, an antient People of *Italy*; who was so averse from all Innovation, especially when it was to proceed from particular Persons; and, I suppose that he might put it out of the Power of Men, fond of their own Notions, to disturb the Constitution at their Pleasures, by advancing private Schemes; as to provide a Statute, that whoever proposed any Alteration to be made, should step out, and do it with a Rope about his Neck: If the Matter proposed were generally approved, then it should pass into a Law; if it went in the Negative, the Proposer to be immediately *hanged*. Great Ministers may talk of what Projects they please; but I am deceived, if a more effectual one could ever be found, for *taking off* (as the present Phrase is) those hot unquiet Spirits, who disturb Assemblies, and obstruct publick Affairs, by gratifying their Pride, their Malice, their Ambition, their Vanity, or their Avarice.

THOSE who, in a late Reign, began the Distinction between the *personal* and *political* Capacity, seem to have had Reason, if they judged of Princes by themselves: For, I think, there is hardly to be found, through all Nature, a greater Difference between two Things, than there is between a representing Commoner, in the Function of his publick Calling, and the same Person, when he acts in the common Offices of Life. Here, he allows himself to be upon a Level with the rest of Mortals: Here, he follows his own Reason, and his own Way; and rather affects a Singularity in his Actions and Thoughts, than servilely to copy either from the wisest of his Neighbours. In short, here his Folly, and his Wisdom, his Reason, and his Passions, are all of his own Growth; not the Eccho, or Infusion of other Men. But when he is got near the Walls of his Assembly, he assumes, and affects an entire Set of very different Airs; he conceives himself a Being of a superior Nature to those *without*, and acting in a Sphere where the vulgar Methods for the Conduct of human Life, can be of no Use. He is listed in a Party, where he neither knows the Temper, nor Designs, nor perhaps the Person of his Leader; but whose Opinions he follows and maintains, with a Zeal and Faith as violent, as a young Scholar does those of a Philosopher, whose Sect he is taught to profess. He hath neither Thoughts, nor Actions, nor Talk, that he can call his own; but all conveyed to him by his Leader, as Wind is through an Organ. The Nourishment he receives hath been not only *chewed*, but *digested*, before it comes into his Mouth. Thus instructed, he followeth his *Party*, right or wrong, through all its Sentiments; and acquires a Courage, and Stiffness of Opinion, not at all congenial with him.

THIS encourages me to hope, that during the present lucid

Interval, the Members retired to their Homes, may suspend a while their *acquired Complexions*; and, taught by the Calmness of the Scene, and the Season, re-assume the native Sedateness of their Temper. If this should be so, it would be wise in them, as individual and private Mortals, to look back a little upon the Storms they have *raised*, as well as those they have *escaped*: To reflect, that they have been Authors of a new and wonderful Thing in *England*; which is, for a House of Commons to lose the universal Favour of the Numbers they represent: To observe, how those whom they thought fit to persecute for Righteousness Sake, have been openly caressed by the People; and to remember, how themselves sat in fear of their Persons from popular Rage. Now, if they would know the Secret of all this unpresidented Proceeding in their *Masters*; they must not impute it to their Freedom in Debate, or declaring their Opinions; but to that unparliamentary Abuse of setting Individuals upon their Shoulders, who were hated by God and Man. For, it seems, the Mass of the People, in such Conjunctures as this, have opened their Eyes, and will not endure to be governed by *Clodius* and *Curio*, at the Head of their *Myrmidons*; although these be ever so numerous, and composed of their own Representatives.

THIS Aversion of the People against the late Proceedings of the Commons, is an Accident, that if it last a while, might be improved to good Uses for setting the Ballance of Power a little more upon an Equality, than their late Measures seem to promise or admit. This Accident may be imputed to two Causes. The first is, an universal Fear and Apprehension of the Greatness and Power of *France*, whereof the People, in general, seem to be very much, and justly possessed; and therefore cannot but resent to see it, in so critical a Juncture, wholly laid aside by their *Ministers*, the Commons. The other Cause is, a great Love, and Sense of Gratitude in the People, towards their present King; grounded upon a long Opinion and Experience of his Merit, as well as Concessions to all their reasonable Desires; so that it is for some Time they have begun to say, and to fetch Instances where he hath, in many Things, been hardly used. How long these Humours may last, (for Passions are momentary, and especially those of a Multitude) or what Consequences they may produce, a little Time will discover. But, whenever it comes to pass, that a popular Assembly, free from such Obstructions, and already possessed of more Power, than an equal Ballance will allow, shall continue to think they have not enough; but by cramping the Hand that holds the Ballance, and by Impeachments, or Dissentions with the Nobles, endeavour still for more; I cannot possibly see, in the common Course of Things, how the same Causes can produce different Effects and Consequences among us, from what they did in *Greece* and *Rome*.

A
MEDITATION
UPON A ж

𝕭𝖗𝖔𝖔𝖒=𝕾𝖙𝖎𝖈𝖐,

AND

Somewhat Beside;

O F

The Same AUTHOR'S.

——*Utile dulci.*

LONDON:

Printed for *E. Curll*, at the *Dial* and *Bible* againſt
St. *Dunſtan*'s Church in *Fleetſtreet* ; and ſold by
J. Harding, at the *Poſt-Office* in St. *Martins-Lane*.
1710.

(Price 6 *d.*)

Given me by John Cliffe Eſq, who had
them of the Bp. of Kilalla in Jreland
whoſe Daughter he married & was
my Lodger. — Clark.

A
MEDITATION
UPON A
BROOM-STICK:
ACCORDING TO

The Style and Manner of the Honourable Robert

Boyle's *Meditations.*

Written in the YEAR 1703.

THIS single Stick, which you now behold ingloriously lying in that neglected Corner, I once knew in a flourishing State in a Forest: It was full of Sap, full of Leaves, and full of Boughs: But now, in vain does the busy Art of Man pretend to vye with Nature, by tying that withered Bundle of Twigs to its sapless Trunk: It is now at best but the Reverse of what it was; a Tree turned upside down, the Branches on the Earth, and the Root in the Air: It is now handled by every dirty Wench, condemned to do her Drugery; and by a capricious Kind of Fate, destined to make other Things clean, and be nasty it self. At length, worn to the Stumps in the Service of the Maids, it is either thrown out of Doors, or condemned to its last Use of kindling a Fire. When I beheld this, I sighed, and said within my self SURELY MORTAL MAN IS A BROOMSTICK; Nature sent him into the World strong and lusty, in a thriving Condition, wearing his own Hair on his Head, the proper Branches of this reasoning Vegetable; till the Axe of Intemperance has lopped off his Green Boughs, and left him a withered Trunk: He then flies to Art, and puts on a *Perriwig*; valuing himself upon an unnatural Bundle of Hairs, all covered with Powder, that never grew on his Head: But now, should this our *Broom-stick* pretend to enter the Scene, proud of those *Birchen* Spoils it never bore, and all covered with Dust, though the Sweepings of the finest Lady's Chamber; we should be apt to ridicule and despise its Vanity. Partial Judges that we are of our own Excellencies, and other Mens Defaults!

BUT a *Broom-stick*, perhaps you will say, is an Emblem of a Tree standing on its Head; and pray what is Man but a topsy-turvy Creature? His Animal Faculties perpetually mounted on his Rational; his Head where his Heels should be, groveling on the Earth. And yet, with all his Faults, he sets up to be a universal Reformer and Correcter of Abuses; a Remover of Grievances; rakes into every Slut's Corner of Nature, bringing hidden Corruptions to the Light, and raiseth a mighty Dust where there was none before; sharing deeply all the while in the very same Pollutions he pretends to sweep away. His last Days are spent in Slavery to Women, and generally the least deserving; till worn to the Stumps, like his Brother *Bezom*, he is either kicked out of Doors, or made use of to kindle Flames for others to warm themselves by.

THOUGHTS

ON

Various SUBJECTS

WE have just Religion enough to make us *hate*, but not enough to make us *love* one another.

REFLECT on Things past, as Wars, Negotiations, Factions, and the like; we enter so little into those Interests, that we wonder how Men could possibly be so busy, and concerned for Things so transitory: Look on the present Times, we find the same Humour, yet wonder not at all.

A WISE Man endeavours, by considering all Circumstances, to make Conjectures, and form Conclusions: But the smallest Accident intervening, (and in the Course of Affairs it is impossible to foresee all) doth often produce such Turns and Changes, that at last he is just as much in doubt of Events, as the most ignorant and unexperienced Person.

POSITIVENESS is a good Quality for Preachers and Orators; because whoever would obtrude his Thoughts and Reasons upon a Multitude, will convince others the more, as he appears convinced himself.

HOW is it possible to expect that Mankind will take *Advice*, when they will not so much as take *Warning*?

I FORGET whether Advice be among the lost Things which, *Ariosto* says, are to be found in the Moon: That and Time ought to have been there.

NO Preacher is listened to, but Time; which gives us the same Train and Turn of Thought, that elder People have tried in vain to put into our Heads before.

WHEN we desire or sollicit any Thing; our Minds run wholly on the good Side, or Circumstances of it; when it is obtained, our Minds run only on the bad ones.

r

IN a *Glass-House*, the Workmen often fling in a small Quantity of fresh Coals, which seems to disturb the Fire, but very much enlivens it. This may allude to a gentle stirring of the Passions, that the Mind may not languish.

RELIGION seems to have grown an Infant with Age, and requires Miracles to nurse it, as it had in its Infancy.

ALL Fits of Pleasure are ballanced by an equal Degree of Pain, or Languor; it is like spending this Year, Part of the next Year's Revenue.

THE latter Part of a wise Man's Life is taken up in curing the Follies, Prejudices, and false Opinions he had contracted in the former.

IF a Writer would know how to behave himself with relation to Posterity; let him consider in old Books, what he finds, that he is glad to know; and what Omissions he most laments.

WHATEVER the Poets pretend, it is plain they give Immortality to none but themselves: It is *Homer* and *Virgil* we reverence and admire, not *Achilles* or *Æneas*. With Historians it is quite the contrary; our Thoughts are taken up with the Actions, Persons, and Events we read; and we little regard the Authors.

WHEN a true Genius appears in the World, you may know him by this infallible Sign; that the Dunces are all in Confederacy against him.

MEN, who possess all the Advantages of Life, are in a State where there are many Accidents to disorder and discompose, but few to please them.

IT is unwise to punish Cowards with Ignominy; for if they had regarded that, they would not have been Cowards: Death is their proper Punishment, because they fear it most.

THE greatest Inventions were produced in the Times of Ignorance; as the Use of the *Compass*. *Gunpowder*, and *Printing*; and by the dullest Nation, as the *Germans*.

ONE Argument to prove that the common Relations of *Ghosts* and *Spectres* are generally false; may be drawn from the Opinion held, that Spirits are never seen by more than one Person at a Time: That is to say, it seldom happens that above one Person in a Company is possest with any high Degree of Spleen or Melancholy.

I AM apt to think, that in the Day of Judgment there will be small Allowance given to the Wise for their want of Morals, or to the Ignorant for their want of Faith; because, both are without Excuse. This renders the Advantages equal of Ignorance and Knowledge. But some Scruples in the Wise, and some Vices in the Ignorant, will perhaps be forgiven upon the Strength of Temptation to each.

THE Value of several Circumstances in History, lessens very much by distance of Time; although some minute Circumstances are very valuable; and it requires great Judgment in a Writer to distinguish.

IT is grown a Word of Course for Writers to say, this *critical Age*, as Divines say, this *sinful Age*.

IT is pleasant to observe, how free the present Age is in laying Taxes on the next. *Future Ages shall talk of this: This shall be famous to all Posterity*. Whereas, their Time and Thoughts will be taken up about present Things, as ours are now.

THE *Camelion*, who is said to feed upon nothing but Air, hath of all Animals the nimblest Tongue.

WHEN a Man is made a spiritual Peer, he loses his Sirname; when a temporal, his Christian Name.

IT is in Disputes as in Armies; where the weaker Side sets up false Lights, and makes a great Noise, that the Enemy may believe them to be more numerous and strong than they really are.

SOME Men, under the Notions of weeding out Prejudices; eradicate Religion, Virtue, and common Honesty.

IN all well-instituted Commonwealths, Care hath been taken to limit Mens Possessions; which is done for many Reasons; and among the rest, for one that perhaps is not often considered: Because when Bounds are set to Mens Desires, after they have acquired as much as the Laws will permit them, their private Interest is at an End; and they have nothing to do, but to take care of the Publick.

THERE are but three Ways for a Man to revenge himself of a censorious World: To despise it; to return the like; or to endeavour to live so as to avoid it. The first of these is usually pretended; the last is almost impossible; the universal Practice is for the second.

Herodotus tells us, that in cold Countries Beasts very seldom have Horns; but in hot they have very large ones. This might bear a pleasant Application.

I NEVER heard a finer Piece of Satyr against *Lawyers*, than that of *Astrologers*; when they pretend by Rules of Art to foretell in what Time a Suit will end, and whether to the Advantage of the Plaintiff or Defendant: Thus making the Matter depend entirely upon the Influence of the Stars, without the least regard to the Merits of the Cause.

THAT Expression in *Apocrypha* about *Tobit*, and his Dog following him, I have often heard ridiculed; yet *Homer* has the same Words of *Telemachus* more than once; and *Virgil* says something like it of *Evander*. And I take the Book of *Tobit* to be partly poetical.

I HAVE known some Men possessed of good Qualities, which were very serviceable to others, but useless to themselves; like a Sun-Dial on the Front of a House, to inform the Neighbours and Passengers, but not the Owner within.

IF a Man would register all his Opinions upon Love, Politicks, Religion, Learning, and the like; beginning from his Youth, and so go on to old Age: What a Bundle of Inconsistencies and Contradictions would appear at last?

WHAT they *do* in Heaven we are ignorant of; what they do *not* we are told expresly; that they neither marry, nor are given in Marriage.

WHEN a Man observes the Choice of Ladies now-a-days, in the dispensing of their Favours; can he forbear *De re eque-* paying some Veneration to the Memory of those *stri.* Mares mentioned by *Xenophon*; who, while their Manes were on; that is, while they were in their Beauty, would never admit the Embraces of an Ass.

IT is a miserable Thing to live in Suspence; it is the Life of a Spider. *Vive quidem, pende tamen, improba, dixit.*

THE Stoical Scheme of supplying our Wants, by lopping off our Desires; is like cutting off our Feet when we want Shoes.

PHYSICIANS ought not to give their Judgment of Religion, for the same Reason that Butchers are not admitted to be Jurors upon Life and Death.

THE Reason why so few Marriages are happy, is, because young Ladies spend their Time in making *Nets*, and not in making *Cages*.

IF a Man will observe as he walks the Streets, I believe he will find the merriest Countenances in Mourning-Coaches.

NOTHING more unqualifies a Man to act with Prudence, than a Misfortune that is attended with Shame and Guilt.

THE Power of Fortune is confest only by the Miserable; for the Happy impute all their Success to Prudence or Merit.

AMBITION often puts Men upon doing the meanest Offices; so climbing is performed in the same Posture with Creeping.

ILL Company is like a Dog, who fouls those most whom he loves best.

CENSURE is the Tax a Man pays to the Publick for being eminent.

A

TRITICAL ESSAY

UPON THE

FACULTIES of the MIND

To - - - - - - -

Sir,

*B*EING *so great a Lover of Antiquities, it was reasonable to suppose you would be very much obliged with any Thing that was new. I have been of late offended with many Writers of Essays and moral Discourses, for running into stale Topicks and thread-bare Quotations, and not handling their Subject fully and closely: All which Errors I have carefully avoided in the following Essay, which I have proposed as a Pattern for young Writers to imitate. The Thoughts and Observations being entirely new, the Quotations untouched by others, the Subject of mighty Importance, and treated with much Order and Perspicuity: It hath cost me a great deal of Time; and I desire you will accept and consider it as the utmost Effort of my Genius.*

A

Tritical ESSAY, &c.

*P*HILOSOPHERS say, that Man is a Microcosm or little World, resembling in Miniature every Part of the great: And, in my Opinion, the Body Natural may be compared to the Body Politick: And if this be so, how can the *Epicureans* Opinion be true, that the Universe was formed by a fortuitous

Concourse of Atoms; which I will no more believe, than that the accidental Jumbling of the Letters in the Alphabet, could fall by Chance into a most ingenious and learned Treatise of Philosophy, *Risum teneatis Amici*, HOR. This false Opinion must needs create many more; it is like an Error in the first Concoction, which cannot be corrected in the second; the Foundation is weak, and whatever Superstructure you raise upon it, must of Necessity fall to the Ground. Thus Men are led from one Error to another, till with *Ixion* they embrace a Cloud instead of *Juno*; or, like the Dog in the Fable, lose the Substance in gaping at the Shadow. For such Opinions cannot cohere; but like the Iron and Clay in the Toes of *Nebuchadnezzar*'s Image, must separate and break in Pieces. I have read in a certain Author, that *Alexander* wept because he had no more Worlds to conquer; which he need not have done, if the fortuitous Concourse of Atoms could create one: But this is an Opinion fitter for that many-headed Beast, the Vulgar, to entertain, than for so wise a Man as *Epicurus*; the corrupt Part of his Sect only borrowed his Name, as the Monkey did the Cat's Claw, to draw the Chesnut out of the Fire.

HOWEVER, the first Step to the Cure is to know the Disease; and although Truth may be difficult to find, because, as the Philosopher observes, she lives in the Bottom of a Well; yet we need not, like blind Men, grope in open Day-light. I hope, I may be allowed, among so many far more learned Men, to offer my Mite, since a Stander-by may sometimes, perhaps, see more of the Game than he that plays it. But I do not think a Philosopher obliged to account for every Phænomenon in Nature; or drown himself with *Aristotle*, for not being able to solve the Ebbing and Flowing of the Tide, in that fatal Sentence he passed upon himself, *Quia te non capio, tu capies me*.

WHEREIN he was at once the Judge and the Criminal, the Accuser and Executioner. *Socrates*, on the other Hand, who said he knew nothing, was pronounced by the Oracle to be the wisest Man in the World.

BUT to return from this Digression; I think it as clear as any Demonstration in *Euclid*, that Nature does nothing in vain; if we were able to dive into her secret Recesses, we should find that the smallest Blade of Grass, or most contemptible Weed, has its particular Use; but she is chiefly admirable in her minutest Compositions, the least and most contemptible Insect most discovers the Art of Nature, if I may so call it; although Nature, which delights in Variety, will always triumph over Art: And as the Poet observes,

Naturam expellas furcâ licet, usque recurret. Hor.

But the various Opinions of Philosophers, have scattered through the World as many Plagues of the Mind, as *Pandora's* Box did those of the Body; only with this Difference, that they have not left Hope at the Bottom. And if Truth be not fled with *Astræa*, she is certainly as hidden as the Source of *Nile*, and can be found only in *Utopia*. Not that I would reflect on those wise Sages, which would be a Sort of Ingratitude; and he that calls a Man ungrateful, sums up all the Evil that a Man can be guilty of.

Ingratum si dixeris, omnia dicis.

But what I blame the Philosophers for, (although some may think it a Paradox) is chiefly their Pride; nothing less than an *ipse dixit*, and you must pin your Faith on their Sleeve. And, although *Diogenes* lived in a Tub, there might be, for ought I know, as much Pride under his Rags, as in the fine spun Garment of the Divine *Plato*. It is reported of this *Diogenes*, that when *Alexander* came to see him, and promised to give him whatever he would ask; the *Cynick* only answered, *Take not from me, what thou canst not give me; but stand from between me and the Light;* which was almost as extravagant as the Philosopher that flung his Money into the Sea, with this remarkable Saying, ———

How different was this Man from the Usurer, who being told his Son would spend all he had got, replied, *He cannot take more Pleasure in spending, than I did in getting it.* These Men could see the Faults of each other, but not their own; those they flung into the Bag behind; *Non videmus id manticæ quod in tergo est.* I may, perhaps, be censured for my free Opinions, by those carping *Momus's*, whom Authors worship as the *Indians* do the Devil, for fear. They will endeavour to give my Reputation as many

Wounds as the Man in the Almanack; but I value it not; and perhaps, like Flies, they may buz so often about the Candle, till they burn their Wings. They must pardon me, if I venture to give them this Advice, not to rail at what they cannot under-stand; it does but discover that self-tormenting Passion of Envy; than which, the greatest Tyrant never invented a more cruel Torment.

> *Invidia Siculi non invenere Tyranni*
> *Tormentum majus.*——— Juven.

I MUST be so bold, to tell my Criticks and Witlings, that they are no more Judges of this, than a Man that is born blind can have any true Idea of Colours. I have always observed, that your empty Vessels sound loudest: I value their Lashes as little, as the Sea did when *Xerxes* whipped it. The utmost Favour a Man can expect from them, is that which *Polyphemus* promised *Ulysses*, that he would devour him the last: They think to subdue a Writer, as *Cæsar* did his Enemy, with a *Veni, vidi, vici*. I confess, I value the Opinion of the judicious Few, a *Rymer*, a *Dennis*, or a *Walsh*; but for the rest, to give my Judgment at once; I think the long Dispute among the Philosophers about a *Vacuum*, may be determined in the Affirmative, that it is to be found in a Critick's Head. They are, at best, but the Drones of the learned World, who devour the Honey, and will not work themselves; and a Writer need no more regard them, than the Moon does the Barking of a little sensless Cur. For, in spight of their terrible Roaring, you may with half an Eye discover the *Ass* under the *Lyon's* Skin.

BUT to return to our Discourse: *Demosthenes* being asked, what was the first Part of an Orator, replied, *Action*: What was the Second, *Action*: What was the Third, *Action*: And so on *ad infinitum*. This may be true in Oratory; but Contemplation, in other Things, exceeds Action. And, therefore, a wise Man is never less alone, than when he is alone:

> *Nunquam minus solus, quàm cum solus.*

AND *Archimedes*, the famous Mathematician, was so intent upon his Problems, that he never minded the Soldier who came to kill him. Therefore, not to detract from the just Praise which belongs to Orators; they ought to consider that Nature, which gave us two Eyes to see, and two Ears to hear, hath given us but one Tongue to speak; wherein, however, some do so abound; that the *Virtuosi*, who have been so long in Search for the perpetual Motion, may infallibly find it there.

SOME Men admire Republicks; because, Orators flourish there most, and are the great Enemies of Tyranny: But my Opinion is, that one Tyrant is better than an Hundred. Besides, these Orators inflame the People, whose Anger is really but a short Fit of Madness.

> *Ira furor brevis est.*———   Horat.

AFTER which, Laws are like Cobwebs, which may catch small Flies, but let Wasps and Hornets break through. But in Oratory, the greatest Art is to hide Art.

> *Artis est celare Artem.*

BUT this must be the Work of Time; we must lay hold on all Opportunities, and let slip no Occasion, else we shall be forced to weave *Penelope*'s Web; unravel in the Night what we spun in the Day. And, therefore, I have observed that Time is painted with a Lock before, and bald behind; signifying thereby, that we must take Time (as we say) by the Forelock; for when it is once past, there is no recalling it.

THE Mind of Man is, at first, (if you will pardon the Expression) like a *Tabula rasa*; or like Wax, which while it is soft, is capable of any Impression, until Time hath hardened it. And at length Death, that grim Tyrant, stops us in the Midst of our Career. The greatest Conquerors have at last been conquered by Death, which spares none from the Sceptre to the Spade.

> *Mors omnibus communis.*

ALL Rivers go to the Sea, but none return from it. *Xerxes* wept when he beheld his Army; to consider that in less than an Hundred Years they would all be dead. *Anacreon* was choqued with a Grape-stone; and violent Joy kills as well as violent Grief.

There is nothing in this World constant, but Inconstancy; yet *Plato* thought, that if Virtue would appear to the World in her own native Dress, all Men would be enamoured with her. But now, since Interest governs the World, and Men neglect the Golden Mean, *Jupiter* himself, if he came on the Earth, would be despised, unless it were as he did to *Danaæ*, in a golden Shower. For Men, now-a-days, worship the rising Sun, and not the setting.

Donec eris fælix, multos numerabis amicos.

THUS have I, in Obedience to your Commands, ventured to expose my self to Censure in this Critical Age. Whether I have done Right to my Subject, must be left to the Judgment of the learned Reader: However, I cannot but hope, that my attempting of it may be an Encouragement for some able Pen to perform it with more Success.

The Prefaces *to* Sir William Temple's Works *Edited by* Swift

1700-1709

LETTERS

Written by
Sir *W. Temple*, Bar.t

AND OTHER
Ministers of State,

Both at Home and Abroad.

CONTAINING,

An ACCOUNT of the most *Important Transactions* that pass'd in *Christendom* from 1665 to 1672.

In Two Volumes.

Review'd by Sir *W. Temple* sometime before his Death:

AND

Published by *Jonathan Swift* Domestick Chaplain to his Excellency the Earl of *Berkeley*, one of the Lords Justices of *Ireland*.

LONDON:

Printed for *J. Tonson*, at Gray's Inn Gate in Gray's Inn Lane; and *A.* and *J. Churchil*, at the *Black Swan* in *Pater-Noster-Row*, and *R. Simpson*, at the *Harp* in S. Paul's Church-yard, MDCC.

TO HIS

Most Sacred Majesty

William III

King of *England*, *Scotland*,
France and *Ireland*, &c.

These Letters of Sir *W. Temple*
having been left to my Care,
they are most humbly presented to YOUR MAJESTY by

Your Majesty's most dutiful
and obedient Subject.

Jonathan Swift.

THE

PUBLISHER'S EPISTLE

TO THE

READER

THE Collection of the following Letters is owing to the diligence of Mr. *Thomas Downton*, who was one of *Sir William Temple*'s Secretaries, during the whole time wherein they bear date. And it has succeeded very fortunately for the Publick, that there is contained in them an Account of all the chief Transactions and Negotiations, which passed in Christendom during the seven Years, wherein they are dated; as, The War with *Holland*, which began in 1665: The Treaty between His Majesty and the Bishop of *Munster*, with the Issue of it: The *French* Invasion of *Flanders* in the Year 1667: The Peace concluded between *Spain* and *Portugal*, by the King's Mediation: The Treaty at *Breda*; The Tripple Alliance; and the Peace of *Aix la Chapelle* in the first Part. And in the second Part; the Negotiations in *Holland* in consequence of those Alliances, with the Steps and Degrees, by which they came to decay: The Journey and Death of Madame: The seisure of *Lorrain*, and his Excellency's recalling; with the first Unkindness between *England* and *Holland*, upon the Yatch's transporting his Lady and his Family: And the beginning of the second *Dutch* War in 1672.

With these are intermixt several Letters, familiar and pleasant.

I found the Book among Sir *William Temple*'s Papers, with many others, wherewith I had the opportunity of being long conversant, having passed several Years in his Family.

I pretend no other Part, than the Care, that Mr. *Downton*'s Book should be correctly transcribed, and the Letters placed, in the Order they were writ. I have also made some literal amendments, especially in the *Latin*, *French* and *Spanish*: These I have

s

taken Care should be translated and printed in another Column, for the Use of such Readers as may be unacquainted with the Originals. Whatever faults there may be in the Translation, I doubt, I must answer, for the greater Part; and must leave the rest to those Friends, who were pleas'd to assist me. I speak only of the *French* and *Latin*; for the few *Spanish* Translations, I believe, need no Apology.

It is generally believed, that this Author, has advanced our English Tongue, to as great a Perfection as it can well bear; and yet, how great a Master he was of it, has I think, never appeared so much, as it will in the following Letters; wherein the Style appears so very different, according to the difference of the Persons, to whom they were address'd; either Men of Business, or Idle; of Pleasure, or Serious; of great or of less Parts or Abilities, in their several Stations. So, that, one may discover, the Characters of most of those Persons, he writes to, from the Stile of his Letters.

At the end of each Volume, is added a Collection, copied by the same hand, of several Letters to this Ambassadour, from the chief Persons employ'd, either at home or abroad in these Transactions, and during six Years course of his Negotiations. Among which are many from Pensionary *John de Witt*, and all the Writings of this kind that I know of, which remain of that Minister so renowned in his time.

It has been justly complained of, as a defect among us, that the English Tongue, has produced no Letters of any value; to supply which, it has been the Vein of late Years, to translate several out of other Languages, tho' I think with little Success. Yet among many Advantages, which might recommend this sort of Writing, it is certain, that nothing is so capable, of giving a true Account of Story, as Letters are; which describe Actions, while they are alive and breathing; whereas all other Relations are of Actions past and dead: So as it hath been observed, that the Epistles of *Cicero* to *Atticus*, give a better account of those times, than is to be found in any other Writer.

In the following Letters, the Reader will every where discover, the Force and Spirit of this Author; but that which will most value them to the Publick, both at home and abroad, is,

First, that the Matters contained in them, were the Ground and Foundation, whereon all the Wars and Invasions, as well as all the Negotiations and Treaties of Peace in Christendom, have since been raised: And next, that they are written by a Person, who had so great a share, in all those Transactions and Negotiations.

By residing in his Family, I know, the Author has had frequent Instances from several great Persons both at home and abroad, to publish some Memoirs of those Affairs and Transactions which are the Subject of the following Papers; *and particularly of the Treaties of the Triple Alliance, and those of Aix la Chapelle*; but his usual Answer was, that whatever Memoirs he had written of those Times and Negotiations, were burnt; however, that perhaps after his Death, some Papers might come out, wherein there would be some Account of them: By which, as he has often told me, he meant these Letters.

I had begun to fit them for the Press during the Author's Life; but never could prevail for Leave to publish them: Tho' he was pleased to be at the Pains of reviewing, and to give me his Directions for digesting them into Order. It has since pleased God to take this great and good Person to Himself; and he having done me the Honour, to leave and recommend to me the Care of his Writings; I thought, I could not at present do a greater Service to my Country, or to the Author's Memory, than by making these Papers publick.

By way of Introduction, I need only take notice, that after the Peace of the *Pyrenees*, and His Majesty's happy Restoration in 1660, there was a general Peace in Christendom (except only the Remainder of a War between *Spain* and *Portugal*) until the Year 1665, when that between *England* and *Holland* began, which produced a Treaty between His Majesty and the Bishop of *Munster*. And this commences the following Letters.

I beg the Readers Pardon for any *Errata*'s which may be in the Printing, occasioned by my Absence.

Miscellanea.

THE
THIRD PART.

CONTAINING

I. *An Essay on* Popular Discontents.

II. *An Essay upon* Health and Long Life.

III. *A Defence of the Essay upon* Antient and Modern Learning.

With some other Pieces.

By the late
Sir WILLIAM TEMPLE, Bar.

Published by *Jonathan Swift*, A. M. Prebendary of *St. Patrick's*, *Dublin*.

LONDON,
Printed for Benjamin Tooke, at the Middle-Temple-Gate in *Fleetstreet*. 1701.

The Publisher

TO THE

READER

THE Two following Essays, *Of Popular Discontents*, and *Of Health and long Life*, were written many Years before the Author's Death: They were Revised and Corrected by himself; and were designed to have been part of a Third Miscellanea, to which some others were to have been added, if the later part of his Life had been attended with any sufficient Degree of Health.

For the Third Paper, relating to the Controversie about *Antient and Modern Learning*, I cannot well Inform the Reader upon what Occasion it was writ, having been at that time in another Kingdom; but it appears never to have been finished by the Author.

The Two next Papers contain the Heads of Two Essays intended to have been written upon the *Different Conditions of Life and Fortune*; and upon *Conversation*. I have directed they should both be Printed among the rest, because I believe there are few who will not be content to see even the First Draughts of any thing from this Author's Hand.

At the End I have added a few Translations from *Virgil*, *Horace*, and *Tibullus*, or rather Imitations, done by the Author above Thirty Years ago; whereof the First was Printed among other Eclogues of *Virgil* in the Year 1679. but without any Mention of the Author. They were indeed not intended to have been made publick, till I was informed of several Copies that were got abroad, and those very imperfect and corrupt. Therefore the Reader finds them here only to prevent him from finding them in other Places, very faulty, and perhaps accompanied with many spurious Additions.

[*Editorial Note by* S w i f t *on page* 231.]

Here it is supposed, the Knowledge of the Antients and Moderns in the Sciences last mentioned, was to have been compared; But, whether the Author designed to have gone through such a Work Himself, or intended these Papers only for Hints to some body else that desired them, is not known.

After which the rest was to follow, written in his own Hand, as before.

LETTERS

TO THE

KING,

THE

Prince of *ORANGE*,

THE

Chief Ministers of State,

AND OTHER

PERSONS.

By Sir W. TEMPLE, *Bar*.

Being the Third and Last Volume.

Published by *Jonathan Swift*, D. D.

LONDON:

Printed for *Tim. Goodwin*, at the *Queen's Head* against St. *Dunstan's Church* ; and *Benj. Tooke*, at the *Middle-Temple-Gate*, in *Fleetstreet*. 1703.

PREFACE.

THE following Papers are the last of this, or indeed of any kind; about which the Author ever gave me his particular Commands. They were Corrected by Himself; and fairly Transcribed in his Life time. I have in all Things followed his Directions as strictly as I could: But Accidents unforeseen having since intervened; I have thought convenient to lessen the Bulk of this *Volume*. To which End I have Omitted several LETTERS Addressed to Persons with whom this *Author* Corresponded without any particular Confidence, farther than upon account of their Posts: Because great Numbers of such LETTERS, procured out of the Office; or, by other means (how justifiable I shall not examine) have been already *Printed*: But running wholly upon long dry Subjects of Business, have met no other Reputation than meerly what the Reputation of the *Author* would give them. If I could have foreseen an End of this Trade, I should upon some Considerations have longer forborn sending these into the *World*. But I daily hear, that new Discoveries of Original LETTERS are hasting to the *Press*: To stop the Current of which, I am forced to an earlier Publication than I designed. And therefore I take this Occasion to inform the *Reader*; that these *Letters* ending with the *Author*'s Revocation from his Employments abroad (which in less than two Years was followed by his Retirement from all publick Business) are the last he ever intended for the *Press*; having been Selected by himself from great Numbers yet lying among his Papers.

If I could have been prevailed with by the *Rhetorick* of *Booksellers*, or any other little Regards; I might easily, instead of *Retrenching*, have made very considerable *Additions*; and by that means have perhaps taken the surest Course to prevent the Interloping of others. But, if the *Press* must needs be loaded; I had rather it should not be by my means. And therefore I may hope to be allowed one Word in the Style of a *Publisher*, (an Office lyable to much Censure, without the least Pretension to Merit or to Praise) that, if I have not been much deceived by others and my self; the *Reader* will hardly find one *Letter* in this *Collection* unworthy of the *Author*, or which does not contain something either of Entertainment or of Use.

MEMOIRS.

PART III.

From the
PEACE concluded 1679.

TO THE
Time of the Author's Retirement from Publick Business.

By Sir WILLIAM TEMPLE *Baronet.*

Et Ille quidem plenus annis abiit, plenus honoribus, illis etiam quos recusavit. Plin. Epist. Lib. 2. Epist. 1.

Publish'd by *Jonathan Swift,* D.D.

LONDON:
Printed for BENJAMIN TOOKE, at the *Middle-Temple Gate* in *Fleet-street.* MDCCIX.

THE
PREFACE

IT was perfectly in complyance to some Persons for whose Opinion I have great Deference, that I so long with-held the Publication of the following Papers. They seem'd to think, that the Freedom of Passages in these Memoirs, might give Offence to several who were still alive; and whose Part in those Affairs which are here related, could not be transmitted to Posterity with any Advantage to their Reputation. But, whether this Objection be in it self of much Weight, may perhaps be Disputed; at least it should have little with me, who am under no Restraint in that Particular; Since I am not of an Age to remember those Transactions, nor had any Acquaintance with those Persons whose Counsels or Proceedings are Condemn'd, and who are all of them now Dead.

BUT, as this Author is very free in exposing the Weakness and Corruptions of ill Ministers, so he is as ready to commend the Abilities and Virtue of others, as may be observ'd from several Passages of these Memoirs; particularly, of the late Earl of *Sunderland*, with whom the Author continu'd in the most intimate Friendship to his Death; and who was Father of that most learned and excellent Lord, now Secretary of State: As likewise, of the present Earl of *Rochester*; and the Earl of *Godolphin*, now Lord Treasurer, represented by this impartial Author, as a Person at that time deservedly entrusted with so great a Part in the Prime Ministry; an Office he now Executes again with such universal Applause, so much to the Queen's Honour and his own, and to the Advantage of his Country, as well as of the whole Confederacy.

THERE are two Objections I have sometimes heard to have been offer'd against those Memoirs that were Printed in the Author's Lifetime, and which these now Publish'd may perhaps be equally liable to. First, as to the Matter; that the Author speaks too much of himself: Next, as to the Style; that he affects the Use of *French* Words, as well as some Turns of Expression peculiar to that Language.

I believe, those who make the former Criticism, do not well consider the Nature of Memoirs. 'Tis to the French (if I mistake not) we chiefly owe that manner of Writing; and Sir *William Temple* is not only the first, but I think the only English-man (at least of any Consequence) who ever attempted it. The best French Memoirs are writ by such Persons as were the Principal Actors in those Transactions they pretend to relate, whether of Wars or Negotiations. Those of Sir *William Temple* are of the same Nature; and therefore, in my Judgment, the Publisher (who sent them into the World without the Author's Privity) gave them a wrong Title, when he call'd them *Memoirs of what pass'd in Christendom, &c.* whereas it should rather have been, *Memoirs of the Treaty at Nimeguen*, which was plainly the Sence of the Author, who in the Epistle tells his Son, that *in Compliance with his Desire, he will leave him some Memoirs of what pass'd in his publick Employments Abroad*; And in the Book it self, when he Deduces an Account of the State of War in *Christendom*, he says it is only to prepare the Reader for a Relation of that famous Treaty; where he and Sir *Lionel Jenkins*, were the only Mediators that continu'd any considerable Time; and as the Author was first in Commission, so in Point of Abilities or Credit, either Abroad or at Home, there was no sort of Comparison between the Two Persons. Those Memoirs therefore are properly a Relation of a General Treaty of Peace, wherein the Author had the Principal as well as the most Honourable part, in Quality of Mediator; so that the frequent Mention of himself, seems not only excusable but necessary. The same may be offer'd in Defence of the following papers; because, during the greatest part of the Period they treat of, the Author was in chief Confidence with the King his Master. To which it may be added, That in the few Preliminary Lines at the Head of the first Page, the Author professes he writ those Papers *for the Satisfaction of his Friends hereafter, upon the Grounds of his Retirement, and his Resolution never to meddle again with publick Affairs.*

As to the Objection against the Style of the former Memoirs, that it abounds in *French* Words and Turns of Expression; it is to be consider'd, that at the Treaty of *Nimeguen*, all Business, either by Writing or Discourse, pass'd in the *French* Tongue; and the Author having liv'd so many Years abroad in that and former Ambassys, where all Business, as well as Conversation, ran in that Language, it was hardly possible for him to write upon publick Affairs without some Tincture of it in his Style; tho' in his other Writings, there be little or nothing of it to be observ'd: And as he has often assur'd me it was a Thing he never affected; so upon the Objections made to his former Memoirs, he blotted out some *French* Words in these, and plac'd *English* in their stead, tho' perhaps not so significant.

THERE is one thing proper to inform the Reader, why these Memoirs are call'd the *Third Part*, there having never been published but one Part before, where in the Beginning, the Author mentions a former Part, and in the Conclusion promises a Third. The Subject of the First Part was chiefly the Triple Alliance, during the Negotiation of which my Lord *Arlington* was Secretary of State and chief Minister: Sir *William Temple* often assur'd me, he had burnt those Memoirs; and for that Reason was content his Letters, during his Ambassies at the *Hague* and *Aix la Chapelle*, should be Printed after his Death, in some manner to supply that Loss.

WHAT it was that mov'd Sir *William Temple* to burn those first Memoirs, may perhaps be conjectur'd from some Passages in the Second Part formerly Printed: In one Place the Author has these Words, *My Lord* Arlington, *who made so great a Figure in the former Part of these Memoirs, was now grown out of all Credit, &c.* In other Parts he tells us, That Lord was of the Ministry which broke the Triple League; advis'd the *Dutch* War and *French* Alliance; and in short, was at the bottom of all those Ruinous Measures which the Court of *England* was then taking; so that, as I have been told from a good Hand, and as it seems very probable, he could not think that Lord a Person fit to be celebrated for his Part in forwarding that famous League while he was Secretary of State, who had made such Counterpaces to destroy it. At the End I have subjoyn'd an Appendix, containing besides one or two other Particulars, a Speech of Sir *William Temple*'s in the House of Commons, and an Answer of the

King's to an Address of that House, relating to the Bill of Exclusion, both which are mention'd in these Memoirs.

I have only further to inform the Reader, that altho' these Papers were Corrected by the Author, yet he had once intended to insert some Additions in several Places, as appear'd by certain Hints or Memorandums in the Margin; but whether they were omitted out of forgetfulness, neglect, or want of Health, I cannot determine: One Passage relating to Sir *William Jones* he was pleas'd to tell me, and I have added it in the Appendix. The rest I know nothing of; but the Thread of the Story is intire without 'em.

JONATHAN SWIFT.

Additions to

THE TALE OF A TUB

Contained in

Miscellaneous Works

1720

MISCELLANEOUS WORKS,

Comical & Diverting:

Rev. Jr. [handwritten] BY Fitzgerald

T. R. D. J. S. D. O. P. I. I.

IN TWO PARTS.

I. The TALE *of a* TUB ; with the *Fragment*, & the BATTEL *of the* BOOKS ; with confiderable *Additions* , & explanatory *Notes*, never before printed.

II. MISCELLANIES in PROSE & VERSE, by the fuppofed Author of the firft part.

LONDON,
Printed by Order of the Society
de propagando, &c.

M. DCC. XX.

THE BOOKSELLERS
ADVERTISEMENT
On this new Edition.

TO give the curious Reader a just Idea of what he may expect in this Volume, I cannot do better than transcribe a part of a Letter sent me with the Copy, from an ingenious Gentleman of my acquaintance, whose advice I have followed exactly.

. . . . You have here also according to your desire my *Tale of a Tub*, with all the Notes you have formerly seen, & several others I have added since. You may make what use you please of it, provided you return it me safe when you have done, & that you let no body see it, or know from whom you had it. You'l perhaps find some of these Notes of no great use, because you understand all without 'em; but some Readers will be apt to wish there were more, to explain some other passages they may not perfectly understand.

I think it's almost needless to tell the Readers, they ought not to impute to the Author the sense given to his words in these Notes; especialy in those taken from his Adversarys, such as M. *Wotton*, one of the Heroes of the piece. Any one that reads the praises given him by our Author, will easily see his reasons for giving the worst turn imaginable to every thing he has written. I once hoped to have found a great many more curious Notes of this kind, in the Remarks made on this Book by D. *Bentley* the Author's principal Hero. I am told this is a Master-piece of modern Criticism, & that this Prince of Pedants has, with a vast deal of laborious learning, shewn that he can interpret almost nine passages of *Antient Authors* in a sense different from that which our Author has given them; but particularly that he has most terribly maul'd this Author with those Arms he had so bountifully bestowed on him in the 160 page of this Treatise, & especially with that of his left hand, of which according to his custom he has been very liberal. I'm informed from some of his Friends, that he expects the Thanks of both Houses of Parliament for this performance, as he had lately those of both our learned & wise Universitys for another of the same kind; but that he does not find the present conjuncture favourable for publishing it. When these Remarks appear you may expect an ample Commentary on this Work; in the mean time you may be satisfied with these few Notes I send you.

As for the Manuscript I told you I had seen, which contains a great deal more than what is printed, I would very willingly have taken a copy of what is ommitted, & have sent it you; but I was not allowed that liberty, having only had leave to read it. I can assure you I found those parts not at all inferior to the others that are printed; but I believe some prudential considerations have hindered their publication. I have writ down the heads of the most material, as near as I can now remember, on the leaves put in at the end of my book, where you'l find a general Table * or Index of the whole work, which may serve for a Recapitulation to those that have read it through. I have extended such parts as have not been printed, somthing more largely than the others, & as near as I can remember in the Authors own words. And who knows of what great use this may be in future Ages, to some learned *Freinshemius*, who may undertake to gratify the World with a Supplement of what has been lost of this curious Treatise.

I would advise you (if it can be conveniently done in the same volume) to print all the comical Pieces of the *Miscellanies in Prose & Verse*, generaly attributed to the same Author: as for the serious Pieces in that Collection, tho' some of them be very good in their kind, yet being of a very different nature, I think you may leave them out; there being but few that buy the volume for their sake, & the generality of Readers will be very glad to find the others in the same volume with the *Tale of a Tub*. The Pieces I mean are, *The Meditation upon a Broomstick*; *Various Thoughts*; *The Tritical Essay*; *The Argument against abolishing Christianity*, The *Predictions* &c. with all the Pieces in Verse, to which I would have you add the *Imitation* of part of the seventh Epist. *Lib. I.* of *Horace*, addressed to the Earl of *Oxford*, which

---

* *See below; pp.* 282. *ff.*

is an excellent Piece. You have not seen perhaps how the last lines of this Epistle of *Horace* (which our Author left untouch'd) have been imitated by one that's no great friend to the Doctor.

> *Qui semel aspexit quantum dimissa petitis*
> *Præstent, mature redeat....*
> *Metiri se quemque suo modulo, ac pede, verum est.*

> This Reverend Dean may teach us all
> What merit goes to fill a Stall;
> To weigh our strength, & be so wise
> As not to swell beyond our size:
> Nor aim at Posts of power & profit
> Due to desert, with little of it.

Although I advise the printing all those pieces together in one volume, because I think it will take very well (especially when done so neat & correct as you are used to doe) yet I would not have any body take this for a proof of their being all of the same Author. So long as Dr. *Swift* does not own the *Tale of a Tub*, I think no man has a right to charge him with it, whatever common Fame may report. I know several persons of good sense, that imagine Sr. *William Temple* to have been the Author of it, & find several passages in his other Writings, pretty much in the same strain. Even Dr. *Wotton*, who is certainly no friend to Dr. *Swift*, seems to be of this opinion, when he says (Def. p. 67) that *in his own Conscience he acquits him from composing it; & believes that the Author is dead, & that it was probably written in* 1697. As for what the Author of the pretended *Key to the Tale of a Tub* says about *Jonathan, & Thomas Swift* having joyn'd in this work, I lay no manner of stress on it. . . .

The passage of that Author here mention'd runs thus.

The Preface of the Bookseller before *the Battle of the Books* shews the cause and design of the whole Work, which was perform'd by * a couple of young Clergymen in the Year 1697, who having

---

* *Generally (and not without sufficient reason) said to be Dr.* Jonathan *and* Thomas Swift; *but since they don't think fit publickly to own it, wherever I mention their names, 'tis not upon any other affirmation than as they are the* reputed Authors.

been Domestick Chaplains to Sir *William Temple*, thought themselves oblig'd to take up his Quarrel in relation to the Controversy then in dispute between him and Mr. *Wotton* concerning *Ancient* and *Modern* Learning.

The * one of 'em began a *Defence* of Sir *William*, under the Title of *A Tale of a Tub*, under which he intended to couch the general History of Christianity; shewing the rise of all the remarkable Errors of the *Roman Church*; in the same order they enter'd, and how the Reformation endeavour'd to root 'em out again, with the different Temper of *Luther* from *Calvin* (and those more violent Spirits) in the way of his Reforming: His aim is to ridicule the stubborn errors of the Romish Church, and the humours of the Fanatick Party, and to shew that their Superstition has somewhat very fantastical in it, which is common to both of 'em, notwithstanding the abhorrence they seem to have for one another.

The Author intended to have it very regular, and withal so particular, that he thought not to pass by the Rise of any one single Error or its Reformation: He design'd at last to shew the purity of the Christian Church in the primitive times, and consequently how weakly Mr. *Wotton* pass'd his judgment, and how partially, in preferring the *modern* Divinity before the *Ancient*, with the confutation of whose Book he intended to conclude. But when he had not yet gone half way, his † Companion borrowing the *Manuscript* to peruse, carried it with him to *Ireland*, and having kept it seven Years, at last publish'd it imperfect; for indeed he was not able to carry it on after the intended method; because *Divinity* (tho it chanc'd to be his Profession) had been the least of his study: However he added to it the *Battle of the Books*, wherein he effectually pursues the main design of lashing Mr. *Wotton*, and having added a jocose Epistle Dedicatory to my Lord *Sommers*, and another to Prince *Posterity*, with a pleasant Preface, and interlarded it with one *Digression* concerning *Criticks*, and another in the *modern* kind, a third in praise of *Digressions*, and a fourth in praise of *Madness* (with which he was not unacquainted) concludes the Book with a *Fragment* which

---

* *Thomas Swift.*   † Dr. *Jonathan Swift.*

the first Author made, and intended should have come in about the middle of the *Tale*, as a Preliminary to *Jack*'s Character.

Having thus shewn the reasons of the little order observ'd in the Book, and the imperfectness of the *Tale*, 'tis so submitted to the Reader's censure.

Thomas Swift is Grandson to Sir *William D'avenant*: *Jonathan Swift* is Cousin German to *Thomas Swift*, both Retainers to Sir *William Temple*.

A TABLE, or INDEX, or KEY,

to the

TALE *of a* TUB, &c.

THE Booksellers Dedication to the Lord Somers: how he finds out that Lord to be the Patron intended by his Author pag. 13-14. Dedicators ridiculous who praise their Patrons for qualitys that do not belong to them. 15-16.

The Bookseller to the Reader, tells how long he has had these Papers, when they were writ, & why he publishes them now. 17.

The DEDICATION to *Posterity*. 18. The Author, aprehending that *Time* will soon destroy almost all the Writings of this Age, complains of his malice against modern Authors & their productions, in hurrying them so quickly off the Scene, 19. & therefor adresses Posterity in favour of his Contemporarys, assures him they abound in wit, & learning, & books; & for instance mentions *Dryden, Tate, Durfey, Bentley, & Wotton.* 19-23.

PREFACE. The occasion & design of this Work. 24-5. Project for employing the Beaux of the Nation 25. of modern Prefaces 25-6. Modern wit how delicate 26. Method for penetrating into an Authors thoughts 26-7. Complaints of every Writer against the multitude of Writers 27. Like the fat Fellow in a crowd 28. Our Author insists on the common privileges of Writers *viz.* to be favourably explained when not understood; & to praise himself in the modern way. 28. This treatise without Satyr, & why, 29. Fame sooner got by Satyr than Panegirick; the subject of the later being narrow & that of the former infinite 30. Difference between Athens & England as to general & particular Satyr, 30-1. The Author designs a Panegyrick on the World, & a modest defence of the Rabble, 32.

I. *Sect.* The INTRODUCTION. 33. A Physico-Mythological Dissertation on the different sorts of Oratorial Machines, 34. Of the Bar & the Bench, 34. The Author fond of the number *Three*, promiseth a Panegyrick on it, 35. Of Pulpits, which are the best, 35. Of Ladders on which the British Orators surpass all others,

35. Of the stage itinerant, the Seminary of the two former. 35-6. A physical reason why those machines are elevated 36. Of the curious contrivance of modern Theaters, 36-7. These 3. Machines emblematicaly represent the various sorts of Authors. 37. 38.

An Apologetical Dissertation for the *Grubstreet* Writers against their revolted Rivals of *Gresham & Wills*. 38-9. Superficial Readers can not easily find out Wisdom, which is compared to several pretty things, 40. Commentarys promised on several Writings of Grubstreet Authors, as *Reynard the Fox*, *Tom Thumb*, *Dr. Faustus*, *Whittington & his Cat*, *The Hind & Panther*, *Tommy Pots*, & *the Wise Men of Gotham*, 41-2. The Authors pen & person worn out in serving the State, 42. Multiplicity of Titles & Dedications, 43.

II. *Sect*. Tale of a Tub. Of a Father & three Sons; his Legacies to them & his Will, 44. Of the young mens carriage at the beginning, & of the genteel qualifications they acquired in Town, 45. Description of a new Sect who adored their Creator the Taylor: Of their Idol, & their System. 47-8. The three Brothers follow the mode against their Father's Will, & get *Shoulderknots* by help of Distinctions, 49. Gold lace by help of Tradition, 51. Flame colour'd sattin lyning by means of a suppos'd Codicil, 52. Silver Fringe by vertue of critical interpretation, 53. and Embroidery of Indian figures by laying aside the plain literal meaning, 54. The Will at last lock'd up, 54. Peter got into a Lords House, & after his death turn'd out his Children, 55.

III. *Sect*. A Digression concerning Criticks, 56. Three sorts of Criticks: the two first sorts now extinct, 56-7. The true Critic's genealogy, 57. Office, 58. Definition, 58. Antiquity of their Race proved from Pausanias, who represents them by Asses browzing on Vines, 58-9. and *Herodotus* by Asses with Horns, 60. & by an Ass that frighted a Scythian Army, 60. And *Diodorus* by a poisonous weed, 61. and *Ctesias* by Serpents that poison with their vomit, 61. & *Terence* by the name of *Malevoli*, 62. The true Critick compared to a Taylor; and to a true Beggar, 62-3. Three characteristicks of a true modern Critick, 63-4.

IV. *Sect*. A Tale of a Tub continued, 65. *Peter* assumes

grandeur and Titles, & to support them turns Projector, 65. The Authors hopes of being translated into foreign languages, 65-6. Peters first Invention of *Terra Australis incognita*, 66. The Second of a Remedy for Worms, 66. The third a Whispering Office, 66. Fourth an Insurance Office, 67. Fifth an universal pickle, 67. Sixth a set of Bulls with leaden feet, 68. Lastly his Pardons to Malefactors, 70. *Peters* brains turned, he plays several tricks, & turns out his Brothers Wives, 71. Gives his Brothers bread for mutton, & for wine, 72-3. Tells huge lyes, of a Cow's milk wou'd fill 3000. Churches, 74. Of a Sign-post as large as 16. Men of War, 74. Of a House that traveled 2000. leagues, 74-5. The Brothers steal a Copy of the Will, break open the cellar door; and are both kick'd out of doors by *Peter*, 75-6.

V. *Sect*. A Digression in the modern kind, 77. Our Author expatiates on his great pains to serve the Publick by instructing, & more by diverting, 78. The Moderns having so far excelled the Ancients, the Author gives them a Receipt for a compleat System of all Arts & Sciences, in a small pocket volume, 78. Several defects discovered in *Homer*, & his ignorance in modern Inventions, &c. 79. 80. Our Author's Writings fit to supply all defects, 80. He justifys his praising his own writings by modern examples, 81-2.

VI. *Sect*. T A L E *of a* T U B continued. The two Brothers ejected agree in a Resolution to reform according to the Will, 83. They take different names & are found to be of different complexions, 84. How *Martin* began rudely, but proceeded more cautiously in reforming his coat, 85. *Jack* of a different temper & full of zeal falls a tearing all to pieces, 86. He endeavours to kindle up *Martin* to the same pitch; but not succeeding they separate, 87. *Jack* runs mad, gets many names, & founds the Sect of *Æolists*, 88-9.

VII. *Sect*. A Digression in praise of Digressions. Digressions suited to modern palates, 90. A proof of depraved appetites, 90. But necessary for modern Writers, 90. Two ways now in use to be book-learned, 1. by learning Titles, 2. by reading Indexes; advantages of this last, 91. & of Abstracts, 91-2. The number of Writers encreasing above the quantity of matter, makes this method necessary, 92. and usefull, 93. The Reader empower'd to transplant this Digression, 94.

VIII. *Sect.* T ALE continued. System of the *Æolists*; they hold *wind* or *Spirit* to be the origin of all things, & to bear a great part in their composition, 95. of the fourth & fifth *animas* attributed by them to Man, 95-6. Of their belching or preaching, 96-7. Their Inspiration from Σκότια 97. They use barrels for Pulpits, 98. Female Officers used for inspiration, & why, 99. The notion opposite to that of a Deity fittest to form a Devil, 99. Two Devils dreaded by the Eolists, 100. Their relation with a northern Nation, 100. The Author's respect for this Sect. 101.

IX. *Sect.* Dissertation on Madness. Great Conquerours of Empires, & Founders of Sects in Philosophy & Religion have generally been persons whose reason was disturbed, 102. A small vapour mounting to the brain may occasion great revolutions, 102. Examples of *Henry IV*. who made great preparations for War, because of his Mistress's absence, 103. And of *Louis XIV*. whose great actions concluded in a *fistula*, 104. Extravagant notions of several great Philosophers, how nice to distinguish from Madness, 104-5-6. M. *Wotton*'s fatal mistake in misapplying his peculiar talents, 106. Madness the source of Conquests & Systems, 107. Advantages of fiction & delusion over truth & reality, 108-9. the outside of things better than the inside, 109. Madness how usefull, 110. A proposal for visiting Bedlam, & employing the divers Members in a way usefull to the Publick, 111-2-3.

X. *Sect.* The Author's Compliment to the Readers. Great civilitys practised between Authors & Readers, & our Author's thanks to the whole Nation, 115. How well satisfyed Authors & Booksellers are, 115. To what occasions we ow most of the present writings, 116. Of a Paultry Scribler our Author is affraid of, & therfor desires Dr. *Bentley*'s protection, 116. He gives here his whole store at one meal, 117. Usefulness of this Treatise to different sorts of Readers; the superficial, the ignorant & the Learned, 117. Proposal for making seven ample Comentarys on this work, & of the usefulness of Comentarys for dark Writers, 118. Useful hints for the Comentators of this Treatise, 118-119.

Abstract of what follows after Sect. IX. in the Manuscript.

The History of Martin.

HOW *Jack* & *Martin* being parted, set up each for himself. How they travel'd over hills & dales, met many disasters, suffered much for the good cause, & strugled with difficultys & wants, not having where to lay their head; by all which they afterwards proved themselves to be right Father's Sons, & *Peter* to be spurious. Finding no shelter near *Peter*'s habitation, *Martin* travel'd northwards, & finding the *Thuringians* & neigbouring people disposed to change, he set up his Stage first among them; where making it his business to cry down *Peter*'s pouders, plaisters, salves, & drugs, which he had sold a long time at a dear rate, allowing *Martin* none of the profit, tho he had been often employed in recommending & putting them off; the good people willing to save their pence began to hearken to *Martin*'s speeches. How several great Lords took the hint & on the same account declared for *Martin*; particularly one, who not having enough of one Wife, wanted to marry a second, & knowing *Peter* used not to grant such licenses but at a swinging price, he struck up a bargain with *Martin* whom he found more tractable, & who assured him he had the same power to allow such things. How most of the other Northern Lords, for their own privat ends, withdrew themselves & their Dependants from *Peters* authority & closed in with *Martin*. How *Peter*, enraged at the loss of such large Territorys, & consequently of so much revenue, thunder'd against *Martin*, and sent out the strongest & most terrible of his *Bulls* to devour him; but this having no effect, & *Martin* defending himself boldly & dexterously, *Peter* at last put forth Proclamations, declaring *Martin* & all his Adherents, Rebels & Traytors, ordaining & requiring all his loving Subjects to take up Arms, & to kill burn & destroy all & every one of them, promising large rewards &c. upon which ensued bloody wars & Desolations.

How *Harry Huff* Lord of Albion, one of the greatest Bullys of those days, sent a Cartel to *Martin* to fight him on a stage, at Cudgels, Quarterstaff, Back-sword &c. Hence the origine of that genteel custom of *Prize-fighting*, so well known & practised to this day among those polite Islanders, tho' unknown every where else. How *Martin* being a bold blustering fellow, accepted the Challenge how they met & fought, to the great diversion of the Spectators; & after giving one another broken heads & many bloody wounds & bruises, how they both drew off victorious; in which their Exemple has been frequently imitated by great Clerks & others since that time. How *Martin*'s friends aplauded his victory; & how Lord *Harrys* friends complimented him on the same score; & particularly Lord *Peter*, who sent him a fine Feather for his Cap, to be worn by him & his Successors, as a perpetual mark of his bold defense of Lord *Peter*'s Cause. How *Harry* flushed with his pretended victory over *Martin*, began to huff *Peter* also, & at last down right quarrelled with him about a Wench. How some of Lord *Harry*'s Tennants, ever fond of changes, began to talk kindly of *Martin*, for which he mauld 'em soundly; as he did also those that adhered to *Peter*: how he turn'd some out of house & hold, others he hanged or burnt &c.

How *Harry Huff* after a deal of blustering, wenching, & bullying, died, & was succeeded by a good natured Boy, who giving way to the general bent of his Tennants, allowed *Martin*'s notions to spread every where & take deep root in Albion. How after his death the Farm fell into the hands of a Lady, who was violently in love with Lord *Peter*. How she purged the whole Country with fire & Sword, resolved not to leave the name or remembrance of *Martin*. How *Peter* triumphed, & set up shops again for selling his own pouders plaisters & salves, which were now called the only true ones, *Martins* being all declared counterfeit. How great numbers of *Martin*'s friends left the Country, & traveling up & down in foreign parts, grew acquainted with many of *Jack*'s followers, & took a liking to many of their notions & ways, which they afterwards brought back into Albion, now under another Landlady more moderate & more cunning than the former. How she endeavoured to keep friendship both with *Peter* & *Martin* & trimm'd for some time between the two, not without countenancing & assisting at the same time many of *Jack*'s followers, but finding no possibility of reconciling all the three Brothers, because each would be Master & allow no other salves pouders or plaisters to be used but his own, she discarded all three, & set up a shop for those of her own Farm, well furnished with pouders plaisters salves & all other drugs necessary, all right & true, composed according to receipts made up by Physicians & Apothecarys of her own creating, which they extracted out of *Peter*'s & *Martin*'s & *Jack*'s Receipt-books; & of this medly or hodgpodge made up a Dispensatory of their own; strictly forbiding any other to be used, & particularly *Peter*'s from which the greatest part of this new Dispensatory was stollen. How the Lady further to confirm this change, wisely imitating her Father, degraded *Peter* from the rank he pretended as eldest Brother, & set up her self in his place as head of the Family, & ever after wore her Fathers old Cap with the fine feather he had got from *Peter* for standing his friend; which has likewise been worn, with no small ostentation to this day, by all her Successors, tho declared Ennemys to *Peter*. How Lady Bess & her Physicians being told of many defects & imperfections in their new medley Dispensatory, resolve on a further alteration, & to purge it from a great deal of *Peter*'s trash that still remained in it; but were prevented by her death. How she was succeeded by a North Country Farmer, who pretended great skill in managing of Farms, tho' he cou'd never govern his own poor litle old Farm, nor yet this large new one after he got it. How this new Landlord, to shew his valour & dexterity, fought against Enchanters, Weeds, Giants, & Windmills, & claimed great Honnour for his victorys, tho' he oftimes beshit himself when there was no danger. How his Successor, no wiser than he, occasion'd great disorders by the new methods he took to manage his Farms. How he attempted to establish in his northern Farm the same Dispensatory used in the southern, but miscarried, because *Jack*'s pouders, pills, salves, & plaisters, were there in great vogue.

How the Author finds himself embarassed for having introduced into his History a new Sect, different from the three he

had undertaken to treat of; & how his inviolable respect to the
sacred number *three* obliges him to reduce these four, as he intends to doe all other things, to that number; & for that end to
drop the former *Martin*, & to substitute in his place Lady *Besses*
Institution, which is to pass under the name of *Martin* in the
sequel of this true History. This weighty point being clear'd, the
Author goes on & describes mighty quarrels & squables between *Jack* & *Martin*, how sometimes the one had the better &
sometimes the other, to the great desolation of both Farms, till
at last both sides concur to hang up the Landlord, who pretended
to die a Martyr for *Martin*, tho he had been true to neither side,
& was suspected by many to have a great affection for *Peter*.

A Digression *on the nature usefulness and necessity of* Wars *and* Quarels.

THIS being a matter of great consequence the Author
intends to treat it methodicaly & at large in a Treatise
apart, & here to give only some hints of what his large
Treatise contains. The State of War natural to all Creatures. War
is an attempt to take by violence from others a part of what they
have & we want. Every man fully sensible of his own merit, &
finding it not duly regarded by others, has a natural right to take
from them all that he thinks due to himself: & every creature
finding its own wants more than those of others has the same
right to take every thing its nature requires. Brutes much more
modest in their pretensions this way than men; & mean men more
than great ones. The higher one raises his pretensions this way,
the more bustle he makes about them, & the more success he
has, the greater Hero. Thus greater Souls in proportion to their
superior merit claim a greater right to take every thing from
meaner folks. This the true foundation of Grandeur & Heroism,
& of the distinction of degrees among men. War therfor necessary to establish subordination, & to found Cities, States, Kingdoms, &c. as also to purge Bodys politick of gross humours.
Wise Princes find it necessary to have wars abroad to keep peace
at home. War, Famine, & Pestilence the usual cures for corrup-

u

tions in Bodys politick. A comparaison of these three. The Author is to write a Panegyrick on each of them. The greatest part of Mankind loves War more than peace: They are but few & mean spirited that live in peace with all men. The modest & meek of all kinds always a prey to those of more noble or stronger apetites. The inclination to war universal: those that cannot or dare not make war in person, employ others to doe it for them. This maintains Bullys, Bravos, Cutthroats, Lawyers, Soldiers, &c. Most Professions would be useless if all were peaceable. Hence Brutes want neither Smiths nor Lawyers, Magistrats nor Joyners, Soldiers nor Surgeons. Brutes having but narrow appetites are incapable of carrying on or perpetuating war against their own species, or of being led out in troops & multitudes to destroy one another. These prerogatives proper to Man alone. The excellency of human nature demonstrated by the vast train of apetites, passions, wants, &c. that attend it. This matter to be more fully treated in the Author's Panegyrick on Mankind.

The History of Martin.

How *Jack* having got rid of the old Landlord & set up another to his mind, quarrel'd with *Martin* & turn'd him out of doors. How he pillaged all his shops, & abolished the whole Dispensatory. How the new Landlord laid about him, maul'd *Peter*, worry'd *Martin*, & made the whole neighborhood tremble. How *Jack*'s friends fell out among themselves, split into a thousand partys, turn'd all things topsy turvy, till every body grew weary of them, & at last the blustering Landlord dying *Jack* was kick'd out of doors, a new Landlord brought in, & *Martin* reestablished. How this new Landlord let *Martin* doe what he pleased, & *Martin* agreed to every thing his pious Landlord desired, provided *Jack* might be kept low. Of several efforts *Jack* made to raise up his head, but all in vain: till at last the Landlord died & was succeeded by one who was a great friend to *Peter*, who to humble *Martin* gave *Jack* some liberty. How *Martin* grew enraged at this, called in a Foreigner & turn'd out the Landlord; in which *Jack* concurred with *Martin*, because this Landlord was entirely devoted to *Peter*, into whose arms he

threw himself, & left his Country. How the new Landlord se-
cured *Martin* in the full possession of his former rights, but
would not allow him to destroy *Jack* who had always been his
friend. How *Jack* got up his head in the North & put himself in
possession of a whole Canton, to the great discontent of *Martin*,
who finding also that some of *Jack*'s friends were allowed to live
& get their bread in the south parts of the country, grew highly
discontent of the new Landlord he had called in to his assistance.
How this Landlord kept *Martin* in order, upon which he fell into
a raging fever, & swore he would hang himself or joyn in with
Peter, unless *Jack*'s children were all turn'd out to starve. Of
several attempts made to cure *Martin* & make peace between
him & *Jack*, that they might unite against *Peter*; but all made
ineffectual by the great adress of a number of *Peter*'s friends, that
herded among *Martin*'s, & appeared the most zealous for his
interest. How *Martin* getting abroad in this mad fit, look'd so
like *Peter* in his air & dress, & talk'd so like him, that many of
the Neighbours could not distinguish the one from the other;
especially when *Martin* went up & down strutting in *Peter*'s
Armour, which he had borrowed to fight *Jack*. What remedys
were used to cure *Martin*'s distemper. &c.

N.B. Some things that follow after this are not in the MS. but
seem to have been written since to fill up the place of what
was not thought convenient then to print.

Sect. XI. The T A L E of a T U B, continued. The Author not
in haste to be at home, shews the difference between a Traveler
weary or in haste, & another in good plight that takes his
pleasure & views every pleasant Scene in his way. 120–121.
The sequel of *Jack*'s adventures; his superstitious veneration
for the H. Scripture, & the uses he made of it. 121-2. his flaming
zeal, & blind submission to the Decrees, 123. his Harangue for
Predestination, 123. he covers roguish tricks with a shew of
devotion; affects singularity in manners & speech, 124. his aversion to musick & painting, 125. His discourses provoke sleep,
his groaning, & affecting to suffer for the good cause. 126. The
great antipathy of *Peter* & *Jack* made them both run into extreams where they often met, 127–8.

The degenerat Ears of this Age cannot afford a sufficient handle to hold men by, 128–129. The senses & passions afford many handles: Curiosity is that by which our Author has held his Readers so long. 130. The rest of this story lost &c. 130-1.

The Conclusion

Of the proper Seasons for [of] publishing books, 132. Of profound Writers, 133. Of the ghost of Wit, 133. Sleep & the Muses nearly related, 133-34. Apology for the Authors fits of dulness, 134. Method & Reason the Lacqueys of Invention, 134. Our Authors great collection of *flowers* of little use till now, 134-135.

A Discourse concerning the Mechanical operation of the Spirit

The Author at a loss what Title to give this piece, finds after much pains that of a *Letter to a friend* to be most in vogue, 171. of modern excuses for haste & neglience &c. 172.

I. *Sect. Mahomet*'s fancy of being carried to Heaven by an Ass, followed by many Christians, 172. A great affinity between this Creature & Man, 173. That talent of bringing his Rider to Heaven the subject of this discourse: but for Ass & Rider the Author uses the synonimous terms of Enlightened Teacher, & Fanatick Hearer, 173. A tincture of Enthousiasm runs through all men & all Sciences, 174. but prevails most in Religion, 174. Enthousiasm defined & distinguished, 174-5. That which is Mechanical & Artificial is treated of by our Author, 175. Tho' Art oftimes changes into Nature: exemples in the Scythian Longheads & English Roundheads, 175-6. Sense & Reason must be laid aside to let this Spirit operate, 176. The Objections about the Manner of the Spirit from above descending on the Apostles, make not against this Spirit that arises within, 177. The methods by which the Assembly helps to work up this Spirit jointly with the Preacher, 177-8.

II. *Sect*. How some worship a good Being, others an evil, 179. Most people confound the bounds of good & evil, 179-80. Vain mortals think the Divinity interested in their meanest actions,

180. The scheme of spiritual mechanism left out, 181. Of the usefulness of quilted nightcaps, to keep in the heat, to give motion & vigour to the litle animals that compose the brain, 181. Sound of far greater use than sense in the operations of the Spirit, as in Musick, 182. Inward light consists of theological po[l]ysyllables & mysterious Texts,182. Of the great force of one Vowel in Canting; & of blowing the nose, hauking spitting & belching, 183. The Author to publish an *Essay on the art of Canting*, 183. Of speaking thro the nose or snuffling: its origine from a disease occasioned by a conflict betwixt the flesh & the Spirit, 184. Inspired vessels, like lanthorns have a sorry sooty outside, 185. Fanaticism deduced from the Ancients in their *Orgyes, Bacchanals*, &c. 186. Of their great lascivousness on those occasions, 187. The Fanaticks of the first centurys, & those of later times generaly agree in the same principle, of improving spiritual into carnal ejaculations, &c. 188.

A PROJECT,

For the universal benefit of Mankind.

The Author having laboured so long & done so much to serve & instruct the Publick, without any advantage to himself, has at last thought of a project which will tend to the great benefit of all Mankind, & produce a handsom Revenue to the Author. He intends to print by Subscription in 96. large volumes in *folio*, an exact Description of *Terra Australis incognita*, collected with great care & pains from 999. learned & pious Authors of undoubted veracity. The whole Work, illustrated with Maps and Cuts agreable to the subject, and done by the best Masters, will cost but a Guiney each volume to Subscribers, one guinea to be paid in advance, & afterwards a guinea on receiving each volume, except the last. This Work will be of great use for all men, & necessary for all familys, because it contains exact accounts of all the Provinces, Colonys & Mansions of that spacious Country, where by a general Doom all transgressors of the law are to be transported: & every one having this work may chuse out the fittest & best place for himself, there being enough for all so as every one shall be fully satisfied.

The Author supposes that one Copy of this Work will be bought at the publick Charge, or out of the Parish rates, for every Parish Church in the three Kingdoms, & in all the Dominions thereunto belonging. And that every family that can command ten pounds *per annum*, even tho' retrenched from less necessary expences, will also subscribe for one. He does not think of giving out above 9 volumes yearly; & considering the number requisite, he intends to print at least 100000. for the first Edition. He's to print Proposals against next Term, with a Specimen, & a curious Map of the Capital City, with its 12 Gates, from a known Author who took an exact survey of it in a dream. Considering the great care & pains of the Author, & the usefulness of the Work, he hopes every one will be ready, for their own good as well as his, to contribute chearfully to it, & not grudge him the profit he may have by it, especially if it comes to a 3. or 4. Edition, as he expects it will very soon.

He doubts not but it will be translated into foreign languages by most Nations of Europe as well as of Asia & Africa, being of as great use to all those Nations as to his own; for this reason he designs to procure Patents & Privileges for securing the whole benefit to himself, from all those different Princes & States, & hopes to see many millions of this great Work printed in those different Countrys & languages before his death.

After this business is pretty well establisht, he has promised to put a Friend on another Project almost as good as this; by establishing Insurance-Offices every where for securing people from shipwreck & several other accidents in their Voyage to this Country; and these Offices shall furnish, at a certain rate, Pilots well versed in the Route, & that know all the Rocks, shelves, quicksands &c. that such Pilgrims & Travelers may be exposed to. Of these he knows a great number ready instructed in most Countrys: but the whole Scheme of this matter he's to draw up at large & communicate to his Friend.

Here ends the Manuscript, there being nothing of the following piece in it.

The Battel of the Books

The Preface tells how this piece was written in 1697. on occasion of a famous dispute about Ancient & Modern Learning, between Sr. *William Temple* & the Earl of *Orrery*, on the one side, & W. *Wotton* & Dr. *Bentley* on the other, 139.

War & Invasions generaly proceed from want & poverty upon plenty & Riches, 141. The *Moderns* quarrel with the *Antients* about the possession of the highest top of Parnassus, & desire them to surrender it, or to let it be levelled, 142. The Answer of the *Antients*, not accepted, a War ensues, 143. in which rivulets of Ink are spilt, & both parties hang out their Trophys, books of Controversy, 144. These books haunted with disorderly Spirits, tho often bound to the peace in Librarys, 144. The Author's advice in this case neglected, occasions a terrible fight in St. James's Library, 145. Dr. *Bentley* the Library keeper a great Enemy to the Antients, 145. The Moderns finding themselves 50000. strong give the Antients ill language, 146-7. *Temple* a favourite of the Antients, 147. An incident of a quarel between a Bee & a Spider, with their Arguments on both sides, 147-8-9-50. *Æsop* applys them to the present dispute, 150-1. The Order of Battel of the Moderns, & names of their Leaders, 151-2. The Leaders of the Antients, 152. Jupiter calls a Council of the Gods & consults the book of Fate, 152-3. & then sends his Orders below, 153. *Momus* brings the news to *Criticism*, whose habitation & company is described, 153-4. She arrives, & sheds her influence on her Son *Wotton*, 155. The Battel described: *Paracelsus* engages *Galen*: *Aristotle* aims at *Bacon* & kills *Des Cartes*, 156. *Homer* overthrows *Gondibert*; kills *Denham* & *Westly*, *Perrault*, & *Fontenelle*, 156-7. Encounter of *Virgil* & *Dryden*, 157. of *Lucan* & *Blackmore*, & of *Creech* & *Horace*, 158. of *Pindar* & *Cowley*, 158. The Episode of *Bentley* & *Wotton*, 159. *Bentleys* Armour, his speech to the modern Generals, 160. *Scaliger's* Answer, 161. *Bentley* & *Wotton* march together, 161. *Bentley* attacks *Phalaris* & *Æsop*, 162. *Wotton* attacks *Temple* in vain, 163. *Boyle* pursues *Wotton*, & meeting *Bentley* in his way he pursues & kills them both, 163-4.

FINIS.   Desunt cœtera.

TEXTUAL NOTES

A TALE OF A TUB

First Edition.

Title: A/ TALE/ OF A/ TUB./ Written for the Universal Improve-/ ment of Mankind./—/ *Diu multumque desideratum.*/—/ To which is added,/ An ACCOUNT of a/ BATTEL/ BETWEEN THE/ Antient and Modern BOOKS/ in St. *James*'s Library./—/ Basima eacabasa eanaa irraurista, diarba da caeo-/ taba fobor camel-anthi. *Iren. Lib.* 1. C. 18/—/ *-Juvatque novos decerpere flores,/ Insignemque meo capiti petere inde coronam,/ Unde prius nulli velarunt tempora Musæ.* Lucret./—/ *LONDON:*/ Printed for *John Nutt*, near *Stationer's -Hall.*/ MDCCIV.

A second and third edition appeared in 1704, a fourth in 1705, and a fifth, much enlarged, in 1710; for facsimile of the title page, see above, page xxxix. It was first included in the collected Works by Hawkesworth in 1755.

The present text is printed from my copy of the Fifth Edition, which includes Swift's latest additions; viz. the *Apology*, and the *Notes* added at the foot of the page, described on the title page as by W. W-tt-n, B.D. and others. It is clear from Swift's letter to Benjamin Tooke, dated from Dublin, June 29, 1710, and from Tooke's reply of July 10 (see *Corr.* i, 183–6, and page xxxi above), that Swift was himself entirely responsible for both. But it is clear also that he did not see the proofs of the whole volume, though he may have suggested certain changes which are found throughout the text; some of these, e.g. on pp. 92, 104, 123, 124, 129, were evidently made to avoid giving offence. Careful collation of the five editions shows quite certainly that errors have crept in during the process of reprinting, and that the text of the first edition is usually the most reliable. I have therefore ventured to restore such readings of the first edition; but all these changes from the text of the fifth edition are indicated below. I have also collated with Hawkesworth's text, as he claimed to have printed from a copy with later corrections made by Swift himself. All names have been printed in full, as was usual in the early collected editions. A few obvious misprints of no significance have been corrected without remark.

Page	Line	Present Text	Variants
13	10	And, being	And, I being 1–4
17	5	Hand	Hands 1, 2
21	18	without	devoid of 1–4
	24	large	huge 1
24	25	*Hobbes*'s H	*Hob's* 5, *Hobs'* 1–4
31	28	*Covent-* 1–3	*Convent-* 4, 5
36	3	sometimes 1–4	sometime 5
37	9	Bombast 1–4	Bombastry 5
40	9	Palate 1–4	Pate 5
41	14	*Metempsychosis* 3, 4	*Metampsychosis* 2, *Metampsycosis* 1,5
	28	1698	1697 1–3
42	2	*Moderns*	*Modern* 1, 2
	b.	Conscience void of Offence	*Conscience void of Offence towards God and towards Man.* 1; *Men.* 2–4
43	29	have 1–4	has 5
45	21	Billets-doux 1	Billetdoux 2–5
	31	in the Town	in Town 1–3

Page	Line	PRESENT TEXT	VARIANTS
50	18	and soon 1–4	and 5
	25	'Tis true, said he, the Word Calendæ 1–4	Calendæ 5
51	26	*in the* 1–3	*to the* 4, 5
54	7	they had no occasion to examine the Will. They remembred 1–4	they remembred 5
55	17	upon 1–3	of 4, 5
56	21	were 1–3	was 4, 5
58	8	to drive away 1, 2	drive away 3–5
61	21	the *True* 1–4	*True* 5
62	6*f.b.**	these 1–4	those 5
63	7*f.b.*	stay 1	stay not 2–5

(*Note:* This sentence is such a tangle of ambiguities that it is not surprising that the 'not' has been introduced and preserved in later editions; but I do not think there can be any doubt that the first edition is as Swift originally wrote it.)

66	25	as likewise of all Eves-droppers, Physicians, Midwives 1–4	as Midwives 5
69	2	and to be 1–4	to be 5
	20	Compliment 1–3	Complement 4, 5
71	3	exceeding 1–4	exceding 5
	18	a *Salute* 1–4	*Salute* 5
	Fn, l. 5	*Crown, and Keys,* (*Notes* 1711.)	*Crown,* 5
72	6	Pheasant, 1–4	Phesants, 5
	21	the Loaf 1	a Loaf 2–5
78	*Fn*, l. 3	ever any (*Notes* 1711.)	any 5
87	17	Peter*'s* 1–3	Peter 4, 5
88	1	Arguments 1–3	Argument 4, 5
92	5	Number 1, 2	Numbers 3–5
	26	Pudenda	Genitals 1–4
93	30	haply 1	happily 2–5
94	1	Guild H. (Yield 1, 2)	Field 3–5

(One of the few significant corrections in Hawkesworth's text, if we may assume that the reading of eds. 1 and 2 was a misprint for 'yeld' or 'yild,' earlier forms of 'guild.')

94	10	please 1, 2	pleases 3–5
95	10	Or 1–4	for 5
96	3	the 1–4	our 5
99	11	a carnal 1	carnal 2–5
	4*f.b.*	over-shot 1	over-short 2–5
103	3	differs 1–4	differ 5
	11	Expectation 1–3	Expectations 4, 5
104	8	—*Teterrima belli Causa*—	*Cunnus teterrima belli Causa*—1–4
	21	the Human	Human 1–5
105	5*f.b.*	thence 1	their 2–4, there 5
107	8	unhappily 1–3	happily 4, 5

* Note : *f.b.* means *from the bottom of the page.*

Page	Line	PRESENT TEXT	VARIANTS
109	1	fade 1, 2	fading 3–5

(N.B. the same phrase 'fade insipid' in *Ode to Congreve*, line 212.)

Page	Line	PRESENT TEXT	VARIANTS
109	6 f.b.	In 1–4	Inn 5
110	21	*Vapo(u)r* 1–4	*Vapours* 5
	3 f.b.	Seasons 1–4	Season 5
111	1	thence 1–4	whence 5
112	11	Window	(omitted) 1–4
116	18	*Part of*	*Part in* 1–4
117	12	Stomachs 1–4	Stomach 5
122	30	*Phrases*	*Phrase* 5
123	22	*Nature*	*Providence* 1–4
124	7	*Fortune*	*Providence* 1–4
125	3	to-bespatter 1–3	to bespatter 4, 5
	16	arrect 1	arrected 2–5
126	1	Occasion	Occasions 1–4
	17	*on the Ear*	*in the Ear* 1–3
127	19	Humo(u)rs 1	Humour 2–5
	20	their Size 1–4	and Size 5
128	22	*may* 1	must 2–5
	23	and 1–4	that 5
129	9 f.b.	*Marks of Grace*	cloven Tongues 1–4
130	28	having 1–4	have 5
132	18	maturely 1	manifestly 2–5
133	26	Acquaintance 1–3	Acquaintants 4, 5

THE BATTLE OF THE BOOKS

Page	Line	PRESENT TEXT	VARIANTS
140	7	kind of 1–3	kind 4, 5
143	9	to levelling 1–3	to the levelling 4, 5
147	2 f.b.	Turn-pikes 1–4	Turk-pikes 5
148	29	Could you not 1–3	Could not you 5
149	25	bestowed on me	bestowed 1–3
150	8	at last 1	at all 2–5
	b.	Conclusions 1, 2	Conclusion 3–5
151	19	*they pretend* 1–4	*to pretend* 5
153	2 f.b.	and headstrong	an headstrong 1–3
154	18	Resentment	Resentments 1–4
	10 f.b.	to oppose 1–4	oppose 5
155	28	*the Day* 1–4	*this Day* 5

A DISCOURSE OF THE CONTESTS AND DISSEN- TIONS IN ATHENS AND ROME

First printed in 1701. For facsimile of the title page, see above, p. 193.
Miscellanies in Prose and Verse, 1711, p. 1.
Miscellanies in Prose and Verse. The First Volume, 1727, p. 1.
The Works of J.S.D.D.D.S.P.D., Dublin, 1735, VOL. I, p. 1.

The present text is taken from the *Works*, 1735; it seems to have been printed by Faulkner from a corrected copy of the 1727 *Miscellanies*. Further changes were made by Swift, or his friends, in proof, but certain errors remained, which have been corrected here, by restoring the reading of the first edition as indicated below. Manuscript corrections in Swift's own copy of the *Miscellanies*, 1727, are indicated by S.

Page	Line	PRESENT TEXT	VARIANTS
195	20	the best Legislators	the Legislators 01, 11, 27
196	17	and common	or common 01, 11
	18	and Dangers	or Dangers 01, 11, 27
	19	is required	are required 01, 11, 27
		Counsel 01, 11	Council 27, 35
197	4	within itself	with itself 01
	17	with the utmost	with utmost 01, 11, 27
	18	each Scale	the several Scales 01, 11, 27
198	19	the Kings 01	the King 11, 27, 35
	22	Age	Ages 01, 11, 27
199	11	this	that 01, 11, 27
	26	Accusations 01, 11, 27	Accusation 35
200	19	for upholding 01, 11	for the upholding 27, 35
	23	Interest	Interests 01
	26	think it an uncontroulable Maxim, that Power is always	conceive, that Power is 01
	27	these	those 01, 11, 27
	33	to be not only 01, 11	not only to be 27, 35
201	1	Defect 01	Defects 11, 27, 35
	2-3	the Rights of the *Many* . . . Privileges of the *Few*	Privileges of the *Many* . . . Rights of the *Few* 01
	20	started S	started at all 01, 11, 27
	22	besides	beside 01
	28	Reasoners S	Reasons 27
	30	pace S	Place 27
	31	make S	makes 27
202	15	of the Legislators	of Legislators 01, 11
	17	every one of S	every of 01, 11, 27
	18	as might	which might 01
	24	States	State 01
	32	several	at several 01, 11
	2 f.b.	Yet	But 01, 11, 27
203	7	Rock that	Rock 01, 11, 27
	13	Dissentions in *Greece* and *Rome*, between the *Nobles* and *Commons*, with the Consequences of them	Dissention(s) between the *Nobles* and *Commons*, with . . ., in *Greece* and *Rome* 01, 11, 27
204	18	the Series	that Series 01
	22	Confusion	Confusions 01, 11
205	27	were	being 01, 11, 27
	30	Articles of	Articles or 01, 11, 27
206	4	Issues	the Issues 01, 11, 27
	18	justly paid	paid justly 01, 11, 27
	23	*Fleet*, and being no ways a Match for the Enemy, set sail to *Athens* ;	(*Persian*) *Fleet*, and being no ways a Match for them, set sail for Athens; 01, 11, 27

Page	Line	Present Text	Variants
206	28	no more than	no otherwise than by 01, 11, 27
	34	Chancellor	the Chancellor 01, 11
	b	But they had soon	But, however, they had, 01, 11, 27
207	9	he who	he that 01, 11, 27
	24	*and he wanted Time to adjust them*	*and he could not then give them up* 01, 11, 27
208	6	powerful	Popular 01
	8	Desire	desires 01, 11, 27
	15	his own	his 01
209	1	recovering	preserving 01, 11, 27
	21	have *popular Assemblies* been	are *popular Assemblies* 01
		deserved	deserve 01
	30	overthrown	overthrew 01, 11, 27
210	1	this great	great 01, 11, 27
	7	on	upon 01, 11
	4*f.b.*	harassed with S	harassed by 01, 11, 27
211	1	*Dissentions*	Dissension 01
	19	those *Grecian*	these *Grecian* 01
	25	Principle	Principles 11, 27
212	4	Stage of the World	Stage 01
	25	These	Those 01, 11, 27
214	5	poorer S	poorest 27
	11	leave S	quit 01, 11, 27

(N.B. an interesting correction of Swift's evidently to avoid the jingle with 'City' and 'acquitted.')

Page	Line	Present Text	Variants
214	28	began 01, 11, 27	begun 35
215	7	he disdaining	disdaining 01, 11, 27
	15	obtained	obtain 01
	27	and	and to 01, 11, 27
216	1	farther	further 01, 11, 27
	5	afterwards	afterward 01, 11, 27
217	3	farther	further 01, 11, 27
	22	the popular	popular 01, 11
	30	lawful for	lawful of, 01
218	16	Destruction	entire Destruction 01
	31	gaining	a gaining 01, 11, 27
219	12	*ancient inherent*	*ancient and inherent* 01, 11
	13	absolute	perfect 01, 11, 27
	25	Account	Accounts 01, 11
220	28	are left	were left 01
	30	to introduce	of introducing 01, 11, 27
	5*f.b.*	He	For he 01, 11, 27
221	1	mutinying	mutining 01, 11
	16	becomes 01	became 11, 27, 35
	18	Man, who S	Man, that 01, 11, 27
	19	ready	just ready 01
223	9	lay	was 01, 11, 27
224	2	Impeachment	Impeaching 01, 11, 27
	5	we	one 01, 11, 27
	9	to reserve	to have reserved 01, 11, 27
	23	expounded 01, 11	expound 27, 35

Page	Line	PRESENT TEXT	VARIANTS
224	24	inconsiderable	paultry 01, 11, 27
	5 f.b.	Persecutors 01, 11, 27	Prosecutors 35
225	6	a Man	one 01, 11, 27
	18	possessed	had 01, 11, 27
	5 f.b.	the	of the 01, 11, 27
226	5	and	or 01, 11, 27
	23–4	no other . . . than	no . . . but 01, 11, 27
228	2	in S	into 01, 11, 27
	15	these	those 01, 11, 27
	5 f.b.	as almost	as 01, 11, 27
	b	towards	toward 01, 11, 27
230	27	who gaining	and gaining 01, 11, 27
	6 f.b.	Thirty	Forty 01
231	12	dreamt of S	dreamt on 01, 11, 27, 35
232	28	Corruptions	Corruption 01
	2 f.b.	so apt	apt 01
233	7 f.b.	averse from S	averse to 01, 11, 27
	3 f.b.	as to provide	that he provided 01, 11, 27

(N.B. Swift deleted 'that' and wrote in 'as' in his copy, the further change being
made presumably in the proofs.)

234	7	Ambition, their Vanity, or	Ambition, or 01, 11, 27
	9 f.b.	neither Thoughts S	neither Opinions, nor Thoughts 01, 11, 27, 35
	6 f.b.	been not only 01, 11, 27	not been only 35
	4 f.b.	followeth his *Party*	follows the *Party* 01, 11, 27
	b	the present	this 01, 11, 27
235	3	native Sedateness 01, 11, 27	Sedateness 35
	16	but to	but for 01
	22	against	to 01; for 11, 27
	6 f.b.	Experience	Sense 01
236	9	from what	than 01

(*Note.* Swift had originally written and printed in 1701 the following final paragraph, which occurs also in some copies of the *Miscellanies*, 1711. But in the
course of printing it was cancelled, leaving page 92 blank, and the following
leaf, G7 (pp. 93–4), was cancelled. It would have been too dangerous for
the *Examiner* to run the risk of being known to have such views on the
advantages of bribery in elections.
    The text is here taken from a copy of the first edition, 1701, pp. 60–62.

There is one thing I must needs add, tho' I reckon it will appear to many as
a very unreasonable Paradox. When the Act passed some years ago against
Bribing of Elections; I remember to have said upon occasion, to some Persons of
both Houses, that we should be very much deceived in the Consequences of that
Act: And upon some Discourse of the Conveniences of it, and the contrary
(which will admit Reasoning enough) they seem'd to be of the same Opinion.
It has appear'd since, that our Conjectures were right: For I think the late
Parliament was the first-fruits of that Act; the Proceedings whereof, as well as
of the present, have been such, as to make many Persons wish that things were
upon the old Foot in that matter. Whether it be that so great a Reformation was
too many Degrees beyond so corrupt an Age as this; or that according to the
present turn and disposition of Men in our Nation, it were a less abuse to Bribe

Elections, than leave them to the discretion of the Chusers. This at least was *Cato*'s Opinion, when things in *Rome* were at a Crisis, much resembling ours; who is recorded to have gone about with great Industry, dealing Money among the People to favour *Pompey* (as I remember) upon a certain Election in opposition to *Cæsar*; And he excused himself for it upon the necessities of the People; an Action that might well have excus'd *Cicero*'s censure of him, that he reasoned and acted, *tanquam in Republica Platonis, non in fæce Romuli.* However it be, 'tis certain that the Talents which qualifie a Man for the Service of his Country in Parliament, are very different from those which give him a dexterity at making his court to the People; and do not often meet in the same subject. Then for the moral part, the difference is inconsiderable; and whoever practices upon the Weakness and Vanity of the People, is guilty of an immoral action as much as if he did it upon their Avarice. Besides, the two Trees may be judged by their Fruits. The former produces a set of popular Men, fond of their own Merits and Abilities, their Opinions, and their Eloquence; whereas the bribing of Elections* seems to be at worst, but an ill means of keeping things upon the old foot, by leaving the defence of our Properties, chiefly in the hands of those who will be the greatest sufferers, whenever they are endangered. It is easie to observe in the late and present Parliament, that several Boroughs and some Counties have been represented by Persons, who little thought to have ever had such hopes before: And how far this may proceed, when such a Way is lay'd open for the Exercise and Encouragement of popular Arts, one may best judge from the Consequences that the same Causes produced both in *Athens* and *Rome.* For, let Speculative Men Reason, or rather Refine as they please; it ever will be true among us, that as long as men engage in the Publick service upon private Ends, and whilst all Pretences to a Sincere *Roman* Love of our Country, are lookt upon as an Affectation, a Foppery, or a Disguise; (which has been a good while our Case, and is likely to continue so;) it will be safer to trust our Property and Constitution in the hands of such, who have pay'd for their Elections, than of those who have obtained them by servile Flatteries of the People.)

*seems to be at worst) though a great and shameful Evil, seems to be at present 11 (Cancelled Page 93).

A MEDITATION UPON A BROOMSTICK

First printed by Curll in 1710, who obtained the copy from his lodger John Cliffe, the son-in-law of the Bishop of Killalla; see facsimile of the title page of the B.M. copy with MS note in Curll's handwriting, p. 237 above.

Miscellanies in Prose and Verse, 1711, p. 231.
Miscellanies in Prose and Verse, 1727, VOL. II, p. 265.
The Works of J.S.D.D.D.S.P.D., Dublin, 1735, VOL. I, p. 235.

The present text is printed from the *Works*, 1735.

Page	Line	PRESENT TEXT	VARIANTS
239	8	in the Year 1703	*August*, 1704 11
	20	its last 10, 11	the last 27, 35
	21	a Fire	Fires 10
	22	MORTAL MAN	Man 10
240	1	*Perriwig*	*Peruque* 10
	8	Defaults!	Faults. 10
	11	mounted on his	a-Cock-Horse and 10

THOUGHTS ON VARIOUS SUBJECTS

Miscellanies in Prose and Verse, 1711, p. 235.
Miscellanies in Prose and Verse, 1727, Vol. I, p. 388.
The Works of J.S.D.D.S.P.D., Dublin, 1735, Vol. I, p. 297.

The present text is taken from the *Works*, 1735, but includes only that portion, which was printed in 1711, and dated Oct. 1, 1706. It is certainly Swift's own work. The *Thoughts* added in the later editions may have been partly contributed by Swift's friends. They will be collected together in Vol. XIV of this edition.

Page	Line	PRESENT TEXT	VARIANTS
241	title	Thoughts on Various Subjects	*Various Thoughts*, Moral and Diverting. Written *October* the 1st. 1706 11
	4	just Religion enough	just enough Religion 11, 27
	7	and the like	*&c.* 11, 27
	18	whoever	he that 11, 27
242	3	may	seems to 11, 27
	13	If a Writer would	Would a Writer 11, 27
	22	infallible Sign	Sign 11, 27
	3 *f.b.*	that above . . . is	to above . . . to be 11, 27
243	2	or	nor 11, 27
	8	History	Story 11, 27
	23	that the Enemy may believe them to be	to make the Enemy believe them 11, 27
	26	Religion, Virtue, and common Honesty	Virtue, Honesty and Religion 11, 27
	29	that perhaps . . . Because	which perhaps . . . That 11, 27
	4 *f.b.*	a censorious World	the Censure of the World 11, 27
244	5	foretell in what Time	to tell when 11, 27
	10	That Expression	The Expression 11, 27
	20	and the like	*&c.* 11, 27
	23	ignorant of	ignorant 11
	6 *f.b.*	*dixit.*	*dixit.* Ovid. Metam 11, 27
245	2	and not	not 11, 27
	12	fouls	Dirts 11, 27

A TRITICAL ESSAY UPON THE FACULTIES OF THE MIND

Miscellanies in Prose and Verse, 1711, p. 247.
Miscellanies in Prose and Verse, 1727, Vol. I, p. 249.
The Works of J.S.D.D.S.P.D., Dublin, 1735, Vol. I, p. 140.

The present text is taken from the *Works*, 1735. Swift's manuscript corrections in his own copy of the *Miscellanies*, 1727, are indicated by S.

Page	Line	PRESENT TEXT	VARIANTS
246	title	(*Undated*)	*August* the 6th. 1707, 11
	10	stale S	State 11, 27
	14	untouched S	untaught 11, 27
247	2	could	would 11, 27
250	19	spun	did 11, 27

THE PREFACES TO SIR WILLIAM TEMPLE'S WORKS

The prefaces to the *Letters* and *Memoirs* were first included in Swift's collected *Works* by Faulkner in 1763, with the following note, see Vol. X, p. 389:

Dr. Warburton, since Bishop of *Gloucester*, having had the Publication of Mr. Pope's Writings (by his last Will,) after his Death, wrote Notes to many of them, and in the Collecting of those Works together, he inserted his Prefaces to the Translation of *Homer*, and to *Shakespear*'s Works; which, we think, will be a sufficient Justification, for inserting the following Prefaces to Sir William Temple's Memoirs and Works, many People, perhaps not having an Opportunity of seeing that great Man's Writings.

The present text and facsimiles of the title-pages of the *Letters*, Vols. I & II, 1700, and Vol. III, 1703, are taken from the copy in the British Museum, with the following inscription in Swift's handwriting:

To
His Excellency, Count Magalotti, Councillor
of State to His Most Serene Highness, the Great
Duke of Tuscany.
By His Excellency's
most obedient
and
most humble Servant,
Johnathan Swift.

The *Miscellanea*, 1701, was printed from the Bodleian copy; and the *Memoirs*, 1709, from the copy in the Forster Collection, which is inscribed by Swift:

To the Right Honble Charles Lord Hallifax
By His most obedient
& most humble Servt.
The Publisher.

APPENDIX

The facsimile of the title page, and the text of the *Additions to the Tale of a Tub* are taken from my own copy of the *Miscellaneous Works, Comical and Diverting*: by T.R.D.J.S.D.O.P.I.I., 1720. But the page references have all been altered to refer to the numbering of this present edition.

THE INDEX

Abstracts, satire on, 79, 91
Academies, in France and Italy, 65; in New-Holland, 171; Academy proposed, with its several schools, 25
Acamoth, 119
Achaian League, 210
Achilles, 242
Aeneas, 242
Aeolists, 89, 95, 121
Aesculapius, 158
Aesop, 40, 139, 150, 151, 162
Aga, 156
Agis, 210
Aix la Chapelle, 270; Treaty of, 257, 259
Alcibiades, 31, 207–8
Aldrovandi Ulisse, *Natural History*, 161
Alexander the Great, 107, 205, 208–9, 247, 248
Analytical Discourse upon Zeal, xxvii, 86
Anatomy, 110
Ancients and Moderns, 42, 59, 78, 91, 139, 142ff., 263
Anima Mundi, 95
Anne, Queen Anne, xxi
Anthony, 222
Antipater, 209–10
Apocrypha, 53; Tobit and his dog, 244
Apology for the Tale, xxviii
Aquinas, 152
Aratus, 210
Archimedes, 39, 249
Argos, 199
Argument against Abolishing Christianity, 278
Ariosto, 241
Aristides, 206, 210, 224
Aristotle, 144, 146, 152, 156, 247; Dialectica, 51; *De Interpretatione*, 51
Arlington, Henry Bennet, first Earl of, 270
Artephius, 41
Ass, Asses, xxv, 116, 128, 150, 162, 163, 173, 182, 249
Astræa, 248
Atterbury, Francis, Bishop of Rochester, xvii
Attica, 187

Bacchus, 186
Bacon, Francis, xxxiv, 156
Bagpipes, 184
Balance of power, 197ff.; disturbance of, 226, 230; necessity of, 228
Balneum Mariæ, 78
Banbury Saint, 184
'Banter,' Alsatia phrase, 7, 10, 132
Bar, the, 34
Barrett, Dr John, ix
Battle of the Books, xxiv, xxviii, xxix, xxxii
Bedlam, 111–3
Beelzebub, 148
Behmen, Jacob, 79
Behn, Mrs Aphra, 158
Belching, 96ff.
Belial, 180
Bellarmin, 41, 152
Bench, the, 34
Bentley, Richard, xvii, xxii, xxiv, 22, 57, 78, 116, 132, 277; his humanity, 145, 150; *Dissertation on Letters of Phalaris*, 63, 139
Berkeley, Charles, second Earl of, xix
—, Lady, xxxiii, xxxiv
Bernier, François, *Grand Mogul*, 178
Billingsgate, 125
Blackmore, Sir Richard, 116, 158
Boccaccio, xxix
Boccalini, 17
Boileau Despreaux, 152
Bowls, Sir John, 111
Boyle, Robert, xxxiv, 239
Brauronia, 187
Breda, Treaty at, 257
Brutus, 222
—, the elder, 111
Buchanan, 152
Buckingham, George Villiers, 2nd Duke of, 7
Bulls, Lord Peter's, 68–9
Burnet, Gilbert, Bishop of Salisbury, xx
Bythus, 119

Cabalism, Cabalist, 4, 118
Cæsar Julius, 211, 219ff., 249
Caligula, 222

x

Callières, François de, *Histoire Poetique de la Guerre entre les Anciens et les Modernes*, xxix, 7–8
Calvin, John, 88
Camden, William, 152
Cant, 108, 125, 180, 189; art of canting, 182–4
Carthage, 196, 200, 202, 211, 218
Celibacy of the clergy, 71
Cercopithecus, Egyptian, 46
Cervantes, *Don Quixote*, 17, 124
Character of the present Set of Wits in this Island, A, xl, 23
Charles II, 42, 130, 259
Charondas, lawgiver to the Sybarites, 233
Christ Church College, Oxford, xvii
Cicero, misquoted, 106; referred to, 258
Circle, squaring of, 174
Clarke, Mary, Ephemerides of, 141
Claudius, Appius, 218
Cleomenes, 210
Cliffe, John, 237
Clothes-philosophy, 46–8
Cloven-tongues, 177, 180
Codrus, 204
Comedies, modern, 39
Commonplace-books, 93, 134
Compendiums, 93
Compleat Jesters, 38
Congreve, William, 133
Constantine the Great, 55
Consuls, method of nomination, 214; office of, opened to all, 216
Contests and Dissensions in Athens and Rome, xx, 193ff.
Coriolanus, 214
Covent-Garden, 26, 31, 155
Cowley, Abraham, xv, 152, 158–9
Creech, Thomas, 158; translation of Lucretius quoted, 36, 61
Creon, probably Cleon, 31
Critical Essay upon the Art of Canting, 183
Criticism, 'a malignant deity,' 153–5
Critics, 56ff., 'dogs under the table,' 64, 117; 'noisy curs,' 120
Cromwell, Oliver, 125, 231
Ctesias quoted, xxv, 60, 61, 92
Cudworth, Ralph, xxxiv
Curll, Edmund, 'a prostitute bookseller,' 12; note by, 237; *Complete Key*, xxx, 279

Curtius, M., 111
Cyrus the Great, 197

Danaë, 251
Darius, 185
Dark Authors, 118
Davenant, Sir William, xxx, 281; *Gondibert*, 156
Davila, Enrico Caterino, 152
Decemviri, 198
Dedications, 13, 15, 26, 30, 43, 82
Defoe, Daniel, xxvi
Delightful Tales, 38
Delphos, 101
Demosthenes, 31, 224, 249
Denham, Sir John, 157
Dennis, John, xxiv, 22, 57, 249
Descartes, 105, 107, 146, 152, 156
de Witt, John, 258
Digressions, 90ff.
Diodorus Siculus, 61, 186, 187, 199, 209, 225, 233
Diogenes, 105, 248
Dionysius Halicarnassus, 198, 211, 215, 216
Dionysus, 186
Discourse concerning the Mechanical Operation of the Spirit, xx, xxvii, 9
Dissertation upon the principal Productions of Grub-street, A, xl, 40
Dogs, republic of, 141
Domitian, 222
Downton, Thomas, 257
Droning, 182
Dryden, John, xxiv, 42, 146, 152; parody of, 3; his Prefaces, 81–2; encounter with Virgil, 157; *Hind and the Panther*, xxiv, 41; *Translation of Virgil*, 22, 33, 43
Dunton, John, 35
Durfey, Tom, xxiv, 22, 133

Eachard, John, *Grounds of the Contempt of the Clergy*, 4
Ears, 125, 129–130; see *General History*
Edwin, Sir Humphrey, Lord Mayor of London, 131, 182
Elixir, the Grand, 174
Elizabeth, Queen, 230, 288
Ely, Bishop of. *See* Turner
Empedocles, 111
Enthusiasm, 107, 174–5, 185; enthusiastic preachers, 98

Ephori, in Sparta, 198, 223; popular practices of, 210
Epicurus, 105, 110, 246, 247
Euclid, 152, 247
Eugenius Philalethes. *See* Vaughan, Thomas
Eutyches, 188
Evander, 244
Exchange, the Royal, 125; Exchange-Women, 88

Fame, 118
Family of Love, 188
Fanaticks, 122ff., 180, 186
Farnaby, Thomas, xxix, 8
Faustus, Dr, 41
Flanders, invasion of in *1667*, 257
Fleet-street, 171
Fontenelle, 157
Forster, John, *Life of Swift* quoted, ix, x
Fortune-tellers in N. America, 186
Fragment, A. See *Discourse*
Freinshemius, Joannes, 278
Friendly Societies, 67

Galen, 156
Gassendi, 152
Gemara, The, 41
General History of Ears, A, xl, 130
Geneva Bibles, 182
George, David, 188
Giffard, Martha, Lady, xii, xxxvi
Glanvil, Joseph, xxxiv
Godolphin, Sidney, 1st Earl, Lord Treasurer, xxxvi, 268
Golden-Fleece, 68, 69
Gondibert, see Davenant
Government, by the one, the few, or the many, 196ff., 201; *Dominatio Plebis,* 209, 217, 219
Gracchi, The, 216, 218
Gresham College, 38, 115, 155, 172
Grub-Street, 38ff.; Grubæan Sages, 40
Guagninus, *Sarmatiæ Europeæ Descriptio,* 178
Gueuses, the, 88
Guicciardini, 152
Guild-Hall, 115

H., T., 171
Hague, The, 270

Halifax, Charles Montague, Earl of, xx; referred to as *Pericles,* 207ff.
Happiness defined, 108–110
Harvey, William, 152
Hawkesworth, John, *Life of Swift,* ix
Helicon, 162
Henry IV of France, 103
Henry VIII, 'Harry Huff,' 287
Hercules, 57, 91
Herodotus, xxv, 60, 92, 94, 152, 185, 186, 205, 244
Hippocrates, 129, 152, 175
History of Martin, xxxii, 286ff.
Hobbes, Thomas, 146, 152; *Leviathan,* 24, 181
Holland, wars in *1665* and *1672,* 257, 259
Homer, 79, 80, 90, 152, 156–7, 160, 162–3, 211, 242, 244
Horace, quoted, 26, 31, 34, 69, 104, 128, 158, 180, 247, 248, 250; Imitation of Ep. 7, Lib, 1, 278–9; translation by Temple, 262
How, John, 111
Huguenots, the, 88
Hybris, 57
Hyde-Park Corner, 26
Hyperbolus, 31

Impeachments, 205, 206, 211, 223ff.
Indexes, xxiv, 91, 93
Indian Figures, 52, 54, 85
Indian Pygmies, 92
Indians, their religion, 179; saints of India, 178
Indulgence, Declaration of, 131
Inns of Court, 31
Insurance Offices, 67, 294
Irenæus, quoted on title of *Tale,* xxxix, 18, 119
Irish, method of smoking, 178
Iroquois Virtuosi, 172
Ixion, 247

Jack, xiii, 84ff., 101, 102, 121ff., 281; Jack of Leyden, *see* John
James I, 29; 'North Country Farmer,' 288
James II, 131
Jehuda Hannasi, 41
Jenkins, Sir Lionel, 269
John of Leyden, 88, 107, 188

Johnson, Samuel, xxii
Jones, John, x
Jones, Sir William, 271
Juno, 247
Jupiter Capitolinus, 46
Juvenal, 249

Key to Tale of a Tub, see Curll
Killala, Bishop of. *See* Lloyd
Kilroot, xv, xvi, xviii
King, William, gazetteer, *Remarks on the Tale of a Tub*, xxviii, 5
King's Bench, Court of, 131, 223
Knox, John, 89

La Bruyère, 17
Ladder, the, 34, 35, 37
Lamachus, 207
Lambinus, Dionysius, 44
Laplanders, 100
Laracor, xxi
La Rochefoucauld, *Maximes*, xxxv
Latria, 97
Lauralco, the Giant (in *Don Quixote*), 124
Laws of the Twelve Tables, 215
Leaden-Hall Market, 73
Lectures upon a Dissection of Human Nature, xl, 77
Leicester-Fields, 28
Leslie, Charles, non-juror, xxii
L'Estrange, Sir Roger, xxiv, 3, 42, 116, 152
Livy, 152
Lloyd, William, Bishop of Killala, 237
Locket's Ordinary, 45
Longheads, 175, 176
Loretto, the chapel of, 74
Lorrain, Paul, ordinary of Newgate, 35
Lorraine, 257
Louis XIV, 104, 126; 'the most Christian King,' 202
Lucan, 158; quoted, 2
Lucretius, 105; quoted, 36, 77, 95, 103, 133, 193, 195, 229
Luther, Martin, 188, 280
Lycurgus, 200
Lyon, John, ix
Lysander, 198, 208

Macaulay, Thomas Babington, Lord, xvii

Madness, digression on, 102ff.
Magna Charta, 231
Mahomet, 172–3
Marathon, 206
Marcellinus, Ammianus, 49
Marcosian Hereticks, 18
Mariana, Juan de, 152
Marius, 219
Marriage, xxxv, 244, 245
Martin, 7, 44, 84ff., 131. See *History of Martin*
Marvell, Andrew, his answer to Parker, *The Rehearsal Transpros'd*, 5
Meal-tub Plot, 42
Meditation on a Broomstick, A, xxxiii, xxxiv, 278
Megalopolis, 97
Melampus, 186
Memorandums, 173
Memoirs, nature of, 269
Mercury, 26, 63, 80
Microcosm, 47
Miltiades, 205, 206, 224
Milton, John, 152
Minellius, Jean, xxix, 8
Mishna, 41
Mobile, 88
Moderns, 77ff.; more ancient than Ancients, 147; their discoveries, 80; deal in invention, 84; self-praise, 28; wit, 92ff., 134; 'write upon Nothing,' 133
Modest Defense of the Proceedings of the Rabble, A, xl, 32
Mogul, the Great, 126
Molière, *L'Avare*, xvii
Momus, 57, 152–4, 163, 248
Moorfields, 115
Moor Park, x, xi, xix
Moses, 112
Moulinavent, 100
Munster, Bishop of, 257, 259
Musgrave, Sir Christopher, 111
Mystical Numbers, 34-5, 118-9

Nero, 198, 222
Neuster, Adam, 188
Newgate, 70, 75, 188
New-Holland, 171
Newton, Sir Isaac, 10
Nicias, 207
Nichols, John, *Supplement to Dr. Swift's Works*, xxxii

Nile, 248
Nimeguen, Treaty at, 269
Ninus, 202
Norman Conquest, 211
Nova Zembla, 153

O Brazile, 78
Occasional Conformity, Bill against, xxi
Occasioned by Sir William Temple's Illness and Recovery, xv
Octavius, 222
Ode to Dr. William Sancroft, xiii
Ode to the Athenian Society, xii
Ode to the Honbl. Sir W. Temple, xiii
Ode to the King On his Irish Expedition, xi
Ogilby, John, 158
Ogling, 189
Oldham, John, 158
Orgya, 186
Orléans, Père d', *Histoire de M. Constance*, 132
Orpheus, 186, 187
Orrery, Charles Boyle, 4th Earl of, 145, 163, 164; *Epistles of Phalaris*, xvi, 139; *Dr. Bentley's Dissertations on Phalaris examin'd*, xvii, xviii, xxiv, 5, 6
Ostracism in Athens, 225
Osyris, 186
Oxford, Robert Harley, 1st Earl of, 278

Painters Wives Island, 78
Pallas, protectress of the Ancients, 153, 156
Panciroli, Guido, *De Artibus Perditis*, 98, 128
Pandora's box, 248
Panegyres, 186
Panegyric, 30ff.
Panegyrical Essay upon the Number Three, A, xl, 35
Panegyrick upon the World, A, xl, 32
Papists, additions to Christianity, 49; oral tradition, 50, 51; resemblance to Fanaticks, 127
Paracelsus, 96, 104, 105, 152, 156
Pardons, 70, 75
Parnassus, 142, 145
Paros, 206
Partition Treaty, xx
Party-factions, 228ff.
Party-leaders, 232–3
Patronage, among the Greeks, 212
Pausanias, quoted, 60, 97, 134

Pembroke, Thomas Herbert, 8th Earl of, xxxiv
Penelope, 250
Pericles, xx, 207, 210, 224
Perrault, Charles, 57, 157
Perseus, 57
Peter, 7, 10, 44, 65ff., 83ff., 127; his Bulls, 68, 286
Peterborough, Charles Mordaunt, 3rd Earl of, xx
Phalaris, 139, 162, 164; edition of his *Epistles*, xvii, 139
Philip II, father of Alexander the Great, 208
Phillipize, 208, 224
Philopœmen, 210
Philosopher's stone, 122, 174
Phocion, xx, 205, 209, 210, 224
Phœnician Tongue, 34
Photius, 187
Pickle, the universal, 67
Pilgrim's Salve, 126
Pindar, 152, 158–9
Planetary Worlds, 174
Plato, 144, 146, 152, 248, 251
Platonicks, 189
Plebiscita, 218
Plutarch, 30, 182, 216, 217
Polybius, 199, 200, 210, 216, 217
Polydore Virgill, 152
Polyperchon, 209
Polyphemus, 249
Pompey, 219ff.
Popular Assemblies, 232
Portland, William Bentinck, 1st Earl of, xx, 210, 224
Predestination, 180
Predictions, &c., 278
Prefaces, 27, 59, 81, 115
Primum Mobile, 47
Profound Writers, 133
Project for the universal benefit of Mankind, A, 293–4
Prologues, 59, 62
Pulpit, the, 34, 35, 37
Puritan faction, the, 230
Pyrenees, peace of, 259
Pysistratus, 205
Pythagoras, 40

Ramble, The, an Ode, xi
Ravaillac, François, 103

Reformation, the, 74, 84ff.

Regiomontanus, 152

Remarks on the Tale of a Tub. See King, William

Resolutions when I come to be old, xviii–xix, xxxvii

Republicks, in Greece and Rome, 200

Revolutions, popular, end in single tyranny, 227

Reynard the Fox, 41

Rochester, Laurence Hyde, 1st Earl of, 268

Rome, 55, 90, 193; government of, 196ff.

Romulus, 211, 212

Rosicrucians, 118

Roundheads, 176

Royal Library. *See* St James's Library

Royal Exchange. *See* Exchange

Royal Society. *See* Gresham College

Russell, Admiral, Lord Oxford, xx

Rymer, Thomas, xxiv, 22, 57, 247

Ryswick, Peace of, 133

St James's Library, 137, 139, 145ff., 152, 153, 155

St Paul's Churchyard, 171

Salamis, 207

Salisbury Plain, 124

Satire, 29ff., 140, 151

Saturninus, 219

Save-all, 79

Scaliger, Julius Cæsar, 130

Scaliger, Joseph Justus, 161

Scipio, Africanus, 217, 218

Scott, Sir Walter, xxvii

Scotland Yard, 115

Scotus, Duns, 41, 144, 152

Scythian Ancestors, 61, 94, 175, 176, 178

Sendivogius, 79

Servius Tullius, 213

Seven Wise Masters, 146

Seymour, Sir Edward, 111

Shaftesbury, Anthony Ashley Cooper, 3rd Earl of, *Letter concerning Enthusiasm*, 3

Sharp, John, Archbishop of York, xiv, xxix

Sheridan, Thomas, xxxiii, xxxiv

Sibyls, 99

Sicily, 208

Sigè, 119

Simon Magus, 188

Six-penny-worth of Wit, 38

Slavonian proverb, 128

Snuffling, 183

Socrates, 14, 33, 40, 247

Solon, 202, 204, 205, 209, 210

Somers, John, Lord, xix–xx, xxii; Dedication to, 13–6, 280

Southwell, Sir Robert, xi

Spain, War with Portugal, 259

Sparta, kings of, 197, 208, 211, 223

Spider and the Bee, The, 147ff.

Spirit, the, 177ff.

Stage-Itinerant, 34, 35, 38

Stillingfleet, Edward, Bishop of Worcester, *The Fanaticism of the Church of Rome*, 127

Stoic, 244

Stymphalian Birds, 58

Summum Bonum, 174

Sunderland, Charles, 3rd Earl of, Secretary of State, 268

Sunderland, Robert, 2nd Earl of, xviii, xxxvi, 268

Sweet Singers of Israel, The, 188

Swift, Deane, ix.

—, Jonathan, at Trinity College, ix; at Moor Park, x–xv, xvi–xviii; at Kilroot, xv, xvi; and the Whigs, xix–xxii; publisher of Temple's writings, xix, xx, xxi, xxxvi, 253ff., *Autobiography*, ix, x; Collected Works, *1735*, xxxv; *Miscellanies in Prose and Verse*, *1711*, xxxiv; *Miscellanies*, *1727*, xxxv; *Odes*, xi–xvi

Swift, Thomas, xii, xxxi, 279, 281

Sylla, 219

Sylva Caledonia, 35

Syracuse, petalism in, 225

Tacitus, 200; *Annals* quoted, 111

Tailors, 46, 62, 113

Tale of a Tub, A, ix, xiiiff., 24–5; adapted to all readers, 117; *Additions to*, 273; authorship of, 279; comment on, xxiiff.; date of, 1, 17; digressions, 280; Notes to, 11; treatises against, 1

Tarquin, the Proud, 213

Tarquinius Priscus, 213

Tasso, 152

Tate, Nahum, xxiv, 22

Telemachus, 244

Temple, Sir William, x–xxi, xxix–xxx, 147, 152, 163, 254ff., 280, 281; attacked by Wotton, 6; imagined author of *A Tale of a Tub*, 279; recall from employments abroad, 266; relations with Swift, xxxvi; relations with William III, 269; his retirement, 266; his style, 258, 268; *Ancient and Modern Learning*, xvi, 139, 262; other *Essays* referred to, 262; *Letters*, xix, xx, xxi, xxxvi, 258, 266; *Memoirs*, xxxvi, 269–70; *Miscellanea*, xx, 261

Terence, 62

Terentius Leo, 218

Terra Australis Incognita, xl, 66, 293–4

Theatres, modern, 36–7, 49

Thebes, 209

Themistocles, xx, 62, 207, 210

Theseus, 57, 204

Thoughts on Various Subjects, xxxv, 241, 278

Thrasybulus, 208

Thucydides, 198

Thuringians, 286

Tiberius, 222

Tibullus, imitation by Temple, 262

Tigellius, 57

Title-pages, 21, 43, 91, 144, 171

Tobinambou, 172

Tobit, 31

Tommy Pots, 41

Tom Thumb, 41

Tooke, Benjamin, bookseller, xxx, xxxi, xxxiii

Translation of the Scriptures, 75

Transubstantiation, 72ff.

Treatises speedily to be published, xxvii, xl

Tribunes of the People, 214, 227

Trinity College, Swift at, ix–xi

Triple Alliance, The, 259

Tritical Essay upon the Faculties of the Mind, xxxv, 246ff.

Troglodyte Philosopher, 116

Turner, Francis, Bishop of Ely, xiii

Tyranny defined, 197–8

Ulysses, 249

Uniformity, Act of, 130

Universal Medicine, 122

Utopia, 248; Utopian Commonwealths, 174

Van Effen, Justus, xxxii

Vapours, causing madness, 102ff.

Vaughan, Thomas, *Anthroposoph a Theomagica*, 79, 119; *Anima Magica Abscondita*, 119

Villanage, abolishing of, 230

Virgil, 33, 139, 146, 157, 242, 244; translated by Swift, xii; translated by Temple, 262

Virtuoso, 39, 65, 98, 155, 172, 181

Vortex, of Descartes, 105

Vossius, Isaac, 152

Walsh, William, 249

Wars and Quarrels, Digression on, 289ff.

Warwick-Lane, 113, 115

Wesley, Samuel, 157

Westminster Drolleries, 38

Westminster-Hall, 112, 115, 125, 171

Whispering-Office, 66

Whiston, William, *Memoirs*, xxii

Whitechapel, 126

Whitehall, 31

Whittington and his Cat, 41

Whore of Babylon, 112, 187

Wilkins, John, Bishop of Chester, 152

William III, xi, xx, 256

Will's Coffee-house, 38, 45, 115

Wind, 95ff.

Wisdom, proverbs concerning, 40

Worms, remedy for the, 66, 127

Wither, George, 146, 152

Wotton, William, xviii, xxiv, xxxvi, 22, 57, 79, 106, 155, 279, 280; *Reflections upon Ancient and Modern Learning*, xvi, 42, 59, 80, 139; *Defence of Reflections . . . with Observations upon the Tale*, xxviii, 5–9, 277, 279

Xenophon, 31, 197; quoted, 79, 198, 199, 225, 244

Xerxes, 249, 250

York, Archbishop of. *See* Sharp

Zeal, 86, 129, 185; see *Analytical Discourse*.

Zibeta Occidentalis, 104

Zoilus, 57